DEPARTMENT OF COMMERCE AND LABOR
COAST AND GEODETIC SURVEY
O. H. TITTMANN
SUPERINTENDENT

GEODESY

THE EFFECT OF TOPOGRAPHY AND ISOSTATIC COMPENSATION UPON THE INTENSITY OF GRAVITY

BY

JOHN F. HAYFORD
Formerly Inspector of Geodetic Work and Chief of the Computing Division

AND

WILLIAM BOWIE
Inspector of Geodetic Work and Chief of the Computing Division
Assistant, Coast and Geodetic Survey

SPECIAL PUBLICATION No. 10

WASHINGTON
GOVERNMENT PRINTING OFFICE
1912

CONTENTS.

<table>
<tr><td></td><td>Page.</td></tr>
<tr><td>General statement</td><td>5</td></tr>
<tr><td>Isostasy defined</td><td>6</td></tr>
<tr><td>Assumptions as to isostasy</td><td>10</td></tr>
<tr><td>Formulæ</td><td>12</td></tr>
<tr><td>Division of the surface of the earth into zones and compartments</td><td>17</td></tr>
<tr><td>Computation of reduction tables for near zones</td><td>19</td></tr>
<tr><td>Computation of reduction tables for distant zones</td><td>23</td></tr>
<tr><td>Explanation of reduction tables</td><td>28</td></tr>
<tr><td>Reduction tables for lettered zones</td><td>30</td></tr>
<tr><td>Reduction tables for numbered zones</td><td>44</td></tr>
<tr><td>Special reduction tables for sea stations</td><td>46</td></tr>
<tr><td>Use of templates</td><td>47</td></tr>
<tr><td>Examples of computations of corrections</td><td>48</td></tr>
<tr><td>Corrections for topography and isostatic compensation, separate zones</td><td>53</td></tr>
<tr><td>Interpolation for outer zones</td><td>58</td></tr>
<tr><td>Method of interpolation for outer zones</td><td>60</td></tr>
<tr><td>Criteria of accepted interpolations for outer zones</td><td>63</td></tr>
<tr><td>Saving by interpolation for outer zones</td><td>64</td></tr>
<tr><td>Change of sign due to distance</td><td>65</td></tr>
<tr><td>Distant topography necessarily considered</td><td>71</td></tr>
<tr><td>Curvature must be considered</td><td>71</td></tr>
<tr><td>Principal facts for 89 stations in the United States</td><td>72</td></tr>
<tr><td>Correction to Helmert's formula of 1901</td><td>75</td></tr>
<tr><td>Comparison of apparent anomalies by new and old methods</td><td>75</td></tr>
<tr><td>Possible relations of anomalies to topography</td><td>77</td></tr>
<tr><td>Comparison of Bouguer anomalies with new-method anomalies</td><td>79</td></tr>
<tr><td>Comparison of free-air anomalies with new-method anomalies</td><td>80</td></tr>
<tr><td>Test by stations not in the United States</td><td>81</td></tr>
<tr><td>Discussion of errors</td><td>86</td></tr>
<tr><td>Errors of observation</td><td>87</td></tr>
<tr><td>Errors of computation</td><td>88</td></tr>
<tr><td>Nature of apparent anomalies</td><td>94</td></tr>
<tr><td>The method not subject to hidden errors</td><td>95</td></tr>
<tr><td>Effects of topography and compensation—why combined</td><td>97</td></tr>
<tr><td>Regional versus local distribution of compensation</td><td>98</td></tr>
<tr><td>Test of depth of compensation</td><td>103</td></tr>
<tr><td>Graphical comparison of three kinds of anomalies</td><td>106</td></tr>
<tr><td>Interpretation of anomalies in terms of masses</td><td>108</td></tr>
<tr><td>Possible relation of new-method anomalies to other things</td><td>112</td></tr>
<tr><td>Relation between new-method anomalies and geologic formations</td><td>113</td></tr>
<tr><td>Discussion of other regional peculiarities</td><td>117</td></tr>
<tr><td>Hypothesis of horizontal displacement of compensation</td><td>121</td></tr>
<tr><td>Comment on Bouguer and free-air anomalies</td><td>122</td></tr>
<tr><td>Comment on Faye method of reduction</td><td>125</td></tr>
<tr><td>Summary</td><td>126</td></tr>
</table>

ILLUSTRATIONS.

Page.

1. Three unit columns showing ideal depth of isostatic compensation 7
2. Three unit columns showing approximate depth of isostatic compensation as used in computations 10
3. Showing station and elementary mass at same elevation. 15
4. Showing elementary mass at greater elevation than station 16
5. Showing elementary mass at less elevation than station 17
6. Showing topography in land zones—three cases 20
7. Graphical computation of reduction table for Zone E 22
8. Graphical representation of values of E for various depths 23
9. Graphical representation of values of E_k 24
10. (a) Template for maps of scale 1/10000 (reduced) 48
10. (b) Template for maps of scale 1/6013500 (reduced) 48
11. Overlapping of corresponding zones for two stations 58
12. Graphical illustration of interpolation 60
13. Map showing location of gravity stations used in the investigation .... In pocket
14. Showing topography and compensation near station 66
15. Showing distant topography and compensation 67
16. Lines of equal anomaly for new method of reduction .... In pocket
17. Lines of equal anomaly for Bouguer method of reduction .... In pocket
18. Lines of equal anomaly for free-air method of reduction .... In pocket
19. Illustration from Supplementary Investigation in 1909 of the Figure of the Earth and Isostasy, showing residuals of Solution H, all stations, with areas of excessive and defective density, and showing also all gravity stations with new-method anomalies .... In pocket

4

EFFECT OF TOPOGRAPHY AND ISOSTATIC COMPENSATION UPON THE INTENSITY OF GRAVITY.

BY

JOHN F. HAYFORD,* *formerly Inspector of Geodetic Work and Chief of the Computing Division,*

AND

WILLIAM BOWIE, *Inspector of Geodetic Work and Chief of the Computing Division, Assistant, Coast and Geodetic Survey*

GENERAL STATEMENT.

In the United States the assumption of isostasy in a definite and reasonable form has been introduced into the computations of the figure and size of the earth from the observed deflections of the vertical. These computations have shown that the assumption of isostasy is substantially correct. They have shown that a close approach to perfect isostatic compensation exists under the United States and adjacent areas. This is important to geology and geophysics. They have also shown that the proper recognition of isostasy in making computations of the figure and size of the earth from observed deflections of the vertical has about doubled the accuracy of such computations by reducing errors of both the accidental and the systematic classes in such work. This increase in accuracy is important to geodesy. These computations and the investigations of which they form a part have been published in full.†

As soon as it was evident that the proper recognition of isostasy in connection with computations of the figure and size of the earth from observed deflections of the vertical would produce a great increase in accuracy, it appeared to be very probable that a similar recognition of isostasy in connection with computations of the shape of the earth from observations of the intensity of gravity would produce a similar increase of accuracy. Logically the next step to be taken was therefore to introduce such a definite recognition of isostasy into gravity computations. Moreover, it appeared that if this step were taken it would furnish a proof of the existence of isostasy independent of the proof furnished by observed deflections of the vertical, and would therefore be of great value in supplementing the deflection investigations and in testing the conclusions drawn from them. In other words, the effects of isostasy upon the direction of gravity at various stations on the earth's surface having been studied, it then appeared to be almost equally important to investigate the effects of isostasy upon the intensity of gravity.

It was evident from the beginning that to properly take into account the possible existence of isostasy in connection with computations of the intensity of gravity a rather extensive revision of formulæ and methods of computation would be necessary, and that the computations must be thorough and must involve a considerable number of gravity stations if the results were to be convincing. Thus it was realized that the problem was both a large and a difficult one. Partly for this reason, Mr. Hayford, as inspector of geodetic work, recommended frequently from 1900 to 1908 that the Coast and Geodetic Survey confine its energy in geodetic observations and

---

* Now Director, College of Engineering, Northwestern University, Evanston, Ill.

† The Figure of the Earth and Isostasy from Measurements in the United States, by John F. Hayford, published in 1909 by the Coast and Geodetic Survey, and Supplementary Investigation in 1909 of the Figure of the Earth and Isostasy, by John F. Hayford, published in 1910 by the Coast and Geodetic Survey. Each of these is a separate publication not included in the annual reports of the survey. They may be obtained by interested parties on application to the Superintendent of the Coast and Geodetic Survey, Washington. D. C.

investigations mainly to deflections of the vertical until that part of the field of investigation had been well covered and reasonably safe conclusions reached, and that then, and not till then, should much energy be expended in gravity observations and the corresponding investigations. This policy was adopted and adhered to.

In the summer of 1908 Mr. Hayford began an extensive study of the theoretical side of the investigation, the revision of formulæ and of methods of computation.

Early in 1909 a long, continuous series of gravity observations with the half-second pendulum apparatus at various stations in the United States was commenced. This series is still in progress. In this publication there are used 89 stations, including those of this series which are available at this time.

In January, 1909, Mr. Bowie became closely associated with Mr. Hayford at the Coast and Geodetic Survey office and was brought into close touch with the investigation set forth in this publication. In October, 1909, he assumed his present position, and has since that time been in charge of the gravity observations and computations of gravity made in the Coast and Geodetic Survey, of which many are utilized in this publication. In certain lines he has extended the investigation beyond its former limits. In the preparation of this publication the two authors have cooperated. They are jointly responsible for the opinions expressed and the statement of conclusions reached.

Miss Sarah Beall, computer, efficiently supervised much of the computing in connection with this investigation, and especially the computation of the reduction tables, the most difficult part of the work. To her and to the various members of the computing division who assisted, the credit is largely due for the unusual rapidity and success of the computations.

In September, 1909, Mr. Hayford presented to the International Geodetic Association at London a paper bearing the same title as the present publication. It has been printed as pages 365–389 of Volume I of the Report of the Sixteenth General Conference of the International Geodetic Association, held at London and Cambridge in September, 1909.

The present investigation is in many respects a counterpart of the previous investigations based on deflections of the vertical, to which reference has already been made. It supplements those investigations, and therefore the three should be studied together to obtain their full force.

The computations of the present investigation have been based upon certain assumptions as to the existence of the condition called isostasy which are substantially identical with the assumptions in the previous investigations involving deflections of the vertical. It is important to the reader to understand clearly the meaning of the word isostasy and of certain related phrases, as otherwise he may fail to understand, or may misunderstand, many statements in this publication. These definitions are given below in substantially the same words as were used in connection with the previous investigations.

ISOSTASY DEFINED.

If the earth were composed of homogeneous material, its figure of equilibrium, under the influence of gravity and its own rotation, would be an ellipsoid of revolution.

The earth is composed of heterogeneous material which varies considerably in density. If this heterogeneous material were so arranged that its density at any point depended simply upon the depth of that point below the surface, or, more accurately, if all the material lying at each equipotential surface (rotation considered) was of one density, a state of equilibrium would exist, and there would be no tendency toward a rearrangement of masses. The figure of the earth in this case would be a very close approximation to an ellipsoid of revolution.

If the heterogeneous material composing the earth were not arranged in this manner at the outset, the stresses produced by gravity would tend to bring about such an arrangement; but as the material is not a perfect fluid, since it possesses considerable viscosity, at least near the surface, the rearrangement will be imperfect. In the partial rearrangement some stresses will still remain, different portions of the same horizontal stratum may have somewhat different densities, and the actual surface of the earth will be a slight departure from the ellipsoid of revolution in the sense that above each region of deficient density there will be a bulge or bump on the ellipsoid, and above each region of excessive density there will be a hollow, relatively speaking. The bumps on this supposed earth will be the mountains, the plateaus, the continents; and the hollows will be the oceans. The excess of material represented by that portion of the continent which is above sea level will be compensated for by a defect of density in the underlying material. The continents will be floated, so to speak, because they are composed of relatively light material; and, similarly, the floor of the ocean will, on this supposed earth, be depressed because it is composed of unusually dense material. This particular condition of approximate equilibrium has been given the name "isostasy."

The adjustment of the material toward this condition, which is produced in nature by the stresses due to gravity, may be called the "isostatic adjustment."

The compensation of the excess of matter at the surface (continents) by the defect of density below, and of surface defect of matter (oceans) by excess of density below, may be called the "isostatic compensation."

Let the depth below sea level within which the isostatic compensation is complete be called the "depth of compensation." At and below this depth the condition as to stress of any element of mass is isostatic; that is, any element of mass is subject to equal pressures from all directions as if it were a portion of a perfect fluid. Above this depth, on the other hand, each element of mass is subject in general to different pressures in different directions—to stresses which tend to distort it and to move it.

Consider the relations of the masses, densities, and volumes, above the depth of compensation, fixed by the preceding definition. The mass in any prismatic column which has for its base a unit area of the horizontal surface which lies at the depth of compensation, for its edges vertical lines (lines of gravity) and for its upper limit the actual irregular surface of the earth (or the sea surface if the area in question is beneath the ocean) is the same as the mass in any other similar prismatic column having any other unit area of the same surface for its base.* Illustration No. 1 represents three such unit columns.

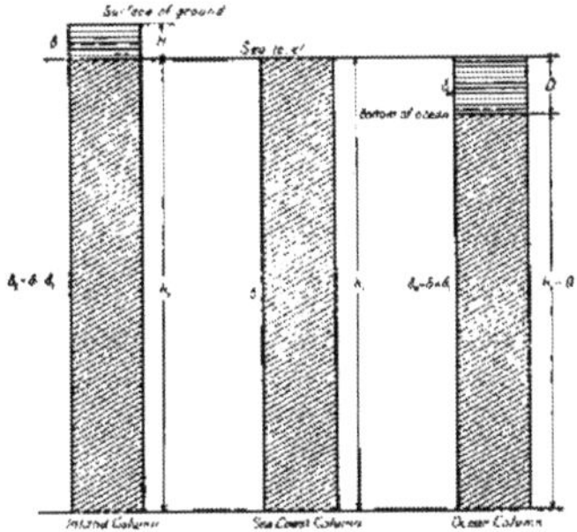

ILLUSTRATION No. 1.—Three unit columns showing ideal depth of isostatic compensation.

Let the depth of compensation be called h_1 and the mean surface density of the solid portion of the earth be called δ. Then the mass of material in a column of unit area at the seacoast is δh_1 † (density times volume).

Let the elevation above sea level of the irregular surface of the earth over the unit area of an inland column be called H. Then the mass of material in the inland column above sea level is δH. Also, let the density of that portion of the inland column between sea level and the depth of compensation be called δ_r. Then the mass of material in the column is expressed by the equation

$$\text{Mass in any land unit column} = \delta H + \delta_r h_1 \tag{1}$$

By definition, at the depth of isostasy, any element of mass is subject to equal pressures from all directions as if it were a portion of a perfect fluid. In order that this may be true, the vertical pressures due to gravity on the various units of area at that depth must all be the

---

* It would be more accurate to use the words "inverted truncated pyramid" instead of "prismatic column." The latter expression has been selected because it is sufficiently exact for the purpose and corresponds to the allowable approximations actually made in the mathematical part of the investigation.

† For the purpose of this demonstration it is assumed that the average density of the earth's crust below the seacoast between sea level and the depth of compensation is equal to the average density of the solid portion of the earth's surface (2.67). This assumption ignores the probability that within a depth as great as 114 kilometers (the assumed depth of compensation) there is probably a slight increase in density with increase of depth, due to increased pressure, the density being some unknown function of the depth. This neglect also appears in various other places in this publication. It is shown later, under the heading "Discussion of errors," that this neglect introduces no appreciable errors into the computation. It is justified, therefore, as a means of avoiding unnecessarily long and complicated statements.

same, and therefore masses of the various unit columns must all be the same. Therefore the mass in a land unit column must be equal to the mass in a seacoast column, or

$$\delta H + \delta_I h_1 = \delta h_1 \tag{1a}$$

From equation (1a) it follows that

$$\delta_I = \frac{\delta(h_1 - H)}{h_1} \tag{2}$$

The difference called δ_1 between δ and δ_I is expressed by the equation

$$\delta_1 = \delta - \frac{\delta(h_1 - H)}{h_1} \tag{2a}$$

$$= \delta \frac{H}{h_1} \tag{3}$$

This difference between the normal density at the surface of the land and also throughout a column at the seacoast on the one hand, and the density of an inland column below sea level on the other hand, is the average compensating defect of density, and this difference multiplied by the depth of compensation is the compensating defect of mass, $\delta_1 h_1$.

The total mass in the inland column may also be expressed by the equation (see illustration No. 1),

$$\text{Mass in any land unit column} = \delta H + \delta h_1 - \delta_1 h_1 \tag{4}$$

As the mass in each unit column is the same, namely δh_1, it is obvious from equation (4) that

$$\delta H = \delta_1 h_1 \tag{4a}$$

This equation is a statement in mathematical symbols that in each unit column the compensating defects of mass below sea level must be exactly equal to the mass above sea level which is considered to be the surface excess.

Equation (3) indicates that the compensating defect of density is proportional to the elevation of the surface above the sea level as δ and h_1 are assumed to be constant.

In an ocean unit column the top of the solid portion happens to be below sea level, being a part of the bottom of the ocean. In the ocean column let the depth of the water be called D and the density of the sea water δ_w. Then the depth of the solid portion of the column will be $h_1 - D$. Let the density of this solid portion be called δ_o. Then the mass of material in this unit column will be expressed by the equation

$$\text{Mass in any ocean unit column} = \delta_w D + \delta_o(h_1 - D) \tag{4b}$$

By definition, this mass must equal the mass of the unit column at the seacoast, hence

$$\delta_w D + \delta_o(h_1 - D) = \delta h \tag{4c}$$

From equation (4c) it follows that

$$\delta_o = \frac{\delta h_1 - \delta_w D}{h_1 - D} \tag{4d}$$

The difference δ_1 between the density of the solid portion of the ocean column δ_o and the normal density δ is expressed by the equation

$$\delta_1 = \frac{\delta h_1 - \delta_w D}{h_1 - D} - \delta \tag{4e}$$

$$= \frac{(\delta - \delta_w)D}{h_1 - D} \tag{4f}$$

The total mass in any ocean unit column may also be expressed by the equation (see illustration No. 1),

$$\text{Mass in any ocean unit column} = \delta_w D + (\delta + \delta_1)(h_1 - D) \tag{5}$$

As the mass in each unit column is the same, namely δh_1, it follows from equation (5) that

$$D(\delta - \delta_w) = \delta_1(h_1 - D) \tag{5a}$$

That is, in the solid portion of each ocean unit column the compensating excess of mass must be exactly equal to the defect of mass in the water portion of the column.

Equation (4f) indicates that the compensating excess of density is nearly proportional to the depth of water, as δ and δ_w are assumed to be constant and $(h_1 - D)$ is approximately constant.

In this publication the mean surface density of the solid portion of the earth, δ, is assumed to be 2.67. The density of sea water, δ_w, is 1.027. With these values $\delta - \delta_w = 0.615\delta$. Hence, for oceanic unit columns, equation (5a) becomes

$$(\delta - \delta_w)D = 0.615\delta D = \delta_1(h_1 - D) \tag{5b}$$

and equation (4f) becomes

$$\delta_1 = \delta \frac{0.615D}{h_1 - D} \tag{6}$$

Note that equation (6) differs from equation (3) only by containing the factor 0.615; in having D, a depth, in the place of H, an elevation; and in having $(h_1 - D)$ as a denominator instead of h_1.

As a concrete illustration, consider three unit columns such as are indicated in illustration No. 1, one beneath a mountain summit at an elevation of 3 kilometers, one underlying an area which is at sea level, a portion of the seashore for example, and the third under the ocean at a point where it is 5 kilometers deep. Let the depth of compensation be assumed to be 114 kilometers below sea level, and the mean surface density $\delta = 2.67$. In the first column the ratio H to h_1 being $\frac{3}{114}$, according to equation (3) the defect of density, δ_1, is $\frac{3}{114}$ of 2.67 or 0.07, and the density of the material below sea level is $2.67 - 0.07 = 2.60$. In the second column the density of the material is 2.67. In the third column the compensating excess of density of the material underlying the ocean is, by equation (6), $\delta\frac{(0.615)(5)}{114-5} = \delta\frac{3}{109} = 0.07$ and the density of the material is therefore $2.67 + 0.07 = 2.74$.

Under such a mountain, therefore, if isostasy exists as defined by the stated assumptions, the average density is about 3 per cent less than under the seacoast, and on the other hand, under a portion of the ocean 5 kilometers deep the average density is about 3 per cent greater than under the seacoast, down to the depth of compensation in each case.

As a rough approximation it may be stated, on the basis of the preceding paragraph, that beneath areas which lie above sea level the density is defective by about 1 per cent for each kilometer of elevation of the surface. Since much of the land portion of the earth's surface is at an elevation of less than 1 kilometer and very little of it above the elevation 3 kilometers, the compensating defects of density beneath most land areas are less than 1 per cent of the mean density and exceed 3 per cent only under a few small areas on very high mountains. Similarly, the compensating excesses of density under ocean areas seldom exceed 3 per cent as the depths exceed 5 kilometers (16 000 feet or 2700 fathoms) in but a small portion of the ocean.

If the condition of equal pressures, that is of equal superimposed masses, is fully satisfied at a given depth, the compensation is said to be complete at that depth. If there is a variation from equality of superimposed masses, the differences may be taken as a measure of the degree of incompleteness of the compensation.

In the above definitions it has been tacitly assumed that g, the intensity of gravity, is everywhere the same at a given depth. Equal superincumbent masses would produce equal pressures only in case the intensity of gravity is the same in the two cases. The intensity of gravity varies with change of latitude and is subject also to anomalous variations which are to some extent associated with the relation to continents and oceanic areas. But even the extreme variations in the intensity of gravity are small in comparison with the variations in density postulated. The extreme variation of the intensity of gravity at sea level on each side of its mean value is only 1 part in 400. Even this small range of variation does not occur except between points which are many thousands of kilometers apart. As will be shown later, the postulated variations in mean densities are about 1 part in 30 on each side of an average value. Hence, it is not advisable to complicate the conception of isostasy and introduce long circumlocutions into its definition in order to introduce the refinement of considering the variations in the intensity of gravity.

The variation of the intensity of gravity with change of depth below the surface need not be considered, as its effect in the various columns of material considered will be substantially the same.

The idea implied in this definition of the phrase "depth of compensation," that the isostatic compensation is complete within some depth much less than the radius of the earth, is not ordinarily expressed in the literature of the subject,* but it is an idea which it is difficult to avoid if the subject is studied carefully from any point of view.

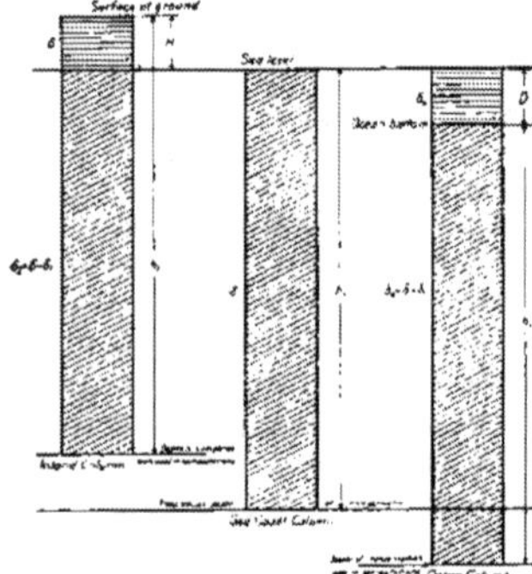

ILLUSTRATION No. 2.—Three unit columns showing approximate depth of isostatic compensation as used in computations.

ASSUMPTIONS AS TO ISOSTASY.

In the computations of the investigation here published the depth of compensation is assumed to be 113.7 kilometers under every separate portion of the earth's surface.

This is substantially the value given in The Figure of the Earth and Isostasy, page 175. It was the best value available at the time the computation of the gravity reduction tables published herein was commenced. A better value, 122 kilometers, became available while these computations were in progress, but too late to be used. (See Supplementary Investigation in 1909 of The Figure of the Earth, p. 77.)

The mean surface density of the earth—that is, the mean density of the solid portion of the earth for the first few miles below the surface—is assumed in this investigation to be 2.67.† The phrase "of the solid portion of the earth" is inserted in the preceding sentence to indicate that the ocean, with a density of only 1.027, is excluded from this mean.

The computations concerned in this investigation were actually made on the assumption indicated in illustration No. 2 instead of those indicated in illustration No. 1 and used on pages 7–9. This slight change was made to simplify and facilitate computations and is justified by the fact that the errors so introduced are negligible, as shown later under the heading "Discussion of errors." In illustration No. 1 and in the corresponding text, the compensation is assumed to extend everywhere to a depth of 113.7 kilometers below sea level. In illustration No. 2 and in the actual computations, the compensation is assumed to extend everywhere to a depth of 113.7 kilometers measured downward from the solid surface of the earth—that is, from the land surface in land areas (above sea level) and from the ocean bottom in oceanic areas (below sea level). For land areas, in computing the direct effect of the topography, the portion above sea level was assumed to have the density δ as indicated in illustration No. 2, but in computing the effect of the isostatic compensation the density was assumed to be $\delta - \delta_1$

---

* See, however, a reference to Pratt's Hypothesis in Helmert's Höhere Geodäsie, II Theil, p. 367.

† For the data and considerations upon which this value is based, see The Solar Parallax and its Related Constants, by William Harkness, Washington, Government Printing Office, 1891, pp. 91–92; see also The Figure of the Earth and Isostasy from Measurements in the United States, p. 128.

above sea level as well as below, δ_1 being computed from formula (3).   The seacoast column is the same in the two illustrations.   Upon the assumption indicated in illustration No. 2 and used in actual computations for oceanic compartments, formula (6) becomes

$$\delta_1 = \delta \frac{0.615\ D}{h_1} \tag{6a}$$

In the computations of this investigation the compensation under each separate portion of the earth's surface is assumed to be uniformly distributed with respect to depth from the surface down to the depth of compensation, 113.7 kilometers.   In other words, the compensating defect or excess of density under a given area is assumed to be, at all depths less than the depth of compensation, exactly equal to the δ_1 of equations (3) and (6), which was defined as being the average defect (or excess) of density.

Elsewhere * it has been assumed temporarily for investigation purposes that the compensating defect (or excess) of density varies with respect to depth, being for example greatest near the surface and diminishing uniformly to zero at the depth of compensation, its average value being δ_1.

In the principal computations of this investigation the isostatic compensation is assumed to be complete under every separate portion of the earth's surface, however small the area considered.   That is, equations (3) and (6) are assumed to be true for every separate unit of area even though a very small unit be chosen, as for example, 1 square foot.

The authors do not believe that any one of these assumptions upon which the computations are based is absolutely accurate.   The mean surface density is probably not exactly 2.67 and the actual surface density in any given area probably does not agree exactly with the mean. The depth of compensation is probably not exactly 113.7 kilometers, and it possibly is somewhat different under different portions of the earth's surface.   The compensation is probably not distributed uniformly with respect to depth.   It is especially improbable that the compensation is complete under each separate small area, under each hill, each narrow valley, and each little depression in the sea bottom.   It is exceedingly improbable, for example, that as each ton of material is eroded from a land area, carried out of a river mouth, and deposited on the ocean bottom, that corresponding changes of isostatic compensation occur at the same time under the eroded area and under the area of deposition at just such a rate as to keep the compensation complete under each.

The authors believe that the assumptions on which the computations are based are a close approximation to the truth.   They believe also that the quickest and most effective way to ascertain the facts as to the distribution of density beneath the surface of the earth is to make the assumptions stated, to base upon them careful computations for many observation stations scattered widely over the earth's surface, and then to compare the computed values with the observed values of the intensity of gravity in order to ascertain how much and in what manner the facts differ from the assumptions.

In this investigation, accordingly, the intensity of gravity at many observation stations has been computed on the assumptions stated.   These computed values have been compared with the observed values at these stations.   The differences between the observed and the computed values, the residuals, are due to two classes of errors.   In the first class are errors in the observations and in the computations.   In the second class are errors in the assumptions. The average and maximum magnitudes of the errors of the first class are fairly well known. The magnitude and character of the residuals which may be produced by them are fairly well known.   It is shown in this publication that the residuals, differences between observed and computed values of the intensity of gravity, are larger than may be accounted for by the first class of errors.   Therefore it is certain that the second class of errors are of appreciable size. In other words, it is certain that the assumptions are appreciably in error.   But, as the residuals are but little larger than may be accounted for by the first class of errors, it is certain that the assumptions are nearly correct.

---

* The Figure of the Earth and Isostasy from Measurements in the United States, pp. 156-163.

The residuals contain evidence not only as to the extent but also as to the manner in which assumptions depart from the truth. To read and interpret this evidence precisely is exceedingly difficult because of the fact that the residuals are small. If the residuals were large, it would be clear that the assumptions were far from the truth, and it would be easy to see in which direction the truth lay. In the actual case it is difficult to ascertain in what way the assumptions should be changed to make them a closer approximation to the whole truth, while still remaining a statement of general laws applicable to the whole United States.

FORMULÆ.

It was desired to compute the intensity of gravity at any selected station on the earth upon the assumptions as to isostasy which have been stated. It was necessary to select the formulæ and methods of computation.

The computations may be most conveniently made in two parts.

First, the intensity of gravity may be computed on an ideal earth having the same size and shape as the ellipsoid of revolution which most nearly coincides with the sea-level surface of the real earth, and having no topography and no variations in density at any given depth below the surface. To convert the real earth into this ideal earth all material on the real earth above sea level must be removed, the water of the ocean must be replaced by material of density equal to the mean surface density of the real earth, and all variations in density at any given depth in the real earth must then be removed by taking out or injecting enough material in each part to make the density conform accurately to the mean density in the real earth at that depth. In this ideal earth the density will increase with increase of depth in the same manner as it does upon an average in the real earth, but in the ideal earth all masses lying at the same depth will have the same density, whereas in the real earth such masses have densities which are known to differ slightly from each other.

This computation was made by using Helmert's formula of 1901,[*] namely,

$$\dagger\,\gamma_0 = 978.046(1 + 0.005\,302\,\sin^2\phi - 0.000\,007\,\sin^2 2\phi) \tag{7}$$

The symbol γ_0 stands for the required value of gravity at a station on the ideal earth above described in the latitude ϕ. On such an ideal earth the value of gravity at the surface would be a function of the latitude only, as expressed by this formula. The numerical value of γ_0 computed from formula (7) is both the acceleration of gravity in centimeters and the attraction of gravity in dynes on a unit mass (1 gram) at the station expressed in the centimeter-gram-second system.

The form of this formula is fixed by theory. The three constants which it contains, namely, 978.046, 0.005 302, and 0.000 007, were computed from a large number of observations of gravity at stations scattered widely over the earth's surface. New and better values of these constants may be obtained by further research and the use of more observations, but at the beginning of this investigation the formula as written was believed to be the best representation available

---

[*] Der normale Theil der Schwerkraft im Meeresniveau, von F. R. Helmert, S. 328–336, Sitzungsberichte / der Königlich Preussischen / Akademie der Wissenschaften / zu Berlin, / Jahrgang 1901 / Erster Halbband, Januar bis Juni. See also Bericht über die relativen Messungen der Schwerkraft mit Pendelapparaten für den Zeitraum von 1900 bis 1903, unter Mitwirkung von F. R. Helmert erstattet von E. Borrass, S. 133–136, Verhandlungen / der vom 4 bis 13 August 1903 in Kopenhagen abgehaltenen / Vierzehnten Allgemeinen Conferenz der / Internationalen Erdmessung / Redigirt vom ständigen Secretär H. G. van de Sande Bakhuyzen. / II. Theil: Spezialberichte. See also The Figure of the Earth and Isostasy from Measurements in the United States, p. 172, for some comments upon this formula.

† After the manuscript of this publication was completed, a letter addressed to the Superintendent, of which the following is a translation, was received from Dr. Helmert:

POTSDAM, *October 31, 1911.*

Mr. Bowie sent to me a small brochure for which I offer my best thanks to the sender and to you. Permit me to make a remark in regard to my formula.

In 1901 I did indeed give:

$$\gamma_0 = 978.046\,(1 + 0.005302\,\sin^2\phi - 0.000007\,\sin^2 2\phi)$$

This formula is based on the value of g in the Vienna system (Sterneck).

The American values of g are, however, referred to Potsdam. The constant 978.046 must, therefore, be modified by the application of −0.016 by which correction it is referred to Potsdam, as I have several times stated in my reports.

I therefore request that in your investigations in North America you will use the value

$$\gamma_0 = 978.030\,(1 + 0.005302\,\sin^2\phi - 0.000007\,\sin^2 2\phi)$$

as being my improved formula.

I know that your scientists think that the value 978.038 is more suitable for the United States. That value of course, may be used. I only wanted to emphasize that, in so far as my work is concerned, the value of g in the United States is not 978.046, but 978.030.

It is clear that the values of gravity in the United States, used in this publication, are based upon Potsdam, as shown on p. 73, and that, therefore, the position taken by Dr. Helmert in this letter is correct. The only manner in which this change ultimately affects the conclusions reached in this publication is shown on p. 75.

of gravity at sea level on the ideal earth described in the preceding paragraph. During the progress of this investigation a small correction to the constant 978.046 was derived, as shown later in this publication. The formula, with this small correction applied, is believed by the authors to be the best available at present for the purpose for which it is intended.

The Helmert formula of 1901 corresponds to a value of 298.3 ± 0.7 for the reciprocal of the flattening of the earth. This is in fair agreement with the best value now available for this quantity as derived from observed deflections in the United States, namely, 297.0 ± 0.5.*

The stations at which observations of gravity were made are situated on the real earth, not the ideal earth, and are in general above sea level, not at sea level. The second portion of the computation of the intensity of gravity at any observation station must therefore take account of the topography which exists upon the real earth, take account so far as is possible of the variations in density beneath the surface of the real earth, and take account of the effect of the elevation of the observation station above sea level.

The correction for elevation was computed by the formula

$$-0.000\ 308\ 6\ H$$

in which H is the elevation of the station above sea level in meters. This correction of the attraction upon a unit mass (1 gram) at the station is in dynes and reduces from sea level to the actual station. It takes account of the increased distance of the station from the attracting mass, the earth, as if the station were in the air at the stated elevation and there were no topography on the earth. This is an old formula and needs no comment other than that it has been adopted in this simple form by Dr. Helmert as being sufficiently accurate.†

The real difficulty of the investigation was encountered when an attempt was made to compute the effect, upon the attraction at a given station, of the topography which exists upon the earth and of the isostatic compensation of that topography which is assumed to exist beneath the surface of the earth. For this purpose new formulæ and new methods of computation were found to be necessary.

It was desired to compute the effect upon the attraction at each station of all the topography of the world and of the isostatic compensation of that topography. It was desired to do this with sufficient accuracy to insure that all constant errors in the computed effects would certainly be less than 1 part in 200 and all accidental errors in the separate parts of the computation less than .0002 dyne. This, it was believed, would insure that the computed total correction for any station would ordinarily be in error in so far as the computation alone is concerned by less than 0.003 dyne. In order to make this computation with the specified degree of accuracy with a minimum expenditure of time and energy the formulæ and methods of computation about to be given were selected and used. This publication contains full information as to the degree of success with which the computations were made, both as to accuracy and rapidity. This degree of success is the proper measure of the excellence of the formulæ and methods of computation selected.

The attraction of any elementary mass, dm, acting upon a mass of 1 gram at the station of observation is, in dynes,

$$\frac{kdm}{D^2} \tag{8}$$

in which k is the gravitation constant and D is the distance from the station to the elementary mass. In order to get the result in dynes all quantities in this formula must be expressed in the centimeter-gram-second system.

The general expression for Newton's law of gravitation is

$$F = k\frac{m_1 m_2}{D^2} \tag{8a}$$

---

* See Supplementary Investigation in 1909 of the Figure of the Earth and Isostasy, pp. 60, 77.

† See p. 651 of "Über die Reduction der auf der physichen Erdoberfläche beobachteten Schwerebeschleunigungen auf ein gemeinsames Niveau Von F. R. Helmert in Sitzungsberichte der Königlich Preussischen Akademie der Wissenschaften 1903 Erster Halbband.

in which m_1 and m_2 are two masses each of dimensions infinitesimal in comparison with the distance D between them and F is the attraction between the two masses. Newton's law of gravitation is frequently expressed merely in the form of a proportion, F being stated to be proportional to $\frac{m_1 m_2}{D^2}$. The gravitation constant, k in formula (8a), is the factor by which the product of two masses divided by the square of their distance asunder must be multiplied in order to express the force exerted by those masses on one another. The gravitation constant is not a mere numeral. Its dimensions are shown by the exponents in $(L^{+3} M^{-1} T^{-2})$ if L, M, T denote the units of length, mass, and time, respectively. That is, the gravitation constant is the cube of a distance divided by the product of a mass and the square of a time.

Formula (8) is merely the special case of formula (8a) which is pertinent to the problem in hand.

The value adopted in this investigation for k in the centimeter-gram-second system is 6673 (10^{-11}). The basis of this adopted value is as follows, as stated by Dr. R. S. Woodward:[*]

In spite of the superb experimental investigations made particularly during the past quarter of a century by Cornu and Baille (Comptes rendus, LXXVI, 1873), Poynting (The Mean Density of the Earth, by J. H. Poynting, London, Charles Griffin & Co., 1894), Boys (Philosophical Transactions, No. 186, 1895), Richarz and Krigar-Menzel (Sitzungsberichte, Berlin Academy, Band 2, 1896), and Braun (Denkschriften, Math. Natur. Classe, Vienna Academy, Bd. LXIV, 1897), it must be said that the gravitation constant is uncertain by some units in the fourth significant figure, and possibly even by one or two units in the third figure.

The results of the investigators mentioned for the gravitation constant are, in C. G. S. units, as follows, the first result having been computed from data given by MM. Cornu and Baille in the publication referred to:

Cornu and Baille (1873)	6668 (10^{-11})
Poynting (1894)	6698 (10^{-11})
Boys (1894)	6657 (10^{-11})
Richarz and Krigar-Menzel (1896)	6685 (10^{-11})
Braun (1897)	6658 (10^{-11})

Regarding these as of equal weight, their mean is 6673 (10^{-11}) with a probable error of ± 5 units in the fourth place, or 1/1330th part. This is of about the same order of precision as that deduced by Prof. Newcomb from astronomical data.

The uncertainty in the adopted value is, however, within allowable limits for the present investigation.

The vertical component at the observation station of the attraction expressed in formula (8) is, in dynes,

$$kdm\frac{\sin \beta}{D^2} \tag{9}$$

in which β is the angle of depression, below the horizon of the station, of the straight line from the station to the elementary mass.

This vertical component is all that is concerned in this investigation. The integral of all such vertical components at the station, corresponding to all the elementary masses which together constitute the earth, is the vertical force due to gravitation which acts on a mass of one gram placed at the station. This vertical force expressed in dynes is necessarily numerically equal to the acceleration (both being expressed in the centimeter-gram-second system) which would be produced by gravitation acting upon any mass at the station left free to fall. They are, of course, affected by the centrifugal force due to the earth's rotation, but this effect need not be considered in the discussion of these formulæ.

The term, gravity, is used in its generally accepted sense; that is, it is the resultant of the earth's gravitation and the centrifugal force due to the earth's rotation.

---

[*] See p. 153 of an address entitled "The Century's Progress in Applied Mathematics," by R. S. Woodward, Bulletin of the American Mathematical Society, 2d Series, Vol. VI, No. 4, pp. 133-163. In this address and in another by the same author entitled "Measurement and Calculation," published in Science, new series, Vol. XV, No. 390, pp. 961-971, June 20, 1902, are given excellent statements of the nature of the gravitation constant and the importance of determining its value accurately.

In general it will be found that throughout this publication the attraction (expressed in dynes) is dealt with directly by preference rather than its numerical equivalent, the acceleration (expressed in centimeters and seconds). This preference is due to the belief that thereby circumlocutions are avoided and greater clearness secured in the conceptions.

If the station and the elementary mass, dm, are at the same elevation referred to sea level

$$\beta = \frac{\theta}{2}$$

and

$$D = 2r \sin \frac{\theta}{2}$$

(see illustration No. 3), in which θ is the angle at the center of the earth subtended between the station and the elementary mass and r is the radius of the earth.

If absolute accuracy were desired it would be necessary to use for r the average radius of curvature, between the station and the mass considered, of the equipotential surface in which they both lie. This average radius depends upon the elevation above sea level and also, since the sea-level surface is an ellipsoid of revolution (not a sphere), it depends upon the latitude of the station and the azimuth of the line from the station to the mass under consideration. But with sufficient accuracy for this investigation r is assumed to be constant with the value 637 000 000 centimeters in this and similar formulæ. This is equivalent to assuming, in deriving these formulæ, that the station is on the surface of a spherical earth having the radius stated. Under the heading "Discussion of errors" it will be shown that this assumption is far within the allowable limits of approximation.

By substituting these values of β and D in (9) there is obtained as the formula for the vertical component of the attraction in dynes upon a unit mass at the station, due to an elementary mass which is at the same elevation as the station,

$$kdm \frac{\sin \frac{\theta}{2}}{4r^3 \sin^2 \frac{\theta}{2}} = kdm \, E \qquad (10)$$

The single symbol E is used to represent that portion of the formula

$$\frac{\sin \frac{\theta}{2}}{4r^3 \sin^2 \frac{\theta}{2}}$$

which depends simply upon the direction and distance of the elementary mass from the station, because later it is most convenient to deal with E separately from k and dm.

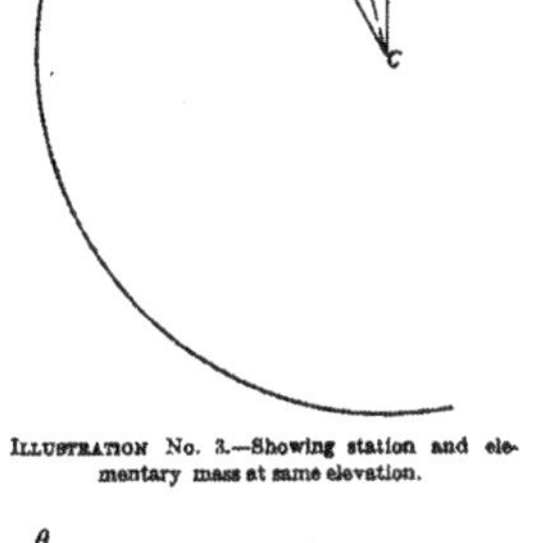

ILLUSTRATION No. 3.—Showing station and elementary mass at same elevation.

To divide both the numerator and denominator of (10) by $\sin \frac{\theta}{2}$ would simplify the expression, but by so doing the close analogy between (10) and the more complicated expressions (15) and (16) would become less obvious.

In each of the illustrations Nos. 3, 4, and 5, S represents the gravity station, and the circle represents the intersection of the level surface which lies at the elevation of the station with a plane defined by the station, the center of the earth (C), and the elementary mass considered..

B is the location of the elementary mass dm, β is the angle between the horizon of the station (SH) and the straight line from the station to B, and D is the distance from the station to B. In illustrations Nos. 4 and 5, D_1 is the distance from the station to a point A at the same elevation as the station and in the same vertical line as B, the location of the elementary mass.

Illustration No. 4 represents the case in which the elementary mass, dm, is higher than the station, the difference of elevation being h. In the triangle SAB, from the law of proportional sines,

$$\sin \beta_c = \frac{h \cos \frac{\theta}{2}}{D} \tag{11}$$

also, in this triangle, according to plane trigonometry,

$$D^2 = D_1^2 + h^2 + 2D_1 h \sin \frac{\theta}{2} \tag{12}$$

From illustration No. 4 it appears that

$$\beta_h = \frac{\theta}{2} \tag{13}$$

and

$$\beta = \beta_h - \beta_c \tag{14}$$

By substituting from formulæ (11), (12), (13), and (14) in (9) there is obtained as the formula for the vertical component of the attraction in dynes upon a unit mass at the station, due to an elementary mass which is higher than the station,

$$kdm \frac{\sin \left(\frac{\theta}{2} - \sin^{-1} \frac{h \cos \frac{\theta}{2}}{\sqrt{D_1^2 + h^2 + 2D_1 h \sin \frac{\theta}{2}}} \right)}{D_1^2 + h^2 + 2D_1 h \sin \frac{\theta}{2}} = kdm \, E_1 \tag{15}$$

Here again a single symbol, E_1, is taken to represent that portion of the formula which depends simply upon the direction and distance of the elementary mass from the station.

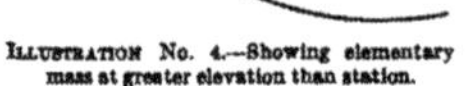

ILLUSTRATION No. 4.—Showing elementary mass at greater elevation than station.

Illustration No. 5 represents the case in which the elementary mass, dm, is lower than the station, the difference of elevation being h. By the same process as that used above it may be shown that the vertical component of the attraction in dynes upon a unit mass at the station, due to an elementary mass which is lower than the station is

$$kdm \frac{\sin \left(\frac{\theta}{2} + \sin^{-1} \frac{h \cos \frac{\theta}{2}}{\sqrt{D_1^2 + h^2 - 2D_1 h \sin \frac{\theta}{2}}} \right)}{D_1^2 + h^2 - 2D_1 h \sin \frac{\theta}{2}} = kdm \, E_2 \tag{16}$$

in which E_2 is used to represent that part of the formula which depends simply upon the direction and distance of the elementary mass from the station.

It is important to note that the only approximation made in deriving formulæ (10), (15), and (16) is that to which attention has already been called, namely that the radius of curvature concerned at each station is 637 000 000 centimeters. In every other respect the derivation of the formulæ is exact regardless of the distance of the attracting mass from the observation station. The attracting mass may even be located at the antipodes of the station. These formulæ were used in connection with all attracting masses which are so far from the station that the curvature of the sea level surface must be taken into account in order to insure that the errors of computation of the effects are less than 1 part in 200.

For masses near the station, the well-known formula for the attraction of a mass having the form of a right cylinder upon a point outside the cylinder and lying in its axis produced was utilized.* This formula, in a convenient form for the present purpose, for the attraction in dynes upon a unit mass (1 gram) at the station, is

$$k2\pi\delta\{\sqrt{c^2+h^2}-\sqrt{c^2+(h+t)^2}+t\} \tag{17}$$

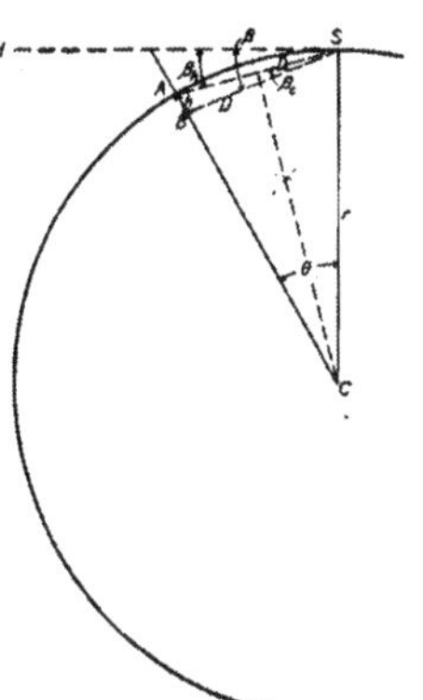

in which k is the gravitation constant, δ is the density of the material, c is the radius of the cylinder, t is the length of an element of the cylinder, and h is the distance from the attracted point, the station, to the nearest end of the cylinder.

For a mass which has the form of a cylindrical shell, that is, the difference of two concentric right cylinders of the same length having different radii, c_1 and c_2, formula (17) becomes

$$k2\pi\delta\{\sqrt{c_2^2+h^2}-\sqrt{c_1^2+h^2}-\sqrt{c_2^2+(h+t)^2}+\sqrt{c_1^2+(h+t)^2}\} \tag{18}$$

This is the attraction in dynes upon a unit mass (1 gram) at the station.

The formulæ (17) and (18) are exact if applied to cylinders and cylindrical shells.

The justification of the radical departure from past practice represented by formulæ (10), (15), and (16), and by the introduction of the gravitation constant into formulæ (17) and

ILLUSTRATION No. 5.—Showing elementary mass at less elevation than station.

(18) is the success attained thereby in securing quick and accurate computations. The reader is therefore requested to suspend judgment until the remainder of this publication has been read and the degree of success has been compared with that obtained by the use of any other formulæ with which comparison is made.

DIVISION OF THE SURFACE OF THE EARTH INTO ZONES AND COMPARTMENTS.

In order to apply formulæ (10), (15), (16), (17), and (18) to the computation of the effect of the topography and the isostatic compensation, the whole surface of the earth was divided into zones by circles, each having the station at its center, and each zone was divided into equal compartments by radial lines. The division adopted is shown in the following table. Illustrations Nos. 10a and 10b, page 48, show the shapes of certain compartments.

* For two statements of this formula see A Treatise on Attractions, Laplace's Function and Figures of the Earth, by John H. Pratt, third edition, p. 46, and Traité de Mécanique Céleste, F. Tisserand, Tome II, pp. 71-72.

Designation of zone	Inner radius of zone			Outer radius of zone			Compartments
	Meters			*Meters*			
A	0			2			1
B	2			68			4
C	68			230			4
D	230			590			6
E	590			1 280			8
F	1 280			2 290			10
G	2 290			3 520			12
H	3 520			5 240			16
I	5 240			8 440			20
J	8 440			12 400			16
K	12 400			18 800			20
L	18 800			28 800			24
M	28 800			58 800			14
N	58 800			99 000			16
O	99 000			166 700			28
	°	′	″	°	′	″	
18	1	29	58	1	41	13	1
17	1	41	13	1	54	52	1
16	1	54	52	2	11	53	1
15	2	11	53	2	33	46	1
14	2	33	46	3	03	05	1
13	3	03	05	4	19	13	16
12	4	19	13	5	46	34	10
11	5	46	34	7	51	30	8
10	7	51	30	10	44		6
9	10	44		14	09		4
8	14	09		20	41		4
7	20	41		26	41		2
6	26	41		35	58		18
5	35	58		51	04		16
4	51	04		72	13		12
3	72	13		105	48		10
2	105	48		150	56		6
1	150	56		180			1

For the numbered zones it was found to be more convenient to use the radii of the zone in degrees and minutes of a great circle than in meters. The inner radius of zone 18 is the same as the outer radius of zone O, that is, on a sphere of the adopted size, radius 637 000 000 centimeters, 1° 29′ 58″ of a great circle (the inner radius of zone 18) has a length 166 700 meters (the outer radius of zone O). Zone A commences at the station, and zone 1 ends at the antipodes of the station. All the zones together cover the earth completely.

Zone A, with a single compartment, is a circle about the station with a radius of 2 meters. Similarly, zone 1, with a single compartment, is a circle about the antipodes of the station with a radius of 29° 04′ (3240 kilometers). Zones 18 to 14 each have a single compartment. All other zones have from 2 to 28 compartments each, the number of compartments being even in each case.

For each zone a special reduction table was prepared in the manner indicated hereafter under the heading, "Computation of reduction tables." This table for each zone gives the relation between the mean elevation of the surface of the ground in each compartment of that zone and the effect of topography and the isostatic compensation in that compartment upon the vertical component of the attraction at the station.

In making the arbitrary selection of radii of zones and of the number of compartments in each zone, it was necessary to consider the effect of the size and shape of the compartment; first, upon the time required to complete the computations; second, upon the accuracy of the computations in so far as it depends upon the accuracy of the estimates made by the computer of the mean elevation within each compartment; and, third, upon the accuracy of certain necessary assumptions in the computation.

The larger the compartments are made, the smaller will be the number of compartments, and therefore the smaller the number of estimates of mean elevation to be made, one for each compartment. But as the compartments are made larger, the time required for each estimate becomes greater. For with a large compartment it is necessary to estimate the mean elevation more closely to secure a given degree of accuracy than with a small compartment; to estimate to the nearest hundred feet, for example, instead of to the nearest thousand feet. Also, the larger the compartment the greater the total range of elevations within the compartment, and therefore the greater the time necessary to secure an estimate of the mean to a given degree of accuracy. Hence the adoption of compartments either too large or too small would have made the time required for the computation greater than would otherwise have been necessary.

There are 317 compartments in all, 199 in the 15 lettered zones near the station, and 118 in the 18 numbered zones, all of which are more than 166 kilometers from the station.

It is believed that the size and shape of each compartment has been so fixed that the error of computation for any compartment is ordinarily less than 0.0002 dyne, and is of the accidental class. The basis of this belief will be indicated in connection with the topic, "Discussion of errors." It is known that notable success has been attained in securing rapid computation.

With the experience now available, a better selection of radii of zones, and of numbers of compartments in each zone could be made. But such a new selection would make it necessary to recompute the reduction tables. It is not probable that the improvement would be sufficient to warrant this recomputation.

COMPUTATION OF REDUCTION TABLES FOR NEAR ZONES.

For zone A, comprising the surface of the earth in a circle around the station with a radius of 2 meters, the reduction table was computed by formula (17).

The effect of the topography in this zone, if the station is on land, is the effect of a cylinder of material having the density, δ, assumed to be the mean surface density of the earth, namely, 2.67, having a radius $c = 200$ centimeters and a length, t, equal to the elevation of the station. In the formula $h = o$ for this case, as the station is at the end of the cylinder in question. The elevation of the surface of the ground in all parts of this small zone is assumed in the computation to be the same as the elevation of the station.

In the computations it was necessary, of course, to express all distances in centimeters to conform to the adopted value of k, which is expressed in the centimeter-gram-second system. (See p. 13.)

The attraction computed is evidently a vertical force, as the station lies in the axis of the cylinder, which is vertical.

The effect of the corresponding isostatic compensation was computed from the same formula (17) with the same values of c and h, but with $t = 11\ 370\ 000$ centimeters, the assumed depth of compensation (it should be remembered that compensation is assumed to begin at the surface of the ground and at the bottom of the sea, see page 10), and with a value of δ_1 from formula (3), page 8, substituted for δ, namely, $\delta_1 = \delta\dfrac{H}{h_1} = 2.67\dfrac{H}{11\ 370\ 000}$, in which H is the elevation of the surface above sea level (assumed to be the same as the elevation of the station).

The isostatic compensation is thus treated as a cylinder of material of a negative density δ_1, or, in other words, as a negative mass just equal to the positive mass which would exist in this zone above sea level if the actual density of all material in the zone above sea level were 2.67.

For a land compartment the computed effect of the topography is positive, an increase in the downward attraction upon a unit mass (1 gram) at the station. The computed effect of the isostatic compensation is negative, a decrease in the downward attraction upon a unit mass at the station. The difference of the two is the resultant effect of the combined topography and isostatic compensation. This resultant effect was computed for various assumed values of the elevation of the station above sea level, and then the reduction table for zone A written as shown on page 30. An inspection of the table will make it clear that as soon as a few of the tabular values had been computed the remainder could be safely interpolated with the required degree of accuracy.

To apply formula (17) to a station at sea, such as those occupied by Dr. Hecker on the Atlantic and Pacific,[*] it is necessary in computing the effect of the topography to substitute for δ in formula (17) the value $(\delta - \delta_w)$ (see pp. 8-9, and illustration No. 2), the defect of density of sea water in comparison with solid earth. The value of h is zero, the station being assumed to be at sea level. The mass thus considered is a mass which is the difference between that actually contained in the cylinder of radius 200 centimeters extending from the station at sea level down to the bottom of the ocean, and the mass which would fill this same cylinder if solid earth with a density of 2.67 were substituted for the sea water.

To apply formula (17) to a station at sea, in computing the effect of the isostatic compensation, it is necessary to substitute for the δ of formula (17) the value of δ_1 computed by formula (6a), page 11, namely

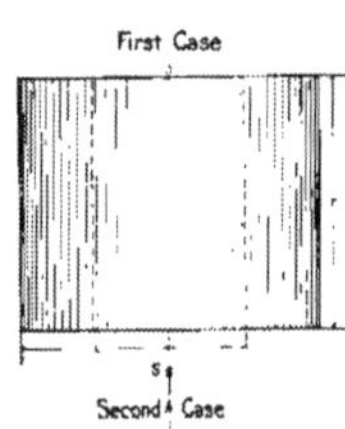

First Case

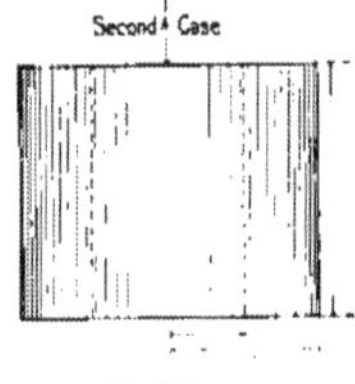

Second Case

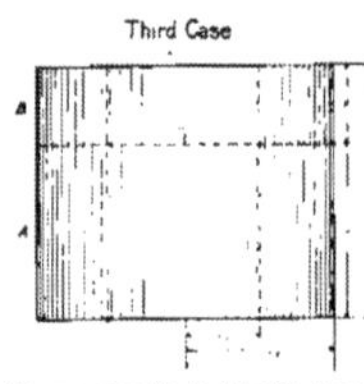

Third Case

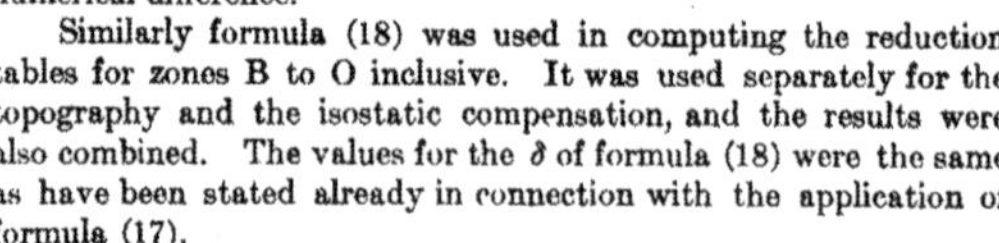

$$\delta_1 = \delta - \frac{0.615\,D}{h_1} = 2.67 \frac{0.615\,D}{11\ 370\ 000}$$

in which D is the depth of the water. In this case the h of formula (17) is not zero but equal to D, as the upper limit of the compensation is at the ocean bottom at a distance D below the station.

For an oceanic compartment the computed effect of the topography (in this case submerged topography, or hydrography) is negative, a decrease in the downward attraction upon a unit mass at the station. That is, the attraction is less than it would be if in the compartment from the ocean bottom to sea level material of density 2.67 were substituted for the sea water which is actually in this space. The computed effect of the isostatic compensation is positive, an increase in the downward attraction upon a unit mass at the station, for the compensation is in this case an excess of density and of mass. The resultant effect is in this case again a numerical difference.

Similarly formula (18) was used in computing the reduction tables for zones B to O inclusive. It was used separately for the topography and the isostatic compensation, and the results were also combined. The values for the δ of formula (18) were the same as have been stated already in connection with the application of formula (17).

In using formula (18) to compute the effect of the topography in land zones three cases arise.

First, when the mean elevation of the surface of the ground in the zone is the same as the elevation of the station, h is zero in formula (18). (See illustration No. 6.) In this case the attracted point, the station, is in the plane of the upper end of the cylindrical shell considered. This cylindrical shell contains all the material in the zone, from the actual surface of the ground down to sea level, the inner and outer radii of the shell being the same as the inner and outer radii of the zone, and the length of an element of the cylindrical shell being the mean elevation of the surface of the ground.

Second, when the station is above the mean elevation of the surface of the ground in the zone, as indicated in the second case in illustration No. 6, h is the difference of elevation between the station and the mean surface of the ground in the zone, and in other respects this case is similar to the first one. For any land zone the computed effect of the topography in either the first or the second case is always positive, an increase in the downward attraction at the station.

ILLUSTRATION No. 6.—Showing topography in land zones—three cases.

* Bestimmung der Schwerkraft / auf dem / Atlantischen Ozean / Sowie in / Rio de Janeiro, Lissabon und Madrid / Mit Neun Tafeln / von O. Hecker; Berlin, 1903. Bestimmung der Schwerkraft / auf dem / Indischen und Groszen Ozean / und / An Deren Küsten / Sowie Erdmagnetische Messungen / Mit Zwölf Tafeln. / von Prof. Dr. O. Hecker; Berlin, 1908.

Third, when the station is below the mean elevation of the surface of the ground in the zone, as indicated in the third case in illustration No. 6, the cylindrical shell containing the topography is considered broken into two separate cylindrical shells, one above the other, indicated as shell A and shell B in the illustration, and formula (18) is applied separately to the two shells. Shell A extends from sea level to the elevation of the station, and its effect is computed exactly as was that of the shell in the first case. Shell B contains the remainder of the material in the zone above sea level. It extends from the level of the station up to the mean elevation of the surface of the ground in the zone. In this shell c_2 and c_1 have the same values as in shell A, h is zero, the station being in the plane of the lower end of the shell, and t is the difference between the elevation of the station and the mean elevation of the surface of the ground in the zone. The effect of the material in shell B is an upward attraction at the station. Hence the resultant effect at the station of the topography in this case is the difference of the separate effects of shell A and shell B. This resultant effect will evidently be positive, a downward attraction, if shell A is longer than shell B, and will be negative if shell B is the longer. If the station is at an elevation exactly one-half of the mean elevation of the surface of the ground in the zone, shell A and shell B are of equal lengths, and the resultant effect is zero.

For oceanic zones the first and second cases arise, but never the third case. Hence for oceanic zones the computed effect is always negative, the downward attraction at the station being always less than it would be if material of density 2.67 were substituted for sea water.

In applying formula (18) to the computation of the effect of the isostatic compensation for land zones all three of the cases described above arise. Hence, in the third case, the effect of the compensation was obtained by computing separately the effects of two shells corresponding to shell A and shell B. In computing the effect of the compensation the length of an element of the shell is 11 370 000 centimeters (the depth of compensation) in the first and second cases, 11 370 000 centimeters minus the difference between the elevation of the station and the mean elevation of the ground in the zone in shell A of the third case, and simply the difference between the elevation of the station and the mean elevation of the surface of the ground in the zone in shell B of the third case. In all these cases, including both shells in the third case, the value to be used for δ in formula (18) is that computed from formula (3), page 8, in which the mean elevation of the surface of the zone is to be used for H and the assumed depth of compensation for h_1. As shell A is always much longer than shell B in connection with the compensation, its effect always predominates, and the computed effect of the compensation for these zones is always negative, a decrease of downward attraction at the station.

In applying formula (18) to the computation of the effect of the isostatic compensation for oceanic zones the second case is the only one which arises, and the computed effect of the compensation is always positive, an increase in the downward attraction at the station. The value to be used for δ in formula (18) is computed from formula (6a), page 11.

For zones B to O the combined effect of topography and compensation is not always a numerical difference of the separate effects. In a few rare cases for land zones, namely, when shell B of the third case happens to be longer than shell A, the effects at the station of the topography and its compensation are both negative, and their combined effect is the numerical sum.

To avoid circumlocutions a few paragraphs just preceding this have been worded as if the mean elevation for the whole of each zone was dealt with in the computation. In zone F, see page 18, which is divided into 10 equal compartments, the effect of the topography or of the compensation in any one compartment upon the vertical component of the attraction at the station is evidently exactly one-tenth of that computed for the whole zone from formula (18), provided the elevation of the surface of the ground is the same throughout the zone. The actual practice was to use formula (18) in computing the effects for a whole zone at once, then to divide the result by the number of compartments in that zone (10 for zone F) to obtain the effect of each compartment. These effects for separate compartments were then tabulated in the reduction tables, and in using these tables the mean elevation for each compartment was used, not the mean elevation for the whole zone.

It was not found necessary to compute each separate value in the reduction tables for zones B to O. For each of these tables a few scattered values, in each of several selected columns, were computed. For each selected column the points so computed were plotted on cross-section paper, using the assumed mean elevation of the compartments as abscissæ and the computed values as ordinates. When the number of plotted points was sufficient to enable one to do so with the required degree of accuracy, a curve was drawn through these points to represent all the required values corresponding to the column in question. The intermediate values for the column were then scaled from the curve and entered in the table, together with the computed values. After the values in a few columns of the table had been so obtained, it obviously became possible to interpolate the values for the remaining columns with the required degree of accuracy. The vertical differences in the columns, filled in from the computations and curves, served as checks in making these interpolations.

Illustration No. 7 shows the curves used as indicated above in connection with the reduction table for zone E. On each curve the computed points are indicated by small circles. The curves were drawn by eye, using a draftsman's flexible ruler. The shape of each curve and its position relative to the other curves furnish a sensitive check for detecting errors in the plotted·values due to the computations or plotting.

As the computations of the reduction tables by formula (18) could be made much more easily than by formulæ (10), (15), and (16), it was desired to extend the use of formula (18) to as many zones as possible. It was found that out to zone L the errors secured by the use of formula (18) in the manner already described were within allowable limits. It appeared that when formula (18) was applied to zone O the principal error arose from the fact that a point in the middle of this zone which is at the same elevation as the station lies 4500 feet below the horizontal plane of the station on account of the curvature of the sea-level surface. It appeared that possibly this particular error could be eliminated and a very close approximation to the truth obtained by using for the h of formula (18) not the difference of elevation between the station and the mean surface of the ground in the zone, but instead the difference of elevation between the station and a point 4500 feet below the mean elevation of the zone. This would have the effect of making the second correction in the table zero if the mean surface of the compartment lay in the horizontal plane of the station. Accordingly, the column headed "Station above compartment, 800 feet," in the reduction table for zone O, was computed with a value $4500 + 800 = 5300$ feet for h, the next column with a value $4500 + 1600 = 6100$ feet for h, and so on. Similarly the values in the column headed "Station below compartment, 800 feet," were computed with the value $4500 - 800 = 3700$ feet. The corrections in the column headed "Station at same elevation as compartment" are applicable to compartments in which the mean elevation of the surface of the ground is the same as that of the station. These values were computed with $h = 4500$ feet in formula (18).

Similar modifications to take account of the curvature approximately were made in the tables for zones M and N, but for zones nearer the station it appeared that such changes would not amount to as much as 0.0001 dyne, and they were therefore not computed.

After computations for zone O were made by formula (18), using the modified method indicated in the preceding two paragraphs, in which method the curvature of the sea-level surface is taken into account in part, certain values of the table were also computed by formulæ (10), (15), and (16), which are exact, the curvature being fully taken into account. This test showed that the tabular values as computed by formula (18) by the method described are each within 0.0002 dyne, and are in error by less than 1 part in 200 on an average. This made it certain that the errors in zones M and N, and other zones nearer the station than zone O, are well within the adopted limits. The test in zone O also indicated that for the next larger zone the adopted limits of error might be exceeded if formula (18) were used, even with the modification described. Therefore formulæ (10), (15), and (16) were used for all zones beyond O.

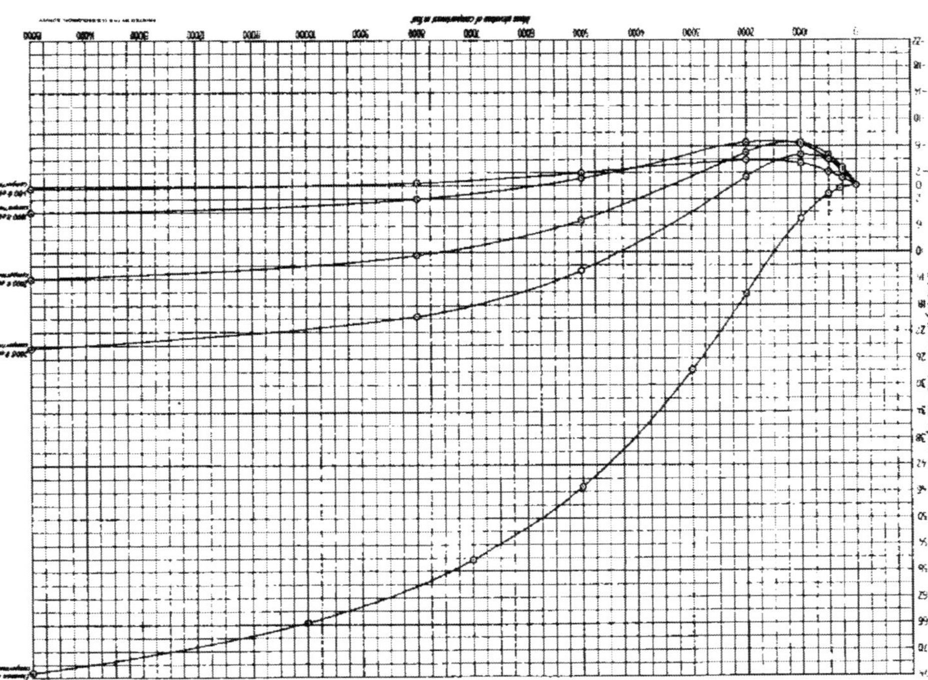

ILLUSTRATION No. 7.—Graphical Computation of Reduction Table for Zone E.

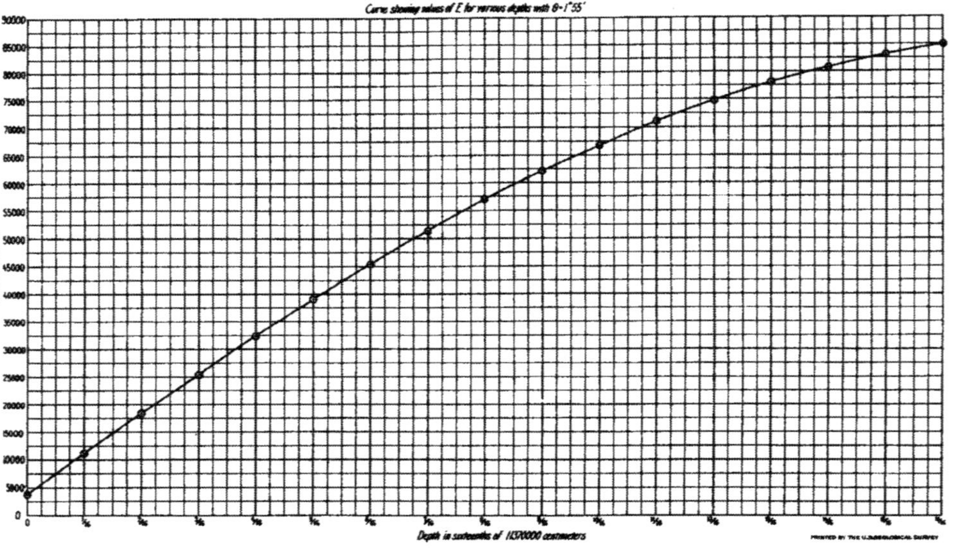

ILLUSTRATION No. 8.—GRAPHICAL REPRESENTATION OF VALUES OF E FOR VARIOUS DEPTHS.

COMPUTATION OF REDUCTION TABLES FOR DISTANT ZONES.

To use these formulæ in computing the effect of the topography within a given zone for a land area it is necessary to integrate the expression $kdmE$ to include all elementary masses within that zone between the surface of the ground and sea level. E is understood in this statement to be the E of formula (10), the E_1 of formula (15), or the E_2 of formula (16) for each elementary mass according to whether it is at the same level as the station, higher than the station or lower than the station, respectively. Since $kdmE$ is the vertical component of the attraction in dynes upon a unit mass at the station due to an elementary mass, dm, the integral stated is evidently the vertical component of the attraction due to all the elementary masses which combined constitute the material lying above sea level in the zone in question. In the integration k is a constant, and the sum of all the elementary masses, dm, is the total mass m, which is known in terms of the volume and density. No difficulty was encountered in dealing with these quantities. But the expression for E is a function of h and θ, which can not, so far as the writers know, be directly integrated with respect to these quantities by calculus. Therefore, an integration by numerical computation was made.

The vertical component of the attraction in dynes upon a unit mass at the station due to all the topography within any zone lying entirely in a land area was therefore expressed as the integral of $kdmE$ or

$$km \text{ (average value of } E \text{ for the zone)} \qquad (19)$$

in which it is understood that the various values of E, of which the average is taken, must correspond to equal elementary masses, of which the sum is m, the total mass represented by the topography in the zone.

Similarly the vertical component of the attraction in dynes upon a unit mass at the station due to the isostatic compensation of the topography within any zone lying entirely in a land area is also represented by formula (19). The negative mass involved is m, the values of E are those fixed by the direction and distance of the compensation from the station, and h is made to vary to cover the whole range occupied by the compensation, namely, from sea level down to the depth 113.7 kilometers below that surface.

The effect of the topography and the effect of its compensation might have been computed separately from formula (19), but it was believed that greater rapidity would be secured without loss of accuracy by combining and dealing directly with the resultant difference of the effects of the topography and its compensation. Accordingly, the actual process followed is that described in the following paragraphs.

The computation will be described first for land zones having an elevation of 100 feet and for the station assumed to be at sea level. The modifications introduced for other elevations, for ocean zones, and for assumed positions of the station above sea level will be stated later.

For a selected value of θ, E was computed by formulæ (10) and (16) for several equally spaced values of h, varying from zero to the depth of compensation. Let the required mean value of an infinite number of such equally spaced values, covering the depth of compensation, be called E_c. By successive trials with increasing numbers of equally spaced values of h it was ascertained how many values were necessary in order to secure the required degree of accuracy in the mean value, E_c, corresponding to the selected value of θ. As E varies continuously according to a law which may be graphically expressed by a smooth and regular curve, it was not difficult with the numerical values at hand to make certain that one had secured the required degree of accuracy. Illustration No. 8 is an example of such a curve, which corresponds to $\theta = 1° 55'$; that is, to compensation which lies in a part of zone 16. (See page 18.) The values of h are plotted as abscissæ and the corresponding values of E as ordinates. The small circles each represent a computed value of E. A smooth curve has been drawn by eye through these computed points. It is evident that as the curve is nearly a straight line between successive computed points but little change would be secured in the mean by computing more points. This is still more clearly and precisely shown in the following table, corresponding to illustration No. 8, and showing the computed values of E and their first and second differences.

Values of E for various depths, with $\theta = 1° 55'$.

Depth	$E(10^{w})$	Difference	Second difference
Centimeters			
0	3684		
1/16×11 370 000	11 026	+7342	− 60
2/16×11 370 000	18 308	+7282	−133
3/16×11 370 000	25 457	+7149	−209
4/16×11 370 000	32 397	+6940	−255
5/16×11 370 000	39 082	+6685	−332
6/16×11 370 000	45 435	+6353	−354
7/16×11 370 000	51 434	+5999	−409
8/16×11 370 000	57 024	+5590	−454
9/16×11 370 000	62 160	+5136	−462
10/16×11 370 000	66 834	+4674	−477
11/16×11 370 000	71 031	+4197	−499
12/16×11 370 000	74 729	+3698	−433
13/16×11 370 000	77 994	+3265	−485
14/16×11 370 000	80 774	+2780	−473
15/16×11 370 000	83 081	+2307	−431
11 370 000	84 947	+1876	
Mean	52 568		

If an infinite number of points were computed on the curve shown in illustration No. 8 and the mean taken, instead of the mean of the finite number of points there shown, the change in the computed mean would be represented by the average ordinate included between the curve and the series of chords joining the computed points which are shown in the illustration. As a convenient rough guide it was assumed that this average ordinate would usually be less than one-eighth of the average second difference shown in the preceding table. That this ratio, one-eighth, is a reasonably safe assumption in such a case may be verified either by trial or by geometry, assuming the short portion of the curve between successive points to be an arc of a circle.

A similar process of reasoning was followed to obtain the mean value of E corresponding to the topography for the same selected value of θ. Let E_T be the required mean value of an infinite number of equally spaced values covering the range from zero to the arbitrarily selected elevation, 100 feet. After E had been computed from formulæ (10) and (15) it usually appeared that in order to secure a sufficiently exact value of E_T it was necessary to compute but two values, one for $h = o$ and one for $h = 100$ feet, the mean of these two being sufficiently accurate.

It will be shown later how topography of a greater elevation than 100 feet was dealt with.

Keeping in mind that the negative mass, which is the isostatic compensation, is necessarily exactly equal to the positive surface excess of mass, which is the topography, formula (19) as applied to the topography and the compensation combined may be written

$$km(E_T - E_c) \text{ or } km\, E_R \tag{20}$$

E_R being written for $E_T - E_c$.

As this process of computing E_R, corresponding to a selected value of θ, is slow it was important to use good judgment in selecting the various values of θ for which the computation was to be made. It was desired to obtain a sufficiently accurate value of E_R for every possible value of θ by computing a moderate number of values for selected values of θ. At first E_R was computed for $\theta = 180°$, that is for the antipodes of the station, and for $\theta = 90°$, midway between the station and its antipodes. Then the computation was made for a few more values of θ at large intervals. It soon became evident that E_R varies quite slowly and at nearly a uniform rate if θ is near 180°, but that for small values of θ, E_R varies at a large and rapidly changing rate. Therefore, to secure a given degree of accuracy in interpolated values it was evidently necessary to compute E_R for closely spaced small values of θ, but only for widely separated large values of θ. The following table shows the various values of E_R actually computed. The values of θ shown in this table were selected by inspection by a step by step process, computations being made first for two values only of θ as already stated, then for values spaced at intervals of 30°, then at intervals of 10° for smaller values only, at intervals of 5° for still smaller values, and so on. All values of E_R intermediate between those shown in the table were obtained by interpolation. Illustration No. 9 shows a part of this table expressed graphically.

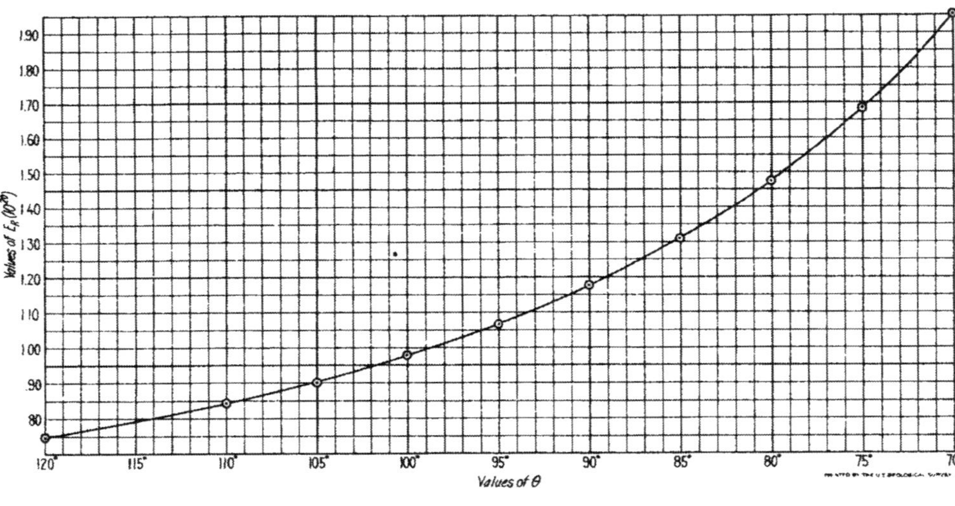

ILLUSTRATION No. 9.—Graphical Representation of Values of E_R.

θ	$E_T\ (10^{20})$	$E_C\ (10^{20})$	$E_R\ (10^{20})$	θ	$E_T\ (10^{20})$	$E_C\ (10^{20})$	$E_R\ (10^{20})$
° ′				° ′			
180 00	+ 61.6112	− 62.1664	− 0.5552	11 30	+ 614.9	− 892.6	− 277.7
170 00	+ 61.8466	− 62.4057	− .5591	11 00	+ 642.8	− 959.3	− 316.5
160 00	+ 62.5618	− 63.1336	− .5718	10 30	+ 673.2	−. 1035.8	− 362.6
150 00	+ 63.7846	− 64.3793	− .5947	10 15	+ 689.6	− 1079.1	− 389.5
140 00	+ 65.5654	− 66.1943	− .6289	10 00	+ 706.8	− 1125.8	− 419.0
130 00	+ 67.9805	− 68.6586	− .6781	9 45	+ 724.8	− 1177.2	− 452.4
120 00	+ 71.1425	− 71.8894	− .7469	9 30	+ 743.9	− 1232.8	− 488.9
110 00	+ 75.2134	− 76.0565	− .8431	9 15	+ 763.9	− 1293.7	− 529.8
105 00	+ 77.6592	− 78.564	− .905	9 00	+ 785.2	− 1359.6	− 574.4
100 00	+ 80.4277	− 81.4071	− .9794	8 45	+ 807.5	− 1432.2	− 624.7
95 00	+ 83.566	− 84.634	− 1.068	8 30	+ 831.2	− 1512.1	− 680.9
90 00	+ 87.1314	− 88.3089	− 1.1775	8 15	+ 856.3	− 1599.9	− 743.6
85 00	+ 91.196	− 92.506	− 1.310	8.00	+ 883.0	− 1697.1	− 814.1
80 00	+ 95.8500	− 97.326	− 1.476	7.45	+ 911.4	− 1805.3	− 893.9
75 00	+101.208	−102.892	− 1.684	7 30	+ 941.8	− 1925.9	− 984.1
70 00	+107.416	−109.368	− 1.952	7 15	+ 974.2	− 2061.3	− 1087.1
65 00	+114.668	−116.972	− 2.304	7 00	+1008.9	− 2213.3	− 1204.4
60 00	+123.222	−125.994	− 2.772	6 45	+1046	− 2391	− 1345
59 00	+125.118	−128.004	− 2.886	6 30	+1086	− 2593	− 1507
58 00	+127.083	−130.088	− 3.005	6 15	+1130	− 2823	− 1693
57 00	+129.120	−132.254	− 3.134	6 00	+1176	− 3087	− 1911
56 00	+131.235	−134.505	− 3.270	5 45	+1228	− 3394	− 2166
55 00	+133.430	−136.848	− 3.418	5 40	+1246	− 3506	− 2260
54 00	+135.710	−139.284	− 3.574	5 35	+1264	− 3624	− 2360
53 00	+138.080	−141.823	− 3.743	5 30	+1284	− 3750	− 2466
52 00	+140.545	−144.470	− 3.925	5 25	+1304	− 3881	− 2577
51 00	+143.111	−147.232	− 4.121	5 20	+1324	− 4020	− 2696
50 00	+145.784	−150.115	− 4.331	5 15	+1344	− 4165	− 2821
49 00	+148.570	−153.128	− 4.558	5 10	+1366	− 4320	− 2954
48 00	+151.476	−156.278	− 4.802	5 05	+1388	− 4482	− 3094
47 00	+154.511	−159.578	− 5.067	5 00	+1412	− 4658	− 3246
46 00	+157.681	−163.037	− 5.356	4 55	+1436	− 4849	− 3413
45 00	+160.996	−166.666	− 5.670	4 50	+1460	− 5056	− 3596
44 00	+164.468	−170.482	− 6.014	4 45	+1486	− 5271	− 3785
43 00	+168.106	−174.493	− 6.387	4 40	+1512	− 5503	− 3991
42 00	+171.920	−178.717	− 6.797	4 35	+1540	− 5743	− 4203
41 00	+175.926	−183.172	− 7.246	4 30	+1568	− 6007	− 4439
40 00	+180.138	−187.877	− 7.739	4 25	+1598	− 6287	− 4689
39 00	+184.569	−192.851	− 8.282	4 20	+1628	− 6582	− 4954
38 00	+189.240	−198.123	− 8.883	4 15	+1660	− 6896	− 5236
37 00	+194.168	−203.716	− 9.548	4 10	+1694	− 7237	− 5543
36 00	+199.376	−209.664	− 10.288	4 05	+1728	− 7601	− 5873
35 00	+204.89	−216.00	− 11.11	4 00	+1764	− 7986	− 6222
34 00	+210.72	−222.76	− 12.04	3 55	+1801	− 8425	− 6624
33 00	+216.92	−230.00	− 13.08	3 50	+1840	− 8883	− 7043
32 00	+223.52	−237.76	− 14.24	3 45	+1881	− 9385	− 7504
31 00	+230.54	−246.10	− 15.56	3 40	+1924	− 9943	− 8019
30 00	+238.04	−255.10	− 17.06	3 35	+1968	− 10525	− 8557
29 00	+246.06	−264.83	− 18.77	3 30	+2014	− 11165	− 9151
28 00	+254.66	−275.38	− 20.72	3 25	+2064	− 11903	− 9839
27 00	+263.92	−286.89	− 22.97	3 20	+2115	− 12685	− 10570
26 00	+273.88	−299.46	− 25.58	3 15	+2170	− 13526	− 11356
25 00	+284.65	−313.27	− 28.62	3 10	+2226	− 14457	− 12231
24 00	+296.32	−328.51	− 32.19	3 05	+2286	− 15462	− 13176
23 00	+309.02	−345.40	− 36.38	3 00	+2350	− 16567	− 14217
22 00	+322.88	−364.24	− 41.36	2 55	+2416	− 17829	− 15413
21 00	+338.08	−385.40	− 47.32	2 50	+2487	− 19214	− 16727
20 00	+354.79	−409.32	− 54.53	2 45	+2562	− 20736	− 18174
19 30	+363.80	−422.48	− 58.68	2 40	+2642	− 22480	− 19838
19 00	+373.27	−436.60	− 63.33	2 35	+2726	− 24402	− 21676
18 30	+383.27	−451.69	− 68.42	2 30	+2817	− 26530	− 23713
18 00	+393.82	−467.96	− 74.14	2 25	+2914	− 28970	− 26056
17 30	+404.98	−485.47	− 80.49	2 20	+3018	− 31703	− 28685
17 00	+416.80	−504.39	− 87.59	2 15	+3128	− 34855	− 31727
16 30	+429.34	−525.04	− 95.70	2 10	+3248	− 38370	− 35122
16 00	+442.6	−547.4	−104.8	2 05	+3377	− 42524	− 39147
15 30	+456.8	−571.9	−115.1	2 00	+3516	− 47164	− 43648
15 00	+472.0	−598.7	−126.7	1 55	+3668	− 52568	− 48900
14 30	+488.2	−628.2	−140.0	1 50	+3833	− 58930	− 55097
14 00	+505.6	−660.6	−155.0	1 45	+4014	− 66117	− 62103
13 30	+524.2	−697.2	−173.0	1 40	+4212	− 74671	− 70459
13 00	+544.2	−737.5	−193.3	1 35	+4431	− 84735	− 80304
12 30	+565.8	−782.6	−216.8	1 30	+4674	− 96711	− 92037
12 00	+589.4	−834.4	−245.0	1 25	+4945	−110993	−106048

It was desired that each value of E_R used in the computation, whether obtained directly or by interpolation, must be correct within 1 part in 200.

Having sufficiently accurate values of E_R for each separate value of θ the next step is essentially an integration with respect to θ as the variable.

The area of any zone lying between the limiting values of θ, θ_1, and θ_2, on the surface of the sphere which is being considered, one having a radius of 637 000 000 centimeters (see p. 15) is

$$2\pi r^2 \ (\cos \theta_1 - \cos \theta_2) \tag{21}$$

or $(6.283186)(637000000)^2(\cos \theta_1 - \cos \theta_2)$

Hence for this zone formula (20) becomes

$$k\partial H \left[(6.283186)(637000000)^2(\cos \theta_1 - \cos \theta_2)\right] \text{ (mean value of } E_R \text{ for the zone)} \tag{22}$$

in which for m there has been substituted its value in terms of density and volume, namely, ∂H(area).

With the numerical values before one it is not difficult to determine that for zones of a moderate width the average value of E_R for the zone is with sufficient accuracy the mean of its values at the two edges of the zone corresponding to θ_1 and θ_2. Therefore, formula (22), which is an expression for the required vertical component of the attraction in dynes upon a unit mass at the station due to the combined effect of both the topography and its isostatic compensation lying in a zone, may be evaluated by making separate numerical computations for separate narrow zones and adding the values.

By examination of the table showing values of E_R it is evident that the separate zones which may be used in this process are wide near the antipodes and decrease in width as θ becomes smaller. The actual widths used did not exceed the following limits and were occasionally less.

Limits of widths of subzones.

θ				Limit of width of subzone	
°	′	°	′	°	′
180	00 to	72	00	2	00
72	00 to	20	00	1	00
20	00 to	10	30	0	30
10	30 to	5	40	0	15
5	40 to	1	25	0	05

It was known from a reconnoissance of the problem that for all distant zones (beyond $\theta = 1° 29' 58''$) the value of the attraction computed from formula (22) would be nearly proportional to H. Therefore, as a time-saving device, it was decided to determine such widths for the selected zones and fix the number of compartments in each zone so that an attraction of 0.0001 dyne for any one compartment would correspond to a value for H of either 100, 1000, or 10 000 feet in that compartment. In that case the computation would consist simply of estimating the mean elevation within the compartment in feet and moving the decimal point a certain number of places to the left to obtain the attraction in dynes.

The arbitrarily selected unit of elevation corresponding to 0.0001 dyne was 10 000 feet for zones 1 to 6 (see tables on pp. 44–46), 1000 feet for zones 7 to 13, and 100 feet for zones 14 to 18. The number of compartments in each zone was arbitrarily fixed as shown in the same tables. By formula (22) the width of the zone was computed which would satisfy the condition that the attraction in one compartment corresponding to a unit of elevation was exactly 0.0001 dyne. For example, for zone 3 having 10 compartments it must be 0.0010 dyne for the zone if the mean elevation in the zone is 10 000 feet.

No difficulty was found in making this computation. An example of the actual arrangement of the numerical work is shown below for zone 12 having 10 compartments.

Computation of limit of zone 12.

[$km. = k\delta H = 0.00543061$ for $H = 1000$ feet.]

θ_1 to θ_2	$\cos \theta_1 - \cos \theta_2$	Area in cm $\times$ (10^{-10})	Area $\times$ km $\times$ (10^{-12})	E_R (10^{8})	Area $\times$ km $\times E_R$
° ′ ″ ° ′ ″					
5 46 34 to 5 40 00	0. 0001905	0. 000004857	0. 00000002638	2198	0. 00005798
5 40 00 to 5 35 00	. 0001425	. 000003633	. 00000001973	2310	. 00004558
5 35 00 to 5 30 00	. 0001405	. 000003582	. 00000001945	2413	. 00004693
5 30 00 to 5 25 00	. 0001383	. 000003526	. 00000001915	2522	. 00004830
5 25 00 to 5 20 00	. 0001363	. 000003475	. 00000001887	2636	. 00004974
5 20 00 to 5 15 00	. 0001341	. 000003419	. 00000001857	2758	. 00005122
5 15 00 to 5 10 00	. 0001321	. 000003368	. 00000001829	2888	. 00005282
5 10 00 to 5 05 00	. 0001299	. 000003312	. 00000001799	3024	. 00005440
5 05 00 to 5 00 00	. 0001278	. 000003258	. 00000001769	3170	. 00005608
5 00 00 to 4 55 00	. 0001257	. 000003205	. 00000001741	3330	. 00005798
4 55 00 to 4 50 00	. 0001236	. 000003151	. 00000001711	3504	. 00005995
4 50 00 to 4 45 00	. 0001215	. 000003098	. 00000001682	3690	. 00006207
4 45 00 to 4 40 00	. 0001194	. 000003044	. 00000001653	3888	. 00006427
4 40 00 to 4 35 00	. 0001173	. 000002991	. 00000001624	4097	. 00006654
4 35 00 to 4 30 00	. 0001151	. 000002934	. 00000001593	4321	. 00006883
4 30 00 to 4 25 00	. 0001131	. 000002884	. 00000001566	4564	. 00007147
4 25 00 to 4 20 00	. 0001109	. 000002827	. 00000001535	4822	. 00007401
4 20 00 to 4 19 12	. 0000176	. 000000449	. 00000000244	4987	. 00001217
					Sum=0.00100034

The change for $1''$ is about 0.000 000 25, therefore, the inner limit of zone 12 is, to the nearest second, $4° 19' 13''$. With that limit the above sum becomes 0.001 000 34 − 0.000 000 25 = 0.001 000 09.

The basis for the arbitrary decisions as to unit elevations and number of compartments in each zone will be indicated under the topic "Discussion of errors." It suffices to state here that the selection was guided by the desirability of making the computations as rapidly as possible subject to the chosen standard of accuracy. Errors of judgment in one direction would make the computation slow, and in the opposite direction would make the computation too inaccurate.

The limits of zones 1 to 18 computed as indicated above are shown in the reduction tables on pages 44–46, as well as on page 18.

To apply formula (22) to the computation for oceanic zones it was necessary merely to take into account the fact that the defect of density represented by sea water is $\delta - \delta_w = 0.615\,\delta$. (See p. 9.) Therefore, if the unit of elevation is 10 000 feet for a land compartment, corresponding to an attraction of 0.0001 dyne, it will be for an oceanic compartment to produce the same effect

$$\frac{10\ 000 \text{ feet}}{0.615} = 16\ 260 \text{ feet} = 2710 \text{ fathoms.}$$

Hence the unit of depth shown for zones 1 to 18 in the reduction tables on pages 44–46.

The attraction computed from formula (22) for a given compartment is not strictly proportional to H as assumed for a first close approximation. The limits of h used in computing E_R must correspond to H. For a land compartment, as H is made greater E_T becomes smaller, as it is an average value covering larger values of h in formula (15). Also as H, the assumed elevation, is made greater E_c tends to become smaller, for the isostatic compensation is assumed to commence at the solid surface of the ground (above sea level) (see illustration No. 2, page 10), and to extend to a depth of 113.7 kilometers measured from that level. The limits of h used in formulæ (15) and (16) must be fixed accordingly. Similar modifications must be inserted for oceanic compartments, the compensation commencing in this case at the ocean bottom, not at the sea level. As E_T and E_c, and their difference E_R, vary slightly for different values of H, the computed attractions in formula (22) are not strictly proportional to H as they would be if E_R were independent of H. This departure from strict proportionality was found upon investigation to be inappreciable for zones 1 to 13. For zones 14 to 18 a few special computations were made to evaluate the corrections for departure from proportionality shown in the reduction tables on page 44. These special computations were made by using the proper limiting values of h as indicated above, comparing the computed values with the values based on the assumption of proportionality and the original computations with $h = 100$ feet, and tabulating the differences as shown in the reduction tables. A few computations only were necessary because the corrections were small, and regular in their variation.

It was also assumed in order to secure a first close approximation to the attraction required that the station is at sea level. In general the station lies above sea level and, therefore, to secure exact results the values of h, used in formulæ (15) and (16) in computing E_T and E_C, must be differences of elevation between the station and the elementary mass, not merely the elevation of the elementary mass as was assumed in the first approximation. To secure the corrections for elevation shown in the reduction tables on page 44 a few special computations were made on the exact basis, compared with the first approximation, and the differences tabulated as corrections for elevation of the station. The corrections for elevation were found to be negligible for zones 1 to 13, and to be small as shown in the reduction tables for zones 14 to 18. Because the corrections are small and their variations regular but few special computations were necessary.

EXPLANATION OF REDUCTION TABLES.

The complete reduction tables for all the zones are given in the following pages. All tabular values are the vertical components of the attraction upon a unit mass at the station expressed in units of the fourth decimal place in dynes. It is equally true that these are corrections in units of the fourth decimal place of centimeters, to the acceleration of gravity, expressed in the centimeter-gram-second system.

These tables cover the whole of the earth's surface, from the station of observation to its antipodes. By their use one may quickly compute the effect upon the attraction of gravity, at any station on the earth, of all the topography of the earth and of its isostatic compensation assumed to be complete and uniformly distributed, with respect to depth, down to a limiting depth of compensation of 113.7 kilometers.

The radii of the zones A to O are given in meters, while those for zones 18 to 1 are in degrees, minutes, and seconds of an arc of a great circle.

The first column of each table from A to O contains values for the mean elevation of the compartment as read from the maps. The second, third, and fourth columns contain the corrections for the topography, the compensation, and the algebraic sum of the corrections for topography and the compensation respectively. These values are computed upon the assumption that the station is at the same elevation as the compartment. For zone A the elevation of the zone is necessarily that of the station, as its radius is only two meters. In the tables for zones B to O corrections for the elevation of the stations above or below the compartments are shown,

The corrections for the topography and compensation, the station being at the same elevation as the compartments, are shown separately in columns 2 and 3 for the zones out to O, in order that certain comparisons may be made between the effects of the assumption of complete local isostatic compensation and of regional isostatic compensation complete within a stated distance from the station. (See pp. 98–102.)

For the regular computations of the combined effect of topography and compensation, one correction is taken from column 4 of each table from zone A to zone O. For zone A this is the only correction. For zones B to L, inclusive, a second correction must be applied, as indicated, to take account of the difference of elevation of the station and of the mean surfaces of the ground in the compartment. To the correction based upon the assumption that the station is at the same elevation as the compartment, taken from the fourth column of the table, is added algebraically the correction for elevation of station above or below the compartment in order to obtain the total effect of topography and compensation. Thus, in zone E, if the mean elevation of the surface of the ground in a compartment is 2000 feet, the first correction is $+0.0016$ dyne, and if in this case the elevation of the station is 3000 feet, 1000 feet above the compartment, the second correction is $+0.0007$ dyne, and the total effect of both the topography of this compartment and its isostatic compensation is to increase the vertical component of the attraction on a unit mass at the station by 0.0023 dyne.

It is understood that, for zones B to L, inclusive, the second correction, namely, for station above or station below compartment, is zero if the elevation of the station is the same as the mean elevation of the surface of the ground in the compartment. This fact is used in interpolation if necessary. For example, in the case just cited in zone E, in which the mean elevation of the surface of the ground in the compartment is 2000 feet, if the station happens to be 100 feet above the compartment, the second correction would be $+0.0001$ dyne, since the table indicates it to be $+0.0002$ if the station is 200 feet above, and it is understood to be zero if the station is at the same elevation as the compartment. Similarly, if in this case the station happens to be 100 feet below the compartment, the second correction would be -0.0001 dyne since the table shows it to be -0.0002 dyne if the station is 200 feet below the compartment.

For zones C to O the first column of the tables contains elevations in both fathoms and in feet. Those in fathoms are depths below sea level and are marked minus. The values in the second, third, and fourth columns, corresponding to depths in fathoms, are computed on the supposition that the station is at sea level and in the following columns, headed "Station above compartment," the station is assumed to be at the stated distances above sea level. Hence, for all water compartments, there will be two corrections in the regular computations, one from the fourth column and one from the proper column beyond the fourth. Thus, in zone E, if the mean depth in the water compartment is 200 fathoms, and the elevation of the station above sea level is 600 feet, the two corrections are -0.0004 dyne and -0.0002 dyne, and the total effect of both topography in this compartment and its isostatic compensation is to decrease the vertical component of the attraction on a unit mass at the station by 0.0006 dyne.

For zones M, N, and O, as already explained in connection with the computation of the tables (p. 22), the second correction does not necessarily become zero when the station is at the same elevation as the compartment. Instead it has the value shown in the tables for these zones in the extra column headed "Station at the same elevation as compartment." In taking out the second corrections for these three zones this extra column must be carefully noted, one must take the second correction from it when the station and compartment happen to be at the same elevation, and one must use the values in this column to control interpolations when the station and compartment are nearly at the same elevation. Thus, if the mean elevation of the surface of a compartment in zone M is 12 000 feet the second correction is $+0.0001$ if the station is also at the elevation 12 000 feet, it is between $+0.0001$ and $+0.0002$ if the station is less than 700 feet above the compartment, and it is between $+0.0001$ and -0.0002 if the station is less than 700 feet below the compartment.

For zones 18 to 14 three corrections are applied. The first is read directly from the map, being 0.0001 dyne for each unit of elevation, the unit in each case being 100 feet, as indicated in the heading of this table. The second is taken from the second column of the table, using the first correction as an argument in entering the table. It takes account of the slight departure of the actual correction from being strictly proportional to the elevation. The third correction is taken from the last part of the table and takes account of the correction due to the elevation of the station above sea level. Thus, in zone 17, if the correction as read from the map is -0.0100 dyne, the elevation of the zone (the zone has but one compartment) being 10 000 feet, then the correction for departure from proportionality is $+0.0001$, and if the elevation of the station above sea level is also 10 000 feet the correction for its elevation is $+0.0003$ and the total effect of topography and compensation of this zone, upon the vertical component of the attraction upon a unit mass, at the station is $-0.0100 + 0.0001 + 0.0003 = -0.0096$ dyne. Similarly, if zone 17 is all upon the ocean, and the average depth of the water is 2710 fathoms (or 100 of the specified units of depth) the correction as read from the map is $+0.0100$ dyne, the correction for departure from proportionality is $+0.0001$, and if the station is at the elevation of 5000 feet the correction for elevation is -0.0001 and the total effect of the topography in this zone and its isostatic compensation is $+0.0100+0.0001-0.0001=0.0100$ dyne.

The unit of elevation for zones 13 to 7 is 1000 feet, and for zones 6 to 1 is 10 000 feet. These large units of elevation make it easy to estimate quickly the mean elevation within each compartment with the required degree of accuracy.

Note that for zones 13–1 there are no corrections for elevation of station and for departure from proportionality.

The reduction tables thus far described are believed to cover all cases which will arise when the gravity station is on land. But in order to provide for the computation of the effects of topography and isostatic compensation on the attraction at a gravity station on a vessel at sea, such as those occupied by Dr. Hecker on the Atlantic and Pacific Oceans, the two supplementary tables for use in connection with gravity stations at sea were prepared. These tables are computed on the supposition that the observation station is at sea level, since the correction for the small elevation above sea level to which the station is limited on board a ship would be less than 0.0001 dyne in every case. But one correction is to be taken out from these tables for each compartment. This correction is to be taken from the first table if that can be done without using any of the values marked with an asterisk. Otherwise it is to be taken from the second table in order to avoid large errors of interpolation which otherwise would occur on account of the large second differences in the first table.

For the remaining zones 18 to 1 no such sea tables are necessary, as the regular tables prepared for land stations cover all cases which will arise.

REDUCTION TABLES FOR LETTERED ZONES.

Zone A.

[Inner radius, zero; outer radius, 2 meters. One compartment.]

Elevation of station and compartment	Correction for—		
	Topography	Compensation	Topography and compensation
Feet			
0	0	0	0
5	+1	0	+1
10	+2	0	+2
100	+2	0	+2
1 000	+2	0	+2
2 000	+2	0	+2
3 000	+2	0	+2
4 000	+2	0	+2
5 000	+2	0	+2
6 000	+2	0	+2
7 000	+2	0	+2
8 000	+2	0	+2
9 000	+2	0	+2
10 000	+2	0	+2
11 000	+2	0	+2
12 000	+2	0	+2
13 000	+2	0	+2
14 000	+2	0	+2
15 000	+2	0	+2

For zone A the correction to gravity is a function only of the elevation of the station, for all land stations, as shown by the above table.

Zone B.

[Inner radius, 2 meters; outer radius, 68 meters. Four compartments.]

Mean elevation of compartment	Correction for— Topography	Correction for— Compensation	Correction for— Topography and compensation	Above 25 feet	Above 50 feet	Above 75 feet	Above 100 feet	Above 125 feet	Below 25 feet	Below 50 feet	Below 75 feet	Below 100 feet	Below 125 feet
Feet													
0	0	0	0	0	0	0	0	0					
10	0	0	0	0	0	0	0	0					
20	+1	0	+1	0	0	0	0	0					
30	+2	0	+2	0	0	-1	-1	-1	-3				
40	+3	0	+3	0	0	-1	-1	-1	-3				
50	+3	0	+3	0	-1	-1	-1	-2	-3	-6			
60	+4	0	+4	0	-1	-1	-1	-2	-3	-6			
70	+4	0	+4	0	-1	-1	-2	-2	-3	-6			
80	+5	0	+5	0	-1	-1	-2	-2	-3	-6	-9		
90	+5	0	+5	-1	-1	-2	-2	-3	-3	-6	-9		
100	+6	0	+6	-1	-1	-2	-2	-3	-3	-6	-9	-12	
150	+8	0	+8	-1	-2	-2	-3	-4	-2	-5	-8	-11	-14
200	+10	0	+10	-1	-2	-3	-4	-5	-2	-5	-7	-10	-12
300	+12	0	+12	-1	-2	-4	-5	-6	-2	-4	-6	-8	-10
400	+14	0	+14	-1	-3	-4	-5	-6	-2	-4	-6	-8	-9
500	+14	0	+14	-1	-3	-4	-5	-7	-2	-3	-5	-7	-8
1 000	+16	0	+16	-2	-3	-5	-6	-7	-2	-3	-5	-6	-7
2 000	+17	0	+17	-2	-3	-5	-6	-7	-2	-3	-5	-6	-7
3 000	+17	0	+17	-2	-3	-5	-6	-7	-2	-3	-5	-6	-7
4 000	+17	0	+17	-2	-3	-5	-6	-7	-2	-3	-5	-6	-7
5 000	+17	0	+17	-2	-3	-5	-6	-7	-2	-3	-5	-6	-7
6 000	+17	0	+17	-2	-3	-5	-6	-7	-2	-3	-5	-6	-7
7 000	+17	0	+17	-2	-3	-5	-6	-7	-2	-3	-5	-6	-7
8 000	+17	0	+17	-2	-3	-5	-6	-7	-2	-3	-5	-6	-7
9 000	+18	-1	+17	-2	-3	-5	-6	-7	-2	-3	-5	-6	-7
10 000	+18	-1	+17	-2	-3	-5	-6	-7	-2	-3	-5	-6	-7
15 000	+19	-1	+18	-2	-3	-5	-6	-7	-2	-3	-5	-6	-7

It is assumed that the mean elevation for any compartment in this zone will never be negative (below sea level) for any gravity station on land.

Zone C.

[Inner radius, 68 meters; outer radius, 230 meters. Four compartments.]

Correction for elevation of station—above compartment:

Mean elevation of compartment	Correction for— Topography	Correction for— Compensation	Correction for— Topography and compensation	Above 50 feet	Above 100 feet	Above 150 feet	Above 200 feet	Above 250 feet	Above 300 feet	Above 350 feet	Above 400 feet	Above 450 feet	Above 500 feet
Fathoms													
− 80	− 9	0	− 9										
− 40	− 4	0	− 4	0	0	0	0						
Feet													
0	0	0	0	0	0	0	0	0	0	0	0	0	0
100	+1	0	+1	0	0	0	0	0	0	0	0	0	-1
150	+2	0	+2	0	0	0	0	0	0	0	0	-1	-1
200	+4	0	+4	0	0	0	0	0	0	0	-1	-1	-1
250	+6	0	+6	0	0	0	0	0	0	0	-1	-1	-2
300	+8	0	+8	0	0	0	0	0	0	0	-1	-1	-2
350	+10	0	+10	0	0	0	0	0	0	-1	-1	-2	-2
400	+12	0	+12	0	0	0	0	0	0	-1	-2	-2	-3
450	+13	0	+13	0	0	0	0	0	0	-1	-2	-2	-3
500	+15	0	+15	0	0	0	0	0	0	-1	-2	-3	-4
550	+16	0	+16	0	0	0	0	0	0	-1	-2	-3	-4
600	+18	0	+18	0	0	0	0	0	-1	-2	-3	-4	-5
700	+20	0	+20	0	0	0	-1	-1	-2	-3	-4	-5	-6
800	+22	0	+22	0	-1	-1	-2	-2	-3	-4	-5	-6	-7
900	+24	0	+24	0	-1	-2	-2	-2	-4	-5	-6	-7	-8
1 000	+26	0	+26	0	-1	-2	-2	-3	-4	-6	-7	-8	-9
1 200	+28	0	+28	-1	-2	-2	-3	-4	-5	-6	-7	-9	-11
1 400	+30	0	+30	-1	-2	-2	-3	-4	-5	-6	-8	-9	-11
1 600	+32	0	+32	-1	-2	-3	-3	-4	-6	-7	-9	-10	-12
2 000	+34	0	+34	-1	-2	-3	-4	-5	-6	-8	-10	-11	-13
2 500	+36	0	+36	-1	-2	-3	-4	-5	-7	-8	-10	-11	-13
3 000	+38	0	+38	-1	-2	-3	-4	-6	-7	-9	-10	-12	-14
5 000	+41	-1	+40	-1	-2	-3	-4	-6	-7	-9	-10	-12	-14
15 000	+44	-2	+42	-1	-2	-3	-4	-6	-7	-9	-11	-12	-14

Correction for elevation of station—below compartment:

Mean elevation of compartment	Below 50 feet	Below 100 feet	Below 150 feet	Below 200 feet	Below 250 feet	Below 300 feet	Below 350 feet	Below 400 feet	Below 450 feet	Below 500 feet
Fathoms										
− 80										
− 40										
Feet										
0										
100	-1	-2								
150	-1	-3	-4							
200	-2	-4	-6	-8						
250	-2	-4	-7	-10	-12					
300	-2	-5	-8	-11	-14	-16				
350	-2	-5	-8	-12	-15	-18	-20			
400	-2	-5	-8	-12	-16	-19	-21	-24		
450	-2	-4	-7	-11	-15	-19	-23	-25	-26	
500	-2	-4	-7	-11	-15	-19	-23	-26	-28	-30
550	-2	-4	-6	-10	-14	-18	-22	-26	-28	-31
600	-2	-4	-6	-10	-14	-18	-22	-26	-29	-32
700	-1	-3	-6	-9	-13	-17	-20	-24	-28	-31
800	-1	-3	-5	-9	-12	-16	-19	-22	-26	-29
900	-1	-3	-5	-8	-11	-15	-18	-21	-24	-27
1 000	-1	-3	-5	-8	-11	-14	-17	-20	-23	-26
1 200	0	-2	-4	-7	-10	-13	-15	-18	-20	-23
1 400	0	-2	-4	-6	-9	-11	-14	-16	-18	-21
1 600	0	-2	-4	-6	-8	-10	-13	-15	-17	-20
2 000	0	-1	-3	-5	-7	-10	-12	-14	-16	-18
2 500	0	-1	-3	-5	-7	-9	-12	-13	-15	-17
3 000	0	-1	-3	-5	-7	-9	-12	-14	-15	-16
5 000	0	-1	-2	-4	-6	-8	-10	-12	-14	-15
15 000	0	-1	-2	-4	-6	-8	-10	-12	-13	-15

Correction for elevation of station —

Mean elevation of compartment	Topography	Compensation	Topography and compensation	Above compartment 100 feet	200 feet	300 feet	400 feet	500 feet	600 feet	700 feet	800 feet	900 feet	1000 feet	1100 feet	1200 feet	1300 feet	1400 feet
Fathoms																	
−200	−11	0	−11	−1	−2	−2	−2										
−150	−7	0	−7	−1	−2	−2	−2	−2	−2	−2							
−100	−4	0	−4	−1	−2	−2	−2	−2	−2	−2	−2	−2	−2				
−50	−1	0	−1	−1	−2	−2	−2	−2	−2	−2	−2	−2	−2	−2	−2	−2	−2
Feet																	
0	0	0	0	0	0	0	0	0	0	0	0	0	0	0	0	0	0
300	+2	0	+2	+1	+2	+3	+3	+3	+4	+4	+4	+3	+3	+3	+3	+3	+3
350	+3	0	+3	+1	+2	+3	+4	+4	+4	+4	+4	+4	+4	+3	+3	+3	+3
400	+3	0	+3	+1	+2	+3	+4	+4	+4	+4	+4	+4	+4	+3	+3	+3	+3
450	+4	0	+4	+1	+3	+4	+4	+4	+4	+4	+4	+4	+4	+3	+3	+3	+3
500	+5	0	+5	+1	+3	+4	+4	+4	+4	+5	+4	+4	+4	+3	+3	+3	+2
550	+6	0	+6	+1	+3	+4	+4	+4	+4	+5	+4	+4	+4	+3	+3	+3	+2
600	+7	0	+7	+1	+3	+4	+4	+4	+4	+5	+4	+4	+4	+3	+3	+3	+2
650	+8	0	+8	+1	+3	+4	+4	+4	+4	+4	+4	+4	+4	+3	+3	+2	+2
700	+8	0	+8	+1	+3	+4	+4	+4	+4	+4	+4	+4	+3	+3	+3	+2	+2
750	+9	0	+9	+1	+3	+4	+4	+4	+4	+4	+4	+4	+3	+3	+2	+2	+1
800	+10	0	+10	+1	+3	+4	+4	+4	+4	+4	+4	+3	+3	+2	+2	+1	+1
850	+11	0	+11	+1	+3	+4	+4	+4	+4	+4	+3	+3	+2	+2	+1	+1	0
900	+12	0	+12	+1	+3	+4	+4	+4	+4	+3	+3	+2	+2	+1	+1	0	0
950	+13	0	+13	+1	+3	+4	+4	+4	+4	+3	+3	+2	+2	+1	+1	0	−1
1000	+14	0	+14	+1	+3	+4	+4	+4	+4	+3	+3	+2	+1	+1	0	0	−1
1050	+15	0	+15	+1	+3	+4	+4	+4	+3	+3	+2	+1	+1	0	−1	−1	−2
1100	+16	0	+16	+1	+3	+3	+4	+4	+3	+3	+2	+1	+1	0	−1	−1	−2
1150	+17	0	+17	+1	+3	+3	+4	+3	+3	+2	+2	+1	0	−1	−2	−2	−3
1200	+18	0	+18	+1	+3	+3	+3	+3	+3	+2	+2	+1	0	−1	−2	−2	−3
1250	+19	0	+19	+1	+3	+3	+3	+3	+2	+2	+1	0	0	−1	−2	−3	−4
1300	+20	0	+20	+1	+3	+3	+3	+3	+2	+2	+1	0	0	−1	−2	−3	−4
1400	+22	0	+22	+1	+3	+3	+3	+2	+2	+1	0	0	−1	−2	−3	−4	−5
1500	+23	0	+23	+1	+2	+3	+3	+2	+2	+1	+1	0	−1	−2	−3	−5	−6
1600	+25	0	+25	+1	+2	+3	+3	+2	+1	+1	0	0	−1	−2	−4	−5	−7
1700	+26	0	+26	+1	+2	+2	+2	+2	+1	+1	0	−1	−2	−3	−4	−6	−7
1800	+28	0	+28	+1	+2	+2	+2	+2	+1	0	0	−1	−2	−3	−5	−7	−8
2000	+30	0	+30	+1	+2	+2	+1	+1	0	−1	−2	−3	−4	−5	−7	−8	−9
2200	+32	0	+32	+1	+1	+1	+1	0	−1	−2	−3	−4	−6	−7	−8	−9	−10
2400	+34	0	+34	0	0	0	0	−1	−2	−3	−4	−5	−6	−8	−9	−10	−11
2600	+36	0	+36	0	−1	−1	−2	−3	−4	−5	−6	−7	−8	−10	−11	−11	−12
2800	+38	0	+38	0	−1	−1	−2	−3	−4	−5	−6	−8	−9	−10	−11	−11	−13
3000	+40	0	+40	0	−1	−1	−2	−3	−4	−5	−7	−8	−9	−11	−12	−12	−14
3200	+42	−1	+41	0	−1	−1	−2	−3	−4	−5	−6	−7	−9	−10	−11	−12	−14
3400	+43	−1	+42	0	−1	−1	−2	−3	−4	−5	−6	−8	−9	−11	−12	−13	−15
3600	+44	−1	+43	0	−1	−2	−2	−3	−4	−5	−6	−8	−9	−11	−13	−14	−15
3800	+45	−1	+44	0	−1	−2	−2	−3	−4	−5	−7	−8	−10	−11	−13	−14	−16
4000	+46	−1	+45	0	−1	−2	−2	−3	−4	−6	−7	−9	−11	−12	−14	−15	−16
4500	+48	−1	+47	0	−1	−2	−3	−4	−5	−6	−8	−9	−11	−12	−14	−16	−17
5000	+50	−1	+49	0	−1	−2	−3	−4	−5	−6	−8	−10	−12	−13	−15	−16	−18
5500	+51	−1	+50	−1	−1	−2	−3	−4	−5	−7	−9	−10	−12	−14	−15	−17	−18
6000	+52	−1	+51	−1	−1	−2	−3	−4	−6	−7	−9	−11	−13	−14	−16	−17	−19
7000	+54	−1	+53	−1	−1	−2	−3	−4	−6	−7	−9	−11	−13	−15	−16	−18	−19
8000	+56	−1	+55	−1	−1	−2	−3	−4	−6	−7	−9	−11	−12	−15	−16	−18	−19
9000	+58	−2	+56	−1	−1	−2	−3	−4	−6	−7	−9	−11	−13	−15	−17	−18	−19
10000	+58	−2	+56	−1	−1	−2	−3	−4	−6	−8	−10	−11	−13	−15	−17	−18	−20
15000	+61	−3	+58	−1	−1	−2	−3	−5	−6	−8	−10	−12	−14	−15	−17	−19	−20

Correction for elevation of station — Below compartment:

Mean elevation of compartment	100 feet	200 feet	300 feet	400 feet	500 feet	600 feet	700 feet	800 feet	900 feet	1000 feet	1100 feet	1200 feet	1300 feet	1400 feet
Fathoms														
−200														
−150														
−100														
−50														
Feet														
0														
300	−2	−3	−4											
350	−2	−3	−5											
400	−2	−3	−5	−6										
450	−2	−3	−5	−7										
500	−3	−4	−6	−8	−10									
550	−3	−4	−6	−9	−11									
600	−3	−5	−7	−9	−11	−14								
650	−3	−5	−7	−9	−12	−15								
700	−3	−5	−7	−9	−12	−15	−16							
750	−3	−5	−7	−9	−12	−15	−17							
800	−3	−5	−7	−10	−13	−16	−18	−20						
850	−3	−5	−7	−10	−13	−16	−18	−21						
900	−3	−5	−7	−10	−14	−17	−19	−21	−24					
950	−3	−5	−7	−10	−14	−17	−19	−22	−25					
1000	−3	−5	−8	−11	−14	−18	−20	−23	−25	−28				
1050	−3	−5	−8	−11	−14	−18	−20	−23	−26	−29				
1100	−3	−5	−8	−11	−14	−18	−21	−24	−27	−29	−32			
1150	−3	−5	−8	−11	−14	−18	−21	−24	−27	−30	−33			
1200	−3	−5	−8	−11	−15	−18	−21	−25	−28	−31	−33	−36		
1250	−3	−5	−8	−11	−15	−18	−21	−25	−28	−31	−34	−37		
1300	−3	−5	−8	−11	−15	−19	−21	−25	−29	−32	−35	−37	−40	
1400	−3	−5	−8	−11	−15	−19	−21	−25	−29	−32	−36	−39	−41	−44
1500	−3	−5	−7	−10	−14	−18	−21	−25	−29	−32	−36	−39	−42	−44
1600	−3	−5	−7	−10	−14	−18	−21	−25	−29	−32	−36	−40	−43	−45
1700	−2	−4	−6	−9	−13	−17	−20	−24	−28	−32	−35	−39	−43	−46
1800	−2	−4	−6	−9	−13	−17	−20	−23	−28	−31	−35	−39	−43	−47
2000	−2	−4	−6	−8	−12	−15	−18	−22	−26	−30	−34	−38	−42	−45
2200	−2	−4	−5	−8	−11	−14	−17	−20	−24	−28	−32	−36	−40	−44
2400	−2	−4	−5	−8	−10	−13	−16	−19	−23	−26	−30	−34	−38	−42
2600	−2	−3	−5	−7	−10	−13	−16	−18	−22	−25	−29	−32	−36	−40
2800	−2	−3	−5	−7	−10	−13	−15	−18	−21	−24	−28	−31	−35	−38
3000	−2	−3	−5	−7	−10	−13	−15	−18	−21	−24	−27	−30	−34	−37
3200	−1	−2	−4	−6	−9	−12	−14	−17	−20	−23	−26	−29	−32	−35
3400	−1	−2	−4	−6	−8	−11	−13	−16	−19	−22	−25	−28	−31	−34
3600	−1	−2	−4	−6	−8	−10	−12	−15	−18	−21	−24	−27	−30	−33
3800	−1	−2	−4	−5	−7	−10	−12	−14	−17	−20	−23	−26	−29	−32
4000	−1	−2	−3	−5	−7	−10	−12	−14	−17	−19	−22	−25	−28	−31
4500	−1	−2	−3	−5	−7	−10	−11	−13	−16	−19	−21	−24	−26	−29
5000	−1	−2	−3	−5	−7	−9	−11	−13	−16	−18	−20	−23	−25	−28
5500	−1	−2	−3	−5	−6	−8	−10	−12	−15	−17	−19	−22	−24	−27
6000	−1	−2	−3	−4	−6	−8	−10	−12	−14	−16	−18	−21	−23	−26
7000	−1	−2	−3	−4	−6	−8	−10	−12	−14	−16	−18	−20	−23	−25
8000	−1	−2	−3	−4	−6	−8	−10	−12	−14	−16	−18	−20	−22	−25
9000	−1	−2	−2	−3	−5	−8	−9	−11	−13	−15	−17	−19	−21	−24
10000	−1	−1	−2	−3	−5	−7	−8	−10	−12	−14	−16	−18	−20	−22
15000	−1	−1	−2	−3	−5	−7	−8	−10	−12	−14	−16	−18	−20	−22

[Inner radius, 590 meters; outer radius, 1280 meters. Eight compartments.]

Mean elevation of compartment	Correction for— Topography	Correction for— Compensation	Correction for— Topography and compensation	Above compartment 200 feet	400 feet	600 feet	800 feet	1000 feet	1200 feet	1400 feet	1600 feet	1800 feet	2000 feet	2500 feet	3000 feet
Fathoms															
−500	−18	+1	−17	−1											
−450	−16	+1	−15	−1	−2										
−400	−13	0	−13	−1	−2	−3									
−350	−11	0	−11	−1	−2	−3	−3	−4							
−300	−9	0	−9	−1	−2	−3	−3	−4	−4	−4					
−250	−6	0	−6	−1	−2	−3	−3	−4	−4	−4	−4				
−200	−4	0	−4	−1	−2	−2	−3	−4	−4	−4	−4	−4	−4		
−150	−2	0	−2	−1	−2	−2	−2	−3	−4	−4	−4	−4	−4		
−100	−1	0	−1	−1	−1	−2	−2	−2	−3	−3	−3	−3	−3	−3	
−50	−1	0	−1	0	−1	−1	−1	−1	−1	−1	−2	−2	−2	−2	−1
Feet															
0	0	0	0	0	0	0	0	0	0	0	0	0	0	0	0
400	+1	0	+1	+1	+2	+2	+3	+3	+3	+3	+4	+4	+4	+4	+3
600	+2	0	+2	+1	+2	+3	+3	+4	+5	+5	+5	+5	+5	+5	+4
800	+3	0	+3	+1	+3	+4	+5	+6	+6	+6	+6	+6	+6	+5	+5
1 000	+5	0	+5	+2	+3	+4	+5	+6	+6	+6	+6	+6	+6	+5	+5
1 200	+7	0	+7	+2	+4	+4	+5	+7	+7	+7	+7	+7	+7	+5	+4
1 400	+9	0	+9	+2	+4	+4	+5	+7	+7	+7	+7	+7	+7	+5	+4
1 600	+11	0	+11	+2	+4	+5	+5	+7	+7	+7	+7	+6	+6	+4	+3
1 800	+14	0	+14	+2	+4	+5	+5	+7	+6	+6	+6	+6	+6	+4	+2
2 000	+17	−1	+16	+2	+4	+5	+5	+7	+6	+6	+6	+6	+5	+3	+1
2 200	+20	−1	+19	+2	+4	+5	+5	+6	+6	+5	+5	+5	+4	+2	0
2 400	+22	−1	+21	+2	+4	+5	+5	+6	+6	+5	+5	+4	+4	+1	−1
2 600	+24	−1	+23	+2	+4	+5	+5	+6	+3	+4	+4	+3	+3	0	−2
2 800	+27	−1	+26	+2	+3	+4	+4	+5	+5	+4	+3	+2	+2	0	−3
3 000	+29	−1	+28	+2	+3	+4	+4	+5	+4	+3	+3	+2	+1	−1	−4
3 200	+31	−1	+30	+2	+3	+3	+4	+4	+4	+3	+2	+2	+1	−2	−5
3 400	+33	−1	+32	+2	+3	+3	+4	+4	+3	+2	+2	+1	0	−3	−6
3 600	+35	−1	+34	+1	+3	+3	+4	+4	+3	+2	+1	0	−1	−4	−7
3 800	+37	−1	+36	+1	+3	+3	+3	+3	+2	+1	0	0	−1	−4	−8
4 000	+38	−1	+37	+1	+3	+3	+3	+3	+2	+1	0	−1	−2	−5	−9
4 200	+40	−1	+39	+1	+2	+2	+2	+2	+1	0	−1	−2	−3	−6	−10
4 400	+42	−1	+41	+1	+2	+2	+2	+2	+1	0	−1	−2	−3	−7	−10
4 600	+43	−1	+42	+1	+2	+2	+2	+2	0	−1	−2	−3	−4	−8	−11
4 800	+45	−1	+44	+1	+2	+2	+1	+1	0	−1	−2	−3	−5	−8	−12
5 000	+46	−1	+45	+1	+2	+2	+1	+1	0	−1	−3	−4	−5	−9	−13
5 200	+48	−1	+47	+1	+2	+2	+1	+1	0	−2	−3	−4	−6	−10	−13
5 400	+49	−1	+48	+1	+2	+2	+1	+1	−1	−2	−3	−4	−6	−10	−14
5 600	+50	−1	+49	+1	+1	+1	0	0	−1	−3	−4	−5	−7	−11	−15
5 800	+52	−2	+50	+1	+1	+1	0	0	−2	−3	−4	−6	−7	−11	−15
6 000	+53	−2	+51	+1	+1	+1	0	0	−2	−3	−5	−6	−8	−12	−16
6 200	+54	−2	+52	+1	+1	0	0	−1	−2	−3	−5	−6	−8	−12	−16
6 400	+55	−2	+53	+1	+1	0	0	−1	−2	−4	−5	−7	−8	−13	−17
6 600	+56	−2	+54	0	+1	0	0	−1	−2	−4	−5	−7	−9	−13	−17
6 800	+57	−2	+55	0	+1	0	0	−1	−3	−4	−6	−7	−9	−13	−18
7 000	+58	−2	+56	0	+1	0	0	−1	−3	−4	−6	−8	−9	−14	−18
7 500	+60	−2	+58	0	+1	0	−1	−2	−3	−5	−6	−8	−10	−14	−19
8 000	+62	−2	+60	0	0	−1	−1	−2	−4	−5	−7	−9	−11	−15	−20
8 500	+64	−2	+62	0	0	−1	−1	−2	−4	−6	−7	−9	−11	−16	−20
9 000	+65	−2	+63	0	0	−1	−2	−3	−4	−6	−8	−9	−11	−16	−21
10 000	+69	−3	+66	0	0	−1	−2	−3	−4	−6	−8	−10	−12	−17	−22
11 000	+71	−3	+68	0	0	−1	−2	−3	−5	−7	−9	−10	−12	−17	−22
12 000	+72	−3	+69	0	0	−1	−3	−3	−5	−7	−9	−11	−13	−18	−23
13 000	+74	−3	+71	0	0	−1	−3	−4	−6	−8	−9	−11	−13	−18	−23
14 000	+76	−4	+72	0	0	−1	−3	−4	−6	−8	−10	−12	−14	−19	−24
15 000	+77	−4	+73	0	0	−1	−2	−4	−6	−8	−10	−12	−14	−19	−24

Mean elevation of compartment	Below compartment 200 feet	400 feet	600 feet	800 feet	1000 feet	1200 feet	1400 feet	1600 feet	1800 feet	2000 feet	2500 feet	3000 feet
Fathoms												
−500												
−450												
−400												
−350												
−300												
−250												
−200												
−150												
−100												
−50												
Feet												
0	−1	−2										
400	−1	−2	−4									
600	−1	−3	−5	−6								
800	−2	−4	−6	−8	−10							
1 000	−2	−5	−7	−9	−12	−14						
1 200	−2	−5	−8	−10	−13	−16	−18					
1 400	−2	−5	−8	−11	−14	−17	−20	−22				
1 600	−2	−5	−8	−12	−16	−19	−23	−26	−28			
1 800	−2	−5	−9	−12	−16	−19	−23	−26	−30	−32		
2 000	−2	−6	−9	−13	−16	−20	−23	−27	−30	−33	−35	
2 200	−2	−6	−10	−13	−17	−21	−25	−28	−32	−35	−45	
2 400	−2	−6	−9	−13	−17	−21	−25	−29	−33	−36	−47	
2 600	−2	−6	−9	−13	−17	−21	−26	−29	−34	−37	−47	−56
2 800	−2	−5	−9	−13	−17	−21	−26	−30	−34	−38	−48	−58
3 000	−2	−5	−9	−13	−17	−21	−26	−30	−35	−39	−49	−59
3 200	−2	−5	−9	−12	−16	−20	−25	−30	−35	−39	−50	−60
3 400	−2	−5	−8	−12	−16	−20	−25	−29	−35	−39	−50	−61
3 600	−2	−5	−8	−12	−16	−20	−24	−29	−34	−39	−50	−60
3 800	−1	−5	−8	−12	−15	−19	−24	−28	−33	−38	−50	−60
4 000	−1	−4	−7	−11	−14	−19	−23	−28	−32	−37	−49	−60
4 200	−1	−4	−7	−11	−14	−18	−22	−27	−32	−36	−48	−60
4 400	−1	−4	−7	−10	−13	−17	−21	−26	−31	−35	−47	−59
4 600	−1	−4	−7	−10	−13	−17	−21	−26	−30	−34	−46	−58
4 800	−1	−4	−7	−10	−13	−17	−21	−25	−29	−33	−45	−58
5 000	−1	−3	−6	−10	−13	−17	−20	−25	−29	−33	−45	−57
5 200	−1	−3	−6	−9	−13	−16	−20	−24	−28	−32	−44	−56
5 400	−1	−3	−6	−9	−12	−16	−20	−24	−28	−32	−43	−55
5 600	−1	−3	−6	−9	−12	−16	−19	−23	−27	−31	−42	−54
5 800	−1	−3	−5	−8	−11	−15	−18	−22	−27	−30	−41	−52
6 000	−1	−3	−5	−8	−11	−14	−18	−22	−26	−30	−41	−51
6 200	−1	−3	−5	−8	−10	−14	−17	−21	−25	−29	−40	−50
6 400	−1	−3	−5	−8	−10	−13	−17	−21	−25	−28	−39	−49
6 600	−1	−3	−5	−8	−10	−13	−16	−20	−24	−28	−38	−48
6 800	−1	−3	−5	−7	−10	−13	−16	−20	−24	−27	−37	−47
7 000	−1	−3	−5	−7	−10	−13	−16	−19	−23	−27	−37	−47
7 500	0	−2	−4	−7	−9	−12	−15	−19	−22	−26	−36	−45
8 000	0	−2	−4	−6	−9	−11	−15	−18	−22	−25	−34	−43
8 500	0	−2	−4	−6	−9	−12	−15	−18	−21	−24	−33	−42
9 000	0	−2	−4	−6	−8	−11	−14	−17	−20	−23	−32	−40
10 000	0	−2	−4	−6	−8	−10	−13	−16	−19	−22	−30	−38
11 000	0	−2	−3	−5	−7	−10	−12	−15	−18	−21	−28	−36
12 000	0	−2	−3	−5	−6	−9	−11	−14	−17	−20	−27	−34
13 000	0	−1	−3	−4	−6	−9	−11	−14	−17	−19	−26	−33
14 000	0	−1	−3	−4	−6	−8	−11	−14	−17	−19	−25	−32
15 000	0	−1	−3	−4	−6	−8	−10	−13	−16	−18	−25	−32

[Inner radius, 1280 meters; outer radius, 2290 meters. Ten compartments.]

Columns 2–4 are grouped under **Correction for**. Columns 5–28 are grouped under **Correction for elevation of station—**, with columns 5–16 under **Above compartment** and columns 17–28 under **Below compartment** (each sub-column headed by a station-height in feet).

Mean elevation of compartment	Topography	Compensation	Topography and compensation	Ab. 250	Ab. 500	Ab. 750	Ab. 1000	Ab. 1250	Ab. 1500	Ab. 1750	Ab. 2000	Ab. 2250	Ab. 2500	Ab. 2750	Ab. 3000	Bel. 250	Bel. 500	Bel. 750	Bel. 1000	Bel. 1250	Bel. 1500	Bel. 1750	Bel. 2000	Bel. 2250	Bel. 2500	Bel. 2750	Bel. 3000
Fathoms																											
−500	−8	+1	−7	−1																							
−450	−7	−1	−6	−1	−2																						
−400	−6	+1	−5	−1	−2	−2																					
−350	−4	0	−4	−1	−2	−2	−3																				
−300	−3	0	−3	−1	−2	−2	−3	−4																			
−250	−2	0	−2	−1	−1	−2	−2	−3	−4	−4																	
−200	−1	0	−1	−1	−1	−1	−2	−2	−3	−3	−3																
−150	−1	0	−1	−1	−1	−1	−1	−2	−2	−2	−2	−2															
−100	0	0	0	−1	−1	−1	−2	−2	−2	−2	−2	−2	−2														
−50	0	0	0	−1	−1	−1	−1	−1	−1	−1	−1	−1	−1	−1	−2												
Feet																											
0	0	0	0	0	0	0	0	0	0	0	0	0	0	0	0												
400	0	0	0	0	+1	+1	+1	+2	+2	+2	+2	+2	+2	+2	+3												
800	+1	0	+1	+1	+1	+2	+2	+3	+3	+3	+4	+4	+4	+4	+5		−1	−2									
1 200	+2	0	+2	+1	+2	+2	+3	+4	+5	+5	+5	+5	+6	+6	+6	−1	−2	−3	−4								
1 600	+4	0	+4	+1	+2	+3	+4	+5	+6	+6	+6	+7	+7	+7	+8	−1	−2	−4	−5	−6	−8						
2 000	+7	−1	+6	+1	+3	+4	+5	+6	+7	+7	+7	+7	+8	+8	+8	−1	−3	−5	−6	−8	−10	−12	−13				
2 200	+8	−1	+7	+1	+3	+4	+5	+6	+7	+7	+7	+8	+8	+8	+9	−1	−3	−5	−7	−8	−10	−12	−14				
2 400	+9	−1	+8	+2	+3	+4	+5	+6	+7	+7	+8	+8	+8	+8	+9	−1	−3	−5	−7	−8	−11	−13	−15	−16			
2 600	+11	−1	+10	+2	+3	+4	+5	+6	+7	+8	+8	+8	+8	+8	+9	−1	−3	−5	−7	−9	−12	−14	−16	−18	−21		
2 800	+12	−1	+11	+2	+3	+4	+5	+6	+7	+8	+8	+8	+8	+8	+9	−1	−3	−6	−8	−9	−12	−14	−17	−19	−22	−24	
3 000	+13	−1	+12	+2	+3	+4	+5	+6	+7	+8	+8	+8	+8	+8	+9	−1	−3	−6	−8	−10	−12	−15	−18	−20	−23	−25	−26
3 200	+15	−1	+14	+2	+3	+4	+5	+6	+7	+8	+8	+8	+8	+8	+9	−1	−3	−7	−8	−10	−13	−16	−19	−21	−24	−26	−28
3 400	+16	−1	+15	+2	+3	+4	+5	+6	+7	+7	+8	+8	+8	+8	+9	−1	−3	−6	−8	−11	−13	−16	−19	−22	−25	−27	−29
3 600	+17	−1	+16	+2	+3	+4	+5	+6	+7	+8	+8	+8	+8	+8	+8	−1	−3	−6	−8	−11	−14	−16	−19	−23	−26	−28	−30
3 800	+19	−1	+18	+2	+3	+4	+5	+6	+7	+7	+8	+8	+8	+8	+8	−2	−3	−6	−9	−11	−14	−17	−20	−23	−27	−29	−31
4 000	+20	−1	+19	+2	+3	+4	+5	+6	+7	+7	+7	+7	+8	+8	+8	−2	−3	−6	−9	−12	−14	−17	−20	−23	−27	−30	−32
4 200	+22	−1	+21	+2	+3	+4	+5	+6	+7	+7	+7	+7	+7	+7	+7	−2	−3	−6	−9	−12	−15	−18	−21	−24	−27	−30	−33
4 400	+23	−1	+22	+2	+3	+4	+5	+6	+7	+7	+7	+7	+7	+7	+7	−2	−3	−6	−9	−12	−15	−18	−21	−24	−27	−30	−33
4 600	+25	−1	+24	+2	+3	+4	+5	+6	+7	+7	+7	+7	+7	+7	+7	−2	−3	−6	−9	−12	−16	−18	−21	−24	−28	−31	−34
4 800	+26	−1	+25	+1	+3	+4	+5	+6	+7	+7	+7	+7	+7	+6	+6	−2	−3	−6	−9	−12	−15	−18	−21	−24	−27	−31	−34
5 000	+28	−2	+26	+1	+3	+4	+5	+6	+6	+6	+6	+6	+6	+6	+6	−2	−3	−6	−9	−12	−15	−18	−21	−24	−27	−31	−35
5 200	+30	−2	+28	+1	+3	+4	+4	+5	+6	+6	+6	+6	+6	+6	+6	−2	−3	−6	−9	−12	−15	−18	−21	−24	−27	−31	−35
5 400	+31	−2	+29	+1	+3	+4	+4	+5	+6	+6	+6	+6	+5	+5	+5	−1	−3	−6	−9	−12	−15	−18	−21	−24	−27	−31	−35
5 600	+32	−2	+30	+1	+3	+4	+4	+5	+6	+6	+5	+5	+5	+5	+5	−1	−3	−6	−9	−12	−15	−18	−20	−24	−27	−31	−35
5 800	+34	−2	+32	+1	+3	+4	+4	+5	+6	+5	+5	+5	+5	+4	+4	−1	−3	−6	−8	−12	−15	−17	−20	−23	−26	−31	−34
6 000	+35	−2	+33	+1	+3	+3	+4	+5	+5	+5	+5	+4	+4	+4	+4	−1	−3	−6	−9	−12	−15	−18	−21	−24	−27	−31	−35
6 200	+36	−2	+34	+1	+3	+3	+4	+5	+5	+5	+4	+4	+4	+4	+3	−1	−3	−6	−9	−12	−15	−18	−21	−24	−27	−31	−35
6 400	+38	−2	+36	+1	+3	+3	+4	+5	+5	+5	+4	+4	+4	+3	+3	−1	−3	−6	−9	−12	−15	−18	−21	−24	−27	−31	−35
6 600	+39	−2	+37	+1	+3	+3	+4	+5	+5	+4	+4	+4	+3	+3	+3	−1	−3	−6	−9	−12	−15	−18	−20	−24	−27	−31	−35
6 800	+40	−2	+38	+1	+2	+3	+4	+4	+5	+4	+4	+3	+3	+2	+2	−1	−3	−6	−8	−12	−15	−17	−20	−23	−26	−31	−34
7 000	+41	−2	+39	+1	+2	+3	+3	+4	+4	+4	+3	+3	+2	+2	+2	−1	−3	−5	−8	−11	−14	−17	−20	−23	−26	−30	−34
7 400	+43	−2	+41	+1	+2	+2	+3	+4	+4	+4	+3	+2	+2	+2	+1	−1	−3	−5	−7	−11	−14	−17	−19	−22	−25	−29	−33
7 800	+45	−2	+43	+1	+2	+2	+3	+3	+4	+3	+3	+2	+2	+1	+1	−1	−2	−5	−7	−10	−13	−16	−18	−22	−25	−29	−32
8 200	+47	−2	+45	+1	+2	+2	+3	+3	+3	+3	+3	+2	+2	+1	0	−1	−2	−5	−7	−10	−13	−16	−18	−21	−24	−28	−31
8 600	+50	−3	+47	+1	+2	+2	+2	+3	+3	+3	+3	+2	+1	+1	0	−1	−2	−4	−7	−10	−13	−15	−17	−21	−24	−28	−31
9 000	+52	−3	+49	+1	+2	+2	+2	+3	+3	+2	+2	+1	0	0	−1	−1	−2	−4	−7	−10	−13	−15	−17	−20	−24	−27	−30
9 500	+55	−3	+52	+1	+2	+2	+2	+2	+3	+2	+2	+1	0	−1	−1	−1	−2	−4	−7	−10	−13	−15	−17	−20	−24	−27	−30
10 000	+57	−3	+54	+1	+2	+2	+2	+2	+2	+2	+1	+1	0	−1	−2	−1	−2	−4	−6	−9	−12	−14	−17	−20	−23	−26	−29
10 500	+58	−3	+55	+1	+2	+2	+2	+2	+2	+2	+1	0	−1	−2	−2	−1	−2	−4	−5	−8	−11	−13	−16	−19	−22	−25	−28
11 000	+60	−3	+57	+1	+2	+2	+2	+2	+2	+2	+1	0	−1	−2	−3	−1	−2	−4	−5	−8	−10	−12	−15	−18	−22	−24	−27
11 500	+62	−3	+59	+1	+1	+1	+2	+2	+2	+2	+1	0	−1	−2	−3	−1	−2	−4	−5	−7	−10	−12	−14	−17	−21	−23	−26
12 000	+64	−4	+60	+1	+1	+1	+1	+2	+2	+1	0	0	−1	−2	−3	−1	−2	−3	−5	−7	−10	−12	−13	−16	−19	−22	−24
13 000	+67	−4	+63	+1	+1	+1	+1	+1	+1	+1	0	−1	−2	−3	−4	−1	−2	−3	−5	−7	−9	−11	−13	−16	−18	−20	−23
14 000	+69	−4	+65	0	+1	+1	+1	+1	+1	0	−1	−2	−3	−4	−5	−1	−2	−3	−5	−6	−8	−11	−13	−15	−17	−19	−21
15 000	+72	−4	+68	0	+1	+1	+1	+1	0	0	−1	−2	−4	−5	−6	−1	−2	−3	−5	−6	−8	−11	−13	−15	−17	−19	−21

[Inner radius, 2290 meters; outer radius, 3520 meters. Twelve compartments.]

Mean elevation of compartment	Correction for—			Correction for elevation of station—Above compartment								
	Topography	Compensation	Topography and compensation	500 feet	1000 feet	1500 feet	2000 feet	2500 feet	3000 feet	3500 feet	4000 feet	4500 feet
Fathoms												
−800	− 8	+1	− 7	−1								
−750	− 7	+1	− 6	−1								
−700	− 7	+1	− 6	−1								
−650	− 6	+1	− 5	−1	−2							
−600	− 5	+1	− 4	−1	−2							
−550	− 5	+1	− 4	−1	−2	−3						
−500	− 4	+1	− 3	−1	−2	−2						
−450	− 3	+1	− 2	−1	−1	−2	−3	−3				
−400	− 2	0	− 2	−1	−1	−2	−2	−3				
−350	− 1	0	− 1	−1	−1	−2	−2	−3				
−300	− 1	0	− 1	−1	−1	−2	−2	−3	−3			
−250	− 1	0	− 1	−1	−1	−2	−2	−2	−2			
−200	0	0	0	−1	−1	−1	−1	−2	−2	−2		
−150	0	0	0	−1	−1	−1	−1	−2	−2	−2	−2	
−100	0	0	0	0	0	−1	−1	−1	−1	−1	−1	
− 50	0	0	0	0	0	0	0	−1	−1	−1	−1	−1
Feet												
0	0	0	0	0	0	0	0	0	0	0	0	0
500	0	0	0	0	0	+1	+1	+2	+2	+2	+2	+2
1 000	0	0	0	+1	+1	+2	+2	+3	+3	+3	+4	+4
1 500	+ 1	0	+ 1	+1	+2	+3	+3	+4	+4	+4	+5	+5
2 000	+ 3	−1	+ 2	+1	+2	+3	+4	+5	+6	+6	+7	+7
2 500	+ 4	−1	+ 3	+1	+2	+4	+4	+5	+6	+7	+7	+8
3 000	+ 6	−1	+ 5	+2	+3	+4	+5	+6	+7	+7	+8	+8
3 500	+ 7	−1	+ 6	+2	+3	+5	+6	+7	+8	+8	+9	+9
4 000	+ 9	−1	+ 8	+2	+3	+5	+6	+7	+8	+8	+9	+9
4 500	+11	−1	+10	+2	+3	+5	+6	+7	+8	+8	+9	+9
5 000	+14	−2	+12	+2	+4	+5	+6	+7	+8	+8	+9	+9
5 200	+15	−2	+13	+2	+4	+5	+6	+7	+8	+8	+9	+9
5 400	+16	−2	+14	+2	+4	+5	+6	+7	+8	+8	+9	+9
5 600	+17	−2	+15	+2	+4	+5	+6	+7	+8	+8	+9	+9
5 800	+17	−2	+15	+2	+4	+5	+6	+7	+8	+8	+9	+9
6 000	+18	−2	+16	+2	+4	+5	+6	+7	+8	+8	+9	+9
6 200	+19	−2	+17	+2	+4	+5	+6	+7	+8	+8	+9	+9
6 400	+21	−2	+18	+2	+4	+5	+6	+7	+8	+8	+9	+9
6 600	+21	−2	+19	+2	+4	+5	+6	+7	+8	+8	+8	+8
6 800	+22	−2	+20	+2	+4	+5	+6	+7	+8	+8	+8	+8
7 000	+23	−2	+21	+2	+4	+5	+6	+7	+8	+8	+8	+8
7 400	+24	−2	+22	+2	+4	+5	+6	+7	+8	+8	+8	+8
7 800	+26	−2	+24	+2	+4	+5	+6	+6	+6	+7	+7	+7
8 200	+28	−2	+26	+2	+3	+5	+6	+6	+6	+7	+7	+7
8 600	+30	−3	+27	+2	+3	+5	+6	+6	+6	+7	+7	+7
9 000	+32	−3	+29	+2	+3	+5	+6	+6	+7	+7	+6	+6
9 500	+34	−3	+31	+2	+3	+5	+6	+6	+6	+6	+6	+6
10 000	+36	−3	+33	+2	+3	+5	+5	+6	+6	+6	+5	+5
10 500	+38	−3	+35	+2	+3	+4	+5	+5	+6	+6	+5	+5
11 000	+40	−3	+37	+2	+3	+4	+4	+5	+5	+5	+4	+4
11 500	+41	−3	+38	+2	+3	+4	+4	+5	+5	+5	+4	+4
12 000	+44	−4	+40	+2	+3	+4	+4	+4	+4	+4	+3	+3
12 500	+46	−4	+42	+2	+3	+4	+4	+4	+4	+4	+3	+3
13 000	+47	−4	+43	+2	+3	+3	+3	+4	+4	+4	+3	+2
13 500	+49	−4	+45	+2	+3	+3	+3	+4	+4	+3	+3	+2
14 000	+50	−4	+46	+1	+2	+3	+3	+3	+3	+2	+2	+1
14 500	+52	−4	+48	+1	+2	+3	+3	+3	+3	+2	+2	+1
15 000	+54	−5	+49	+1	+2	+3	+3	+3	+2	+1	+1	0

Mean elevation of compartment	Correction for elevation of station—Below compartment											
	400 feet	800 feet	1200 feet	1600 feet	2000 feet	2400 feet	2800 feet	3200 feet	3600 feet	4000 feet	4400 feet	4800 feet
Feet												
0												
500	0											
1 000	0	0										
1 500	−1	−1	−1									
2 000	−1	−2	−3	−4	− 5							
2 500	−1	−2	−3	−5	− 6	−7						
3 000	−1	−2	−4	−6	− 7	−8	−10					
3 500	−1	−2	−4	−6	− 8	−9	−11	−12				
4 000	−2	−3	−5	−7	− 9	−11	−12	−14	−15	−17		
4 500	−2	−3	−5	−7	−10	−12	−13	−15	−17	−19	−22	
5 000	−2	−4	−6	−8	−10	−12	−14	−16	−18	−21	−23	−25
5 200	−2	−4	−6	−9	−11	−13	−15	−17	−19	−22	−24	−26
5 400	−2	−4	−6	−9	−11	−14	−16	−18	−20	−22	−24	−27
5 600	−2	−4	−6	−9	−11	−14	−16	−18	−20	−22	−25	−28
5 800	−2	−4	−6	−9	−11	−14	−16	−18	−20	−22	−25	−28
6 000	−2	−4	−6	−9	−11	−14	−16	−18	−21	−23	−26	−29
6 200	−2	−4	−6	−9	−12	−14	−16	−18	−21	−24	−26	−29
6 400	−2	−4	−6	−9	−12	−14	−16	−19	−22	−25	−27	−30
6 600	−2	−4	−6	−9	−12	−14	−17	−20	−23	−26	−28	−31
6 800	−2	−4	−6	−9	−12	−14	−17	−20	−23	−26	−29	−32
7 000	−2	−4	−6	−9	−13	−15	−17	−20	−23	−26	−29	−32
7 400	−2	−4	−6	−9	−12	−17	−20	−23	−26	−30	−30	−33
7 800	−2	−4	−6	−9	−12	−14	−17	−20	−23	−27	−30	−33
8 200	−2	−4	−6	−9	−11	−14	−17	−20	−24	−27	−30	−34
8 600	−2	−4	−6	−9	−11	−14	−17	−20	−24	−27	−30	−34
9 000	−2	−4	−6	−9	−11	−14	−17	−20	−24	−27	−31	−34
9 500	−2	−4	−6	−9	−11	−14	−17	−20	−23	−27	−31	−34
10 000	−2	−4	−6	−9	−11	−14	−16	−19	−23	−27	−31	−34
10 500	−2	−4	−6	−8	−10	−13	−16	−19	−22	−27	−31	−34
11 000	−2	−4	−6	−8	−10	−13	−16	−19	−23	−26	−30	−33
11 500	−2	−4	−6	−7	−10	−13	−15	−18	−21	−26	−29	−32
12 000	−3	−4	−5	−7	−10	−13	−15	−18	−21	−25	−29	−32
12 500	−3	−3	−5	−7	−10	−12	−15	−17	−21	−25	−28	−32
13 000	−3	−3	−5	−7	− 9	−12	−14	−16	−20	−24	−28	−32
13 500	−2	−3	−5	−7	− 9	−12	−14	−16	−20	−24	−28	−32
14 000	−1	−3	−5	−7	− 9	−12	−14	−16	−20	−23	−27	−31
14 500	−1	−3	−5	−7	− 9	−11	−13	−16	−19	−23	−26	−30
15 000	−1	−3	−5	−7	− 7	−11	−13	−16	−19	−22	−26	−29

Zone H.

[Inner radius, 3520 meters; outer radius, 5240 meters. Sixteen compartments.]

In the table below, the three columns under "Correction for —" are Topography, Compensation, and Topography and compensation. The remaining columns fall under "Correction for elevation of station —": the first twelve (600–7200 feet) are for a station *above* the compartment, the last twelve (600–7200 feet) for a station *below* the compartment.

Mean elevation of compartment	Topography	Compensation	Topography and compensation	Above 600 ft	Above 1200 ft	Above 1800 ft	Above 2400 ft	Above 3000 ft	Above 3600 ft	Above 4200 ft	Above 4800 ft	Above 5400 ft	Above 6000 ft	Above 6600 ft	Above 7200 ft	Below 600 ft	Below 1200 ft	Below 1800 ft	Below 2400 ft	Below 3000 ft	Below 3600 ft	Below 4200 ft	Below 4800 ft	Below 5400 ft	Below 6000 ft	Below 6600 ft	Below 7200 ft
Fathoms																											
−1 200	− 8	+1	− 7	−1																							
−1 100	− 6	+1	− 5	−1																							
−1 000	− 6	+1	− 5	−1	−2																						
− 900	− 5	+1	− 4	−1	−2	−2																					
− 800	− 4	+1	− 3	−1	−2	−2	−3																				
− 700	− 3	+1	− 2	−1	−2	−2	−3	−3																			
− 600	− 2	+1	− 1	−1	−1	−1	−2	−3	−4																		
− 500	− 2	+1	− 1	−1	−1	−1	−2	−2	−3	−3																	
− 400	− 1	0	− 1	0	−1	−1	−1	−2	−2	−2	−3																
− 300	0	0	0	0	−1	−1	−1	−2	−2	−2	−2	−2															
− 200	0	0	0	0	−1	−1	−1	−1	−1	−2	−2	−1	−1														
− 100	0	0	0	0	−1	−1	−1	−1	−1	−1	−1	−1	−1	−1	0												
Feet.																											
0	0	0	0	0	0	0	0	0	0	0	0	0	0	0	0												
500	0	0	0	0	+1	+1	+1	+1	+1	+1	+1	+2	+2	+2	+2												
1 000	0	0	0	0	+1	+1	+1	+2	+2	+2	+2	+2	+3	+3	+3	0											
1 500	+ 1	−1	0	0	+1	+1	+2	+2	+3	+3	+3	+3	+4	+4	+4	0	−1										
2 000	+ 1	−1	0	0	+1	+2	+2	+3	+3	+3	+4	+4	+4	+5	+5	−1	−1	−2									
2 500	+ 2	−1	+ 1	0	+1	+2	+3	+3	+4	+4	+5	+5	+5	+6	+6	−1	−1	−2	−3								
3 000	+ 3	−1	+ 2	+1	+2	+3	+4	+4	+5	+5	+6	+6	+6	+7	+7	−1	−2	−3	−4	−5							
3 500	+ 3	−1	+ 2	+1	+2	+3	+4	+5	+6	+6	+7	+7	+7	+8	+8	−1	−2	−3	−5	−6	−7						
4 000	+ 4	−1	+ 3	+1	+3	+4	+5	+5	+6	+6	+7	+8	+8	+9	+9	−1	−2	−4	−5	−7	−7	−10					
4 500	+ 5	−1	+ 4	+1	+3	+4	+5	+6	+7	+7	+8	+8	+8	+9	+9	−1	−3	−4	−6	−7	−9	−10					
5 000	+ 7	−2	+ 5	+1	+3	+4	+5	+6	+7	+7	+8	+8	+8	+9	+9	−1	−3	−5	−6	−8	−10	−11	−13				
5 200	+ 8	−2	+ 6	+1	+3	+4	+5	+6	+7	+7	+8	+8	+8	+9	+9	−1	−3	−5	−7	−9	−10	−12	−14				
5 400	+ 8	−2	+ 6	+1	+3	+4	+5	+6	+7	+7	+8	+8	+8	+9	+9	−1	−3	−5	−7	−9	−10	−12	−14	−15			
5 500	+ 9	−2	+ 7	+1	+3	+4	+5	+6	+7	+7	+8	+8	+9	+10	+10	−1	−3	−5	−7	−9	−11	−13	−15	−16			
5 800	+ 9	−2	+ 7	+2	+3	+5	+6	+6	+7	+7	+8	+8	+9	+10	+10	−1	−3	−5	−7	−9	−11	−13	−15	−16			
6 000	+10	−2	+ 8	+2	+3	+5	+6	+6	+7	+7	+8	+8	+9	+10	+10	−1	−3	−6	−8	−10	−12	−14	−16	−17	−19		
6 200	+10	−2	+ 8	+2	+3	+5	+6	+7	+8	+8	+9	+9	+9	+10	+10	−1	−4	−6	−8	−10	−12	−14	−16	−18	−20		
6 400	+11	−2	+ 9	+2	+3	+5	+6	+7	+8	+8	+9	+9	+9	+10	+10	−2	−4	−6	−8	−11	−13	−15	−17	−19	−21		
6 600	+11	−2	+ 9	+2	+3	+5	+6	+7	+8	+8	+9	+9	+9	+10	+10	−2	−4	−6	−9	−11	−13	−15	−17	−19	−21	−22	
6 800	+12	−2	+10	+2	+3	+5	+6	+7	+8	+8	+9	+9	+9	+10	+10	−2	−4	−7	−9	−11	−13	−15	−17	−20	−22	−23	
7 000	+12	−2	+10	+2	+3	+5	+6	+7	+8	+8	+9	+9	+9	+10	+10	−2	−4	−7	−9	−11	−13	−15	−18	−20	−22	−23	
7 200	+13	−2	+11	+2	+3	+5	+6	+7	+8	+8	+9	+9	+9	+10	+10	−2	−4	−7	−9	−11	−13	−16	−18	−20	−23	−24	−26
7 400	+13	−2	+11	+2	+3	+5	+6	+7	+8	+8	+9	+9	+9	+10	+10	−2	−4	−7	−9	−11	−14	−16	−18	−21	−23	−25	−27
7 600	+14	−2	+12	+2	+3	+5	+6	+7	+8	+8	+9	+9	+9	+10	+10	−2	−4	−7	−9	−12	−14	−16	−18	−21	−24	−25	−28
7 800	+15	−2	+13	+2	+3	+5	+6	+7	+8	+8	+9	+9	+9	+10	+10	−2	−4	−7	−9	−12	−14	−17	−19	−22	−24	−26	−29
8 000	+16	−3	+13	+2	+3	+5	+6	+7	+8	+8	+9	+9	+9	+10	+10	−2	−4	−7	−9	−12	−14	−17	−19	−22	−24	−27	−29
8 500	+18	−3	+15	+2	+3	+5	+6	+7	+8	+8	+9	+9	+9	+10	+10	−2	−4	−7	−9	−12	−15	−18	−20	−23	−25	−28	−30
9 000	+19	−3	+16	+2	+3	+5	+6	+7	+8	+8	+8	+9	+9	+9	+9	−1	−4	−7	−10	−12	−15	−18	−20	−23	−25	−28	−30
9 500	+20	−3	+17	+2	+3	+5	+6	+7	+8	+8	+8	+8	+9	+9	+9	−1	−4	−7	−10	−12	−15	−18	−20	−23	−26	−29	−31
10 000	+22	−3	+19	+2	+3	+5	+6	+6	+7	+7	+8	+8	+8	+9	+9	−1	−4	−7	−10	−12	−15	−18	−20	−24	−27	−30	−33
10 500	+23	−3	+20	+2	+3	+5	+6	+6	+7	+7	+8	+8	+8	+9	+9	−1	−4	−7	−10	−12	−15	−18	−21	−24	−27	−30	−33
11 000	+25	−3	+22	+2	+3	+5	+6	+6	+7	+7	+7	+8	+8	+8	+8	−1	−4	−7	−10	−12	−15	−18	−21	−24	−28	−31	−34
11 500	+27	−4	+23	+1	+3	+4	+5	+6	+7	+7	+7	+7	+8	+8	+8	−1	−4	−7	−10	−13	−15	−18	−21	−24	−28	−31	−34
12 000	+29	−4	+25	+1	+3	+4	+5	+6	+7	+7	+7	+7	+7	+8	+8	−1	−4	−7	−10	−13	−15	−18	−21	−25	−28	−31	−34
12 500	+30	−4	+26	+1	+3	+4	+5	+6	+7	+7	+7	+7	+7	+7	+7	−1	−4	−7	−10	−13	−15	−18	−21	−25	−28	−32	−35
13 000	+32	−4	+28	+1	+3	+4	+5	+6	+7	+7	+7	+7	+7	+7	+7	−1	−4	−7	−10	−13	−15	−18	−21	−25	−28	−32	−36
13 500	+33	−4	+29	+1	+3	+4	+5	+6	+7	+7	+7	+6	+6	+6	+6	−1	−4	−7	−10	−13	−15	−18	−21	−25	−28	−32	−36
14 000	+34	−4	+30	+1	+3	+4	+5	+5	+7	+7	+7	+6	+6	+6	+6	−1	−4	−7	−10	−12	−15	−18	−21	−25	−28	−32	−36
14 500	+37	−5	+32	+1	+3	+4	+5	+5	+6	+6	+6	+6	+6	+6	+6	−1	−4	−7	−10	−12	−15	−18	−21	−25	−28	−32	−36
15 000	+38	−5	+33	+1	+3	+4	+5	+5	+6	+6	+6	+6	+5	+5	+5	−1	−4	−7	−10	−12	−15	−18	−21	−25	−28	−32	−36

[Inner radius, 5210 meters; outer radius, 8440 meters. Twenty compartments.]

Correction for elevation of station — Above compartment

Mean elevation of compartment	Topography	Compensation	Topography and compensation	1000 feet	2000 feet	3000 feet	4000 feet	5000 feet	6000 feet	7000 feet	8000 feet	9000 feet	10000 feet	11000 feet	12000 feet
Fathoms															
−2 000	−14	+3	−11	−2											
−1 800	−11	+2	−9	−2	−3										
−1 600	−9	+2	−7	−1	−3	−4									
−1 400	−7	+2	−5	−1	−3	−4	−5								
−1 200	−5	+2	−3	−1	−2	−4	−4	−6							
−1 000	−4	+2	−2	−1	−2	−3	−4	−5	−6	−6					
− 800	−2	+1	−1	−1	−2	−2	−4	−4	−5	−6	−6				
− 600	−2	+1	−1	−1	−1	−2	−3	−3	−4	−4	−4	−5			
− 400	−1	+1	0	−1	−1	−2	−2	−2	−3	−3	−4	−4	−4		
− 200	0	0	0	0	−1	−1	−1	−1	−1	−2	−2	−2	−2	−2	
Feet.															
0	0	0	0	0	0	0	0	0	0	0	0	0	0	0	0
500	0	0	0	0	0	0	+1	+1	+1	+1	+1	+1	+2	+2	+2
1 000	0	0	0	0	+1	+1	+1	+2	+2	+3	+3	+3	+3	+3	+3
1 500	+1	−1	0	+1	+1	+2	+2	+2	+3	+3	+4	+4	+4	+4	+4
2 000	+1	−1	0	+1	+2	+2	+3	+3	+4	+5	+5	+5	+5	+6	+6
2 500	+1	−1	0	+1	+2	+3	+3	+4	+5	+5	+6	+6	+6	+7	+7
3 000	+1	−1	0	+1	+2	+3	+4	+5	+5	+6	+7	+7	+7	+8	+8
3 500	+3	−2	+1	+1	+2	+3	+5	+5	+6	+7	+7	+8	+8	+9	+9
4 000	+3	−2	+1	+2	+3	+4	+5	+6	+7	+8	+8	+9	+9	+10	+10
4 500	+4	−2	+2	+2	+3	+4	+6	+6	+7	+8	+9	+9	+10	+10	+10
5 000	+4	−2	+2	+2	+3	+4	+6	+7	+8	+9	+10	+10	+10	+11	+11
5 500	+5	−2	+3	+2	+3	+5	+6	+7	+8	+9	+10	+10	+11	+11	+12
6 000	+6	−2	+4	+2	+4	+5	+7	+8	+9	+10	+11	+11	+11	+12	+12
6 500	+8	−3	+5	+2	+4	+6	+7	+8	+9	+10	+11	+11	+12	+12	+13
7 000	+8	−3	+5	+2	+4	+6	+8	+9	+10	+11	+12	+12	+12	+13	+13
7 500	+9	−3	+6	+2	+4	+6	+8	+9	+10	+11	+12	+12	+13	+13	+14
8 000	+11	−4	+7	+2	+4	+6	+8	+9	+10	+11	+13	+13	+13	+13	+14
8 200	+12	−4	+8	+2	+5	+6	+8	+9	+10	+12	+13	+13	+13	+14	+14
8 400	+12	−4	+8	+2	+5	+6	+8	+9	+11	+12	+13	+13	+13	+14	+14
8 600	+13	−4	+9	+2	+5	+7	+8	+10	+11	+12	+13	+13	+14	+14	+14
8 800	+13	−4	+9	+2	+5	+7	+9	+10	+11	+12	+13	+13	+14	+14	+14
9 000	+13	−4	+9	+2	+5	+7	+9	+10	+11	+12	+13	+13	+14	+14	+14
9 200	+14	−4	+10	+2	+5	+7	+9	+10	+11	+12	+13	+14	+14	+14	+14
9 400	+14	−4	+10	+2	+5	+7	+9	+10	+11	+12	+13	+14	+14	+14	+14
9 600	+15	−4	+11	+2	+5	+7	+9	+10	+11	+12	+13	+14	+14	+14	+15
9 800	+15	−4	+11	+2	+5	+7	+9	+10	+11	+12	+14	+14	+14	+14	+15
10 000	+16	−4	+12	+2	+5	+7	+9	+10	+11	+12	+14	+14	+14	+14	+15
10 200	+17	−5	+12	+3	+5	+7	+9	+10	+11	+13	+14	+14	+14	+14	+15
10 400	+18	−5	+13	+3	+5	+7	+9	+10	+11	+12	+14	+14	+14	+14	+15
10 600	+18	−5	+13	+3	+5	+7	+9	+11	+12	+13	+14	+14	+14	+14	+15
10 800	+19	−5	+14	+3	+5	+7	+9	+11	+12	+13	+14	+14	+14	+14	+15
11 000	+19	−5	+14	+3	+5	+7	+9	+11	+12	+13	+14	+14	+14	+14	+15
11 500	+20	−5	+15	+3	+5	+7	+9	+11	+12	+13	+14	+14	+14	+14	+15
12 000	+22	−5	+17	+3	+6	+8	+10	+11	+12	+13	+14	+14	+14	+14	+15
12 500	+24	−6	+18	+3	+6	+8	+10	+11	+12	+13	+14	+14	+14	+14	+14
13 000	+25	−6	+19	+3	+6	+8	+10	+11	+12	+13	+14	+14	+14	+14	+14
13 500	+26	−6	+20	+3	+6	+8	+10	+11	+12	+13	+14	+14	+14	+14	+14
14 000	+28	−6	+22	+3	+6	+8	+10	+11	+12	+13	+14	+14	+14	+14	+14
14 500	+30	−7	+23	+3	+6	+8	+10	+11	+13	+14	+14	+14	+14	+14	+13
15 000	+31	−7	+24	+3	+6	+8	+9	+11	+11	+12	+13	+13	+13	+13	+13

Correction for elevation of station — Below compartment

Mean elevation of compartment	1000 feet	2000 feet	3000 feet	4000 feet	5000 feet	6000 feet	7000 feet	8000 feet	9000 feet	10000 feet	11000 feet	12000 feet
Fathoms												
−2 000												
−1 800												
−1 600												
−1 400												
−1 200												
−1 000												
− 800												
− 600												
− 400												
− 200												
Feet.												
0												
500	−1											
1 000	−1											
1 500	−1	−2										
2 000	−1	−2										
2 500	−1	−2	−4									
3 000	−1	−2	−4									
3 500	−1	−3	−4	−6								
4 000	−1	−3	−5	−6								
4 500	−2	−3	−5	−7								
5 000	−2	−4	−6	−7	−8							
5 500	−2	−4	−6	−8	−9	−11	−13					
6 000	−2	−5	−7	−9	−10	−12	−14					
6 500	−2	−5	−7	−10	−12	−14	−16					
7 000	−2	−5	−8	−10	−12	−14	−16					
7 500	−2	−5	−8	−11	−13	−15	−17	−21				
8 000	−3	−7	−10	−13	−16	−18	−21	−22				
8 200	−3	−7	−10	−13	−16	−19	−22	−22				
8 400	−3	−8	−11	−14	−17	−19	−22	−23				
8 600	−3	−8	−11	−14	−17	−20	−23	−24				
8 800	−3	−6	−9	−12	−15	−18	−20	−23	−26			
9 000	−3	−7	−10	−13	−16	−19	−21	−23	−26	−27		
9 200	−3	−7	−10	−13	−16	−19	−21	−24	−27	−27		
9 400	−3	−7	−10	−13	−16	−19	−22	−24	−27	−28		
9 600	−3	−7	−10	−13	−16	−19	−22	−25	−28	−28		
9 800	−3	−7	−10	−13	−16	−19	−22	−25	−28	−31	−34	
10 000	−3	−7	−10	−13	−16	−20	−23	−26	−29	−32	−32	
10 200	−3	−7	−10	−13	−16	−20	−23	−26	−29	−32	−32	
10 400	−3	−7	−11	−15	−18	−22	−26	−30	−33	−37	−40	
10 600	−3	−7	−11	−15	−18	−22	−26	−30	−33	−37	−40	
10 800	−3	−7	−11	−14	−17	−21	−24	−28	−31	−34	−37	
11 000	−3	−7	−11	−14	−18	−21	−25	−28	−31	−34	−37	−39
11 500	−3	−7	−11	−14	−18	−21	−25	−29	−32	−35	−39	−40
12 000	−3	−7	−11	−15	−18	−22	−26	−30	−33	−37	−40	−43
12 500	−3	−7	−11	−15	−19	−22	−26	−30	−34	−38	−41	−45
13 000	−3	−7	−11	−15	−19	−23	−27	−31	−35	−39	−42	−46
13 500	−3	−7	−11	−15	−19	−23	−27	−31	−36	−40	−43	−47
14 000	−3	−7	−11	−15	−19	−24	−28	−32	−36	−41	−44	−48
14 500	−3	−7	−11	−15	−20	−24	−28	−32	−37	−41	−45	−49
15 000	−3	−7	−11	−15	−20	−24	−28	−33	−38	−42	−46	−50

Zone J.

[Inner radius, 8440 meters; outer radius, 12 400 meters. Sixteen compartments.]

Mean elevation of compartment	Correction for — Topography	Correction for — Compensation	Correction for — Topography and compensation	Above compartment 1000 feet	Above 2000 feet	Above 3000 feet	Above 4000 feet	Above 5000 feet	Above 6000 feet	Above 7000 feet	Above 8000 feet	Above 9000 feet	Above 10000 feet	Above 11000 feet	Above 12000 feet	Below compartment 1000 feet	Below 2000 feet	Below 3000 feet	Below 4000 feet	Below 5000 feet	Below 6000 feet	Below 7000 feet	Below 8000 feet	Below 9000 feet	Below 10000 feet	Below 11000 feet	Below 12000 feet
Fathoms																											
−1 200	−4	+3	−1	−1	−2	−3	−4																					
− 800	−2	+2	0	−1	−1	−2	−3	−4	−4	−4																	
− 400	0	+1	+1	−1	−1	−1	−1	−2	−2	−2	−2	−3															
Feet																											
0	0	0	0	0	0	0	0	0	0	0	0	0	0	0	0	+1											
1 000	0	−1	−1	0	+1	+1	+1	+1	+1	+1	+2	+2	+2	+2	+2	0	−1										
2 000	0	−1	−1	+1	+2	+2	+2	+3	+3	+4	+4	+4	+4	+4	+5	0	−1	−2									
3 000	+1	−2	−1	+1	+2	+2	+3	+4	+4	+5	+5	+6	+6	+6	+7	0	−1	−2									
4 000	+2	−3	−1	+1	+2	+3	+4	+5	+5	+6	+6	+7	+8	+8	+9	0	−1	−2	−3								
5 000	+3	−3	0	+1	+2	+4	+5	+6	+6	+7	+8	+9	+10	+10	+11	−1	−1	−2	−4	−7							
6 000	+4	−4	0	+1	+3	+4	+5	+7	+8	+8	+9	+10	+12	+13	+13	−1	−1	−3	−5	−7	−8						
7 000	+6	−5	+1	+2	+3	+5	+7	+8	+9	+10	+11	+12	+13	+14	+14	−2	−3	−4	−6	−8	−10	−11					
8 000	+7	−5	+2	+2	+4	+5	+7	+8	+10	+11	+12	+13	+14	+15	+16	−2	−4	−5	−7	−9	−11	−13	−15				
8 500	+8	−5	+3	+2	+4	+6	+7	+9	+10	+11	+12	+13	+14	+15	+16	−2	−4	−6	−7	−10	−12	−14	−16				
9 000	+9	−6	+3	+2	+4	+6	+7	+9	+10	+11	+12	+14	+15	+16	+17	−2	−4	−6	−8	−10	−12	−15	−17	−18			
9 500	+10	−6	+4	+2	+4	+6	+7	+9	+11	+12	+13	+14	+15	+16	+17	−2	−4	−6	−8	−11	−13	−16	−18	−20			
10 000	+12	−7	+5	+2	+4	+6	+8	+9	+11	+12	+13	+14	+15	+17	+18	−2	−5	−7	−9	−11	−14	−16	−19	−21	−24		
10 500	+13	−7	+6	+2	+4	+6	+8	+9	+11	+12	+13	+15	+16	+17	+18	−2	−5	−7	−10	−12	−14	−17	−20	−22	−25		
11 000	+14	−7	+7	+2	+4	+6	+8	+10	+12	+13	+14	+15	+16	+18	+19	−2	−5	−7	−10	−12	−15	−17	−21	−24	−27	−29	
11 500	+15	−8	+7	+2	+4	+7	+8	+10	+12	+13	+14	+16	+17	+18	+19	−2	−5	−8	−10	−13	−15	−18	−21	−24	−27	−29	
12 000	+16	−8	+8	+2	+4	+7	+9	+11	+12	+14	+15	+16	+17	+18	+20	−2	−5	−8	−10	−13	−16	−19	−22	−25	−28	−30	−32
12 500	+17	−8	+9	+2	+5	+7	+9	+11	+13	+14	+15	+16	+18	+19	+20	−2	−5	−8	−11	−14	−17	−20	−23	−26	−29	−31	−33
13 000	+19	−9	+10	+2	+5	+7	+9	+11	+13	+14	+15	+16	+18	+19	+20	−2	−5	−8	−11	−14	−17	−20	−23	−27	−30	−32	−35
13 500	+20	−9	+11	+3	+5	+7	+9	+11	+13	+14	+16	+17	+18	+19	+20	−2	−6	−8	−11	−14	−17	−21	−24	−28	−31	−33	−36
14 000	+21	−9	+12	+3	+5	+7	+9	+11	+13	+14	+16	+17	+19	+20	+21	−2	−6	−8	−11	−14	−18	−21	−25	−28	−32	−34	−37
14 500	+23	−10	+13	+3	+5	+8	+10	+11	+13	+14	+16	+17	+19	+20	+21	−2	−6	−9	−11	−15	−18	−22	−26	−29	−32	−35	−38
15 000	+24	−10	+14	+3	+6	+8	+10	+12	+14	+15	+17	+18	+19	+20	+21	−2	−6	−9	−11	−15	−19	−22	−26	−29	−33	−36	−39

Zone K.

[Inner radius, 12 400 meters; outer radius, 18 800 meters. Twenty compartments.]

Mean elevation of compartment	Topography	Compensation	Topography and compensation	Above 600 feet	Above 1200 feet	Above 1800 feet	Above 2400 feet	Above 3000 feet	Above 3600 feet	Above 4200 feet	Above 4800 feet	Above 5400 feet	Above 6000 feet	Above 6600 feet	Above 7200 feet	Below 600 feet	Below 1200 feet	Below 1800 feet	Below 2400 feet	Below 3000 feet	Below 3600 feet	Below 4200 feet	Below 4800 feet	Below 5400 feet	Below 6000 feet	Below 6600 feet	Below 7200 feet
Fathoms																											
-1 200	-3	+4	+1	-1	-1	-1																					
- 800	-1	+2	+1	0	-1	-1	-1	-1	-1																		
- 400	0	+1	+1	0	-1	-1	-1	-1	-1	-1	-1	-1	-1	-1	-1												
Feet																											
0	0	0	0	0	0	0	0	0	0	0	0	0	0	0	0	0											
1 000	0	-1	-1	0	0	0	0	+1	+1	+1	+1	+1	+1	+1	+1	0	-1	-1									
2 000	0	-1	-1	0	+1	+1	+1	+1	+1	+1	+2	+2	+2	+2	+2	0	-1	-1	-1	-1							
3 000	0	-2	-2	0	+1	+1	+1	+2	+2	+2	+2	+2	+2	+3	+3	0	-1	-2	-2	-2	-2						
4 000	+1	-3	-2	0	+1	+1	+1	+2	+2	+2	+3	+3	+3	+4	+4	0	-1	-2	-2	-2	-2	-2					
5 000	+2	-4	-2	0	+1	+1	+1	+2	+2	+3	+3	+4	+4	+5	+5	0	-1	-2	-3	-3	-3	-4	-4				
6 000	+3	-5	-2	+1	+1	+2	+2	+3	+3	+3	+4	+4	+5	+5	+6	0	-1	-2	-3	-3	-4	-4	-5	-5	-6		
7 000	+4	-6	-2	+1	+1	+2	+2	+3	+3	+4	+4	+5	+6	+6	+7	0	-1	-2	-3	-3	-4	-4	-5	-6	-6	-7	
8 000	+5	-7	-2	+1	+1	+2	+3	+3	+4	+5	+5	+6	+6	+7	+7	0	-1	-2	-3	-3	-4	-5	-5	-6	-7	-8	-8
8 500	+5	-7	-2	+1	+1	+2	+3	+3	+4	+5	+5	+6	+7	+7	+8	0	-1	-2	-3	-4	-4	-5	-6	-6	-7	-8	-9
9 000	+5	-7	-2	+1	+1	+2	+3	+3	+4	+5	+5	+6	+7	+7	+8	0	-1	-2	-3	-4	-4	-5	-6	-7	-8	-9	-9
9 500	+6	-8	-2	+1	+1	+2	+3	+4	+4	+5	+6	+7	+8	+8	+9	0	-1	-2	-3	-4	-4	-5	-6	-7	-8	-9	-10
10 000	+7	-8	-1	+1	+1	+2	+3	+4	+4	+5	+6	+7	+8	+8	+9	0	-1	-2	-4	-5	-5	-6	-7	-8	-9	-10	-11
10 500	+8	-9	-1	+1	+1	+2	+3	+4	+5	+6	+6	+7	+8	+8	+9	0	-1	-2	-4	-5	-5	-6	-7	-8	-9	-10	-11
11 000	+8	-9	-1	+1	+2	+3	+4	+4	+5	+6	+7	+7	+8	+9	+10	0	-1	-3	-4	-5	-5	-6	-7	-8	-9	-10	-11
11 500	+9	-9	0	+1	+2	+3	+4	+4	+5	+6	+7	+8	+9	+9	+10	0	-2	-3	-5	-6	-6	-7	-8	-9	-10	-11	-12
12 000	+10	-10	0	+1	+2	+3	+4	+4	+5	+6	+7	+8	+9	+9	+10	0	-2	-3	-5	-6	-6	-7	-8	-9	-10	-11	-12
12 500	+10	-10	0	+1	+2	+3	+4	+5	+6	+6	+7	+8	+9	+10	+11	0	-2	-3	-5	-6	-6	-7	-8	-9	-10	-11	-12
13 000	+12	-11	+1	+1	+2	+3	+4	+5	+6	+7	+8	+8	+9	+10	+11	-1	-2	-3	-5	-6	-7	-8	-9	-10	-11	-12	-13
13 500	+12	-11	+1	+1	+2	+3	+4	+5	+6	+7	+8	+9	+10	+10	+11	-1	-2	-4	-5	-6	-7	-8	-9	-10	-11	-12	-13
14 000	+13	-11	+2	+1	+2	+3	+4	+5	+6	+7	+8	+9	+10	+10	+11	-1	-2	-4	-5	-6	-7	-8	-9	-10	-11	-13	-14
14 500	+14	-12	+2	+1	+2	+3	+4	+5	+6	+7	+8	+9	+10	+11	+12	-1	-2	-4	-5	-6	-7	-8	-10	-11	-12	-13	-14
15 000	+15	-12	+3	+1	+2	+3	+4	+5	+6	+7	+8	+9	+10	+11	+13	-1	-2	-4	-5	-6	-7	-9	-10	-12	-13	-14	-14

Zone L.

[Inner radius, 18 800 meters; outer radius, 28 800 meters. Twenty-four compartments.]

Correction for—

Mean elevation of compartment	Topography	Compensation	Topography and compensation
Fathoms			
−1 500	−2	+6	+4
−1 200	−1	+4	+3
− 900	−1	+3	+2
− 600	0	+2	+2
− 300	0	+1	+1
Feet			
0	0	0	0
1 000	0	−1	−1
2 000	0	−2	−2
3 000	0	−3	−3
4 000	+1	−4	−3
5 000	+1	−5	−4
6 000	+1	−5	−4
7 000	+2	−7	−5
8 000	+3	−8	−5
8 500	+3	−9	−6
9 000	+3	−9	−6
9 500	+3	−9	−6
10 000	+4	−10	−6
10 500	+4	−10	−6
11 000	+5	−11	−6
11 500	+5	−11	−6
12 000	+6	−12	−6
12 500	+6	−12	−6
13 000	+7	−13	−6
14 000	+8	−14	−6
15 000	+9	−15	−6

Correction for elevation of station—Above compartment

Mean elevation of compartment	700 feet	1400 feet	2100 feet	2800 feet	3500 feet	4200 feet	4900 feet	5600 feet	6300 feet	7000 feet	7700 feet	8400 feet
Fathoms												
−1 500	0											
−1 200	0	−1	−1									
− 900	0	−1	−1	−1	−1	−1	−1					
− 600	0	−1	−1	−1	−1	−1	−1	−1	−1			
− 300	0	0	0	0	−1	−1	−1	−1	−1	−1	−1	−1
Feet												
0	0	0	0	0	0	0	0	0	0	0	0	0
1 000	0	0	0	0	0	0	+1	+1	+1	+1	+1	+1
2 000	0	0	0	0	+1	+1	+1	+1	+1	+1	+1	+1
3 000	0	0	0	0	+1	+1	+1	+1	+2	+2	+2	+2
4 000	0	+1	+1	+1	+1	+1	+1	+2	+2	+2	+2	+3
5 000	0	+1	+1	+1	+2	+2	+2	+3	+3	+3	+3	+3
6 000	0	+1	+1	+1	+2	+2	+2	+3	+3	+4	+4	+4
7 000	0	+1	+1	+1	+2	+2	+2	+3	+4	+4	+5	+5
8 000	0	+1	+1	+2	+2	+2	+3	+3	+4	+4	+5	+5
8 500	0	+1	+1	+2	+2	+2	+3	+3	+4	+4	+5	+5
9 000	0	+1	+1	+2	+2	+3	+3	+4	+4	+5	+5	+6
9 500	0	+1	+2	+2	+3	+3	+4	+4	+5	+5	+6	+6
10 000	+1	+1	+2	+2	+3	+3	+4	+4	+5	+6	+6	+6
10 500	+1	+1	+2	+2	+3	+3	+4	+5	+5	+6	+6	+7
11 000	+1	+1	+2	+2	+3	+3	+4	+5	+5	+6	+6	+7
11 500	+1	+1	+2	+3	+3	+4	+4	+5	+5	+6	+6	+7
12 000	+1	+1	+2	+3	+3	+4	+5	+5	+6	+6	+7	+7
12 500	+1	+1	+2	+3	+3	+4	+5	+5	+6	+7	+7	+8
13 000	+1	+1	+2	+3	+3	+4	+5	+5	+6	+7	+7	+8
14 000	+1	+1	+2	+3	+3	+4	+5	+5	+6	+7	+7	+8
15 000	+1	+2	+3	+4	+4	+5	+6	+6	+7	+8	+8	+9

Correction for elevation of station—Below compartment

Mean elevation of compartment	700 feet	1400 feet	2100 feet	2800 feet	3500 feet	4200 feet	4900 feet	5600 feet	6300 feet	7000 feet	7700 feet	8400 feet
Fathoms												
−1 500												
−1 200												
− 900												
− 600												
− 300												
Feet												
0												
1 000	0											
2 000	0	0										
3 000	0	0	0	−1								
4 000	0	−1	−1	−1	−1							
5 000	0	−1	−1	−1	−2	−2	−2					
6 000	0	−1	−1	−1	−2	−2	−2	−3				
7 000	0	−1	−1	−2	−2	−3	−3	−3	−4			
8 000	0	−1	−1	−2	−2	−3	−3	−4	−4	−4		
8 500	0	−1	−1	−2	−2	−3	−3	−4	−4	−5	−5	
9 000	0	−1	−1	−2	−2	−3	−3	−4	−4	−5	−6	−6
9 500	0	−1	−2	−2	−3	−3	−4	−4	−5	−5	−6	−6
10 000	−1	−1	−2	−2	−3	−3	−4	−4	−5	−6	−6	−7
10 500	−1	−1	−2	−2	−3	−3	−4	−5	−6	−6	−7	−7
11 000	−1	−1	−2	−2	−3	−3	−4	−4	−5	−6	−7	−7
11 500	−1	−1	−2	−3	−3	−4	−4	−5	−5	−6	−7	−8
12 000	−1	−1	−2	−3	−3	−4	−5	−5	−6	−6	−7	−8
12 500	−1	−1	−2	−3	−3	−4	−5	−5	−6	−7	−8	−9
13 000	−1	−1	−2	−3	−3	−4	−5	−5	−6	−7	−8	−9
14 000	−1	−1	−2	−3	−3	−4	−5	−5	−6	−7	−8	−9
15 000	−1	−2	−3	−3	−4	−5	−6	−6	−7	−8	−9	−10

Zone M.

[Inner radius, 28 800 meters; outer radius, 58 800 meters. Fourteen compartments.]

Correction for—

Mean elevation of compartment	Topography	Compensation	Topography and compensation	At same elevation as compartment
Fathoms				
−1 500	− 3	+23	+20	
−1 200	− 2	+19	+17	
− 900	− 1	+14	+13	
− 600	− 1	+10	+ 9	
− 300	0	+ 4	+ 4	
Feet				
0	0	0	0	0
1 000	0	− 4	− 4	0
2 000	0	− 8	− 8	0
3 000	+ 1	−13	−12	0
4 000	+ 1	−17	−16	0
5 000	+ 2	−21	−19	+1
6 000	+ 2	−25	−23	+1
7 000	+ 3	−29	−26	+1
8 000	+ 4	−33	−29	+1
8 500	+ 5	−35	−30	+1
9 000	+ 5	−37	−32	+1
9 500	+ 6	−39	−33	+1
10 000	+ 7	−42	−35	+1
10 500	+ 7	−43	−36	+1
11 000	+ 8	−46	−38	+1
11 500	+ 9	−48	−39	+1
12 000	+ 9	−49	−40	+1
12 500	+10	−52	−42	+1
13 000	+11	−54	−43	+1
14 000	+13	−58	−45	+1
15 000	+15	−62	−47	+1

Correction for elevation of station—Above compartment

Mean elevation of compartment	700 feet	1400 feet	2100 feet	2800 feet	3500 feet	4200 feet	4900 feet	5600 feet	6300 feet	7000 feet	7700 feet	8400 feet
Fathoms												
−1 500	−1											
−1 200	−1	−1	−1									
− 900	−1	−1	−1	−1	−2	−2	−2	−2				
− 600	0	0	−1	−1	−1	−1	−1	−1	−1	−1		
− 300	0	0	0	0	−1	−1	−1	−1	−1	−1	−2	−2
Feet												
0	0	0	0	0	0	0	0	0	0	0	0	0
1 000	0	0	0	+1	+1	+1	+1	+1	+1	+1	+2	+2
2 000	0	0	+1	+1	+1	+1	+1	+2	+2	+2	+3	+3
3 000	0	+1	+1	+1	+2	+2	+2	+3	+3	+3	+4	+4
4 000	+1	+1	+1	+1	+2	+2	+3	+3	+4	+4	+5	+5
5 000	+1	+1	+1	+2	+2	+3	+3	+3	+4	+5	+5	+6
6 000	+1	+1	+2	+2	+3	+3	+4	+4	+5	+6	+6	+7
7 000	+1	+1	+2	+3	+3	+4	+5	+5	+6	+7	+7	+8
8 000	+1	+1	+2	+3	+4	+4	+5	+6	+7	+8	+8	+9
8 500	+1	+1	+2	+3	+4	+4	+5	+6	+7	+8	+8	+9
9 000	+1	+2	+2	+3	+4	+4	+5	+6	+7	+8	+9	+10
9 500	+1	+2	+2	+3	+4	+4	+6	+6	+8	+9	+9	+10
10 000	+1	+2	+2	+3	+4	+5	+6	+7	+8	+10	+10	+11
10 500	+1	+2	+2	+3	+4	+5	+6	+7	+9	+10	+10	+11
11 000	+1	+2	+3	+3	+4	+5	+6	+7	+9	+10	+11	+12
11 500	+1	+2	+3	+3	+4	+5	+6	+7	+9	+10	+11	+12
12 000	+1	+2	+3	+4	+5	+6	+7	+8	+10	+11	+12	+13
12 500	+1	+2	+3	+4	+5	+6	+7	+8	+10	+11	+12	+13
13 000	+1	+2	+3	+4	+5	+6	+7	+8	+11	+12	+13	+14
14 000	+1	+2	+3	+4	+5	+7	+8	+9	+11	+12	+14	+15
15 000	+2	+3	+4	+5	+7	+8	+9	+11	+12	+13	+15	+16

Correction for elevation of station—Below compartment

Mean elevation of compartment	700 feet	1400 feet	2100 feet	2800 feet	3500 feet	4200 feet	4900 feet	5600 feet	6300 feet	7000 feet	7700 feet	8400 feet
Fathoms												
−1 500												
−1 200												
− 900												
− 600												
− 300												
Feet												
0												
1 000												
2 000	0											
3 000	0	0										
4 000	−1	−1	−1									
5 000	−1	−1	−2	−2	−3	−3	−3					
6 000	−1	−2	−2	−2	−3	−3	−4	−4				
7 000	−1	−2	−2	−3	−3	−4	−5	−5	−6			
8 000	−1	−2	−3	−4	−4	−5	−6	−6	−7	−7		
8 500	−1	−2	−3	−4	−4	−5	−6	−6	−7	−7		
9 000	−2	−2	−3	−4	−4	−5	−6	−6	−7	−7	−8	
9 500	−2	−2	−3	−4	−4	−5	−6	−7	−7	−8	−8	−9
10 000	−2	−2	−3	−4	−5	−6	−7	−7	−8	−8	−9	−9
10 500	−2	−3	−3	−4	−5	−6	−7	−8	−8	−9	−9	−10
11 000	−2	−3	−3	−4	−5	−6	−7	−8	−8	−9	−10	−10
11 500	−2	−3	−3	−4	−5	−6	−7	−8	−8	−9	−10	−11
12 000	−2	−3	−4	−5	−6	−7	−7	−8	−9	−9	−10	−11
12 500	−2	−3	−4	−5	−6	−7	−8	−8	−9	−10	−11	−12
13 000	−2	−3	−4	−5	−6	−7	−8	−9	−9	−10	−11	−13
14 000	−2	−3	−4	−5	−7	−8	−8	−9	−10	−11	−12	−13
15 000	−2	−3	−4	−5	−7	−8	−9	−10	−11	−12	−14	−15

The distance from the station to the middle of this zone is 43.8 km (=27.2 miles) and the curvature is 495 feet.

Zone N.

[Inner radius, 58 800 meters; outer radius, 99 000 meters. Sixteen compartments.]

Correction for—

Mean elevation of compartment	Topography	Compensation	Topography and compensation	At same elevation as compartment
Fathoms				
−1 500	−1	+18	+17	0
−1 200	−1	+15	+14	0
− 900	0	+10	+10	0
− 600	0	+ 7	+ 7	0
− 300	0	+ 4	+ 4	0
Feet				
0	0	0	0	0
500	0	− 2	− 2	0
1 000	0	− 3	− 3	0
1 500	0	− 5	− 5	0
2 000	0	− 6	− 6	0
2 500	0	− 8	− 8	0
3 000	0	−10	−10	0
3 500	0	−11	−11	0
4 000	0	−13	−13	0
4 500	+1	−15	−14	0
5 000	+1	−17	−16	0
6 000	+1	−20	−19	0
7 000	+1	−23	−22	0
8 000	+1	−26	−25	0
9 000	+2	−30	−28	+1
10 000	+2	−32	−30	+1
11 000	+3	−36	−33	+1
12 000	+3	−39	−36	+1
13 000	+4	−43	−39	+1
14 000	+4	−45	−41	+1
15 000	+5	−49	−44	+1

Correction for elevation of station— Above compartment

Mean elevation of compartment	700 feet	1400 feet	2100 feet	2800 feet	3500 feet	4200 feet	4900 feet	5600 feet	6300 feet	7000 feet	7700 feet	8400 feet
Fathoms												
−1 500	−1											
−1 200	−1	−1	−1									
− 900	0	−1	−1	−1	−1	−1						
− 600	0	0	0	0	−1	−1	−1	−1	−1			
− 300	0	0	0	0	0	0	0	−1	−1	−1	−1	−1
Feet												
0	0	0	0	0	0	0	0	0	0	0	0	0
500	0	0	0	0	0	0	0	0	0	0	+1	+1
1 000	0	0	0	0	0	0	0	0	0	+1	+1	+1
1 500	0	0	0	0	0	0	0	0	+1	+1	+1	+1
2 000	0	0	0	0	0	0	0	+1	+1	+1	+1	+1
2 500	0	0	0	0	+1	+1	+1	+1	+1	+1	+1	+1
3 000	0	0	0	0	+1	+1	+1	+1	+1	+1	+1	+1
3 500	0	0	0	0	+1	+1	+1	+1	+1	+1	+1	+2
4 000	0	0	0	+1	+1	+1	+1	+1	+1	+1	+2	+2
4 500	0	0	0	+1	+1	+1	+1	+1	+2	+2	+2	+2
5 000	0	+1	+1	+1	+1	+1	+1	+2	+2	+2	+2	+2
6 000	0	+1	+1	+1	+1	+1	+1	+2	+2	+2	+2	+2
7 000	+1	+1	+1	+1	+1	+1	+1	+2	+2	+2	+2	+2
8 000	+1	+1	+1	+1	+1	+1	+2	+2	+2	+3	+3	+3
9 000	+1	+1	+1	+1	+1	+2	+2	+2	+2	+3	+3	+3
10 000	+1	+1	+1	+1	+2	+2	+2	+2	+3	+3	+3	+4
11 000	+1	+1	+1	+1	+2	+2	+2	+3	+3	+3	+4	+4
12 000	+1	+1	+1	+2	+2	+2	+2	+3	+3	+4	+4	+4
13 000	+1	+1	+1	+2	+2	+2	+3	+3	+4	+4	+4	+4
14 000	+1	+1	+1	+2	+2	+2	+3	+3	+4	+4	+5	+5
15 000	+1	+1	+1	+2	+3	+3	+3	+4	+4	+4	+5	+5

Correction for elevation of station— Below compartment

Mean elevation of compartment	700 feet	1400 feet	2100 feet	2800 feet	3500 feet	4200 feet	4900 feet	5600 feet	6300 feet	7000 feet	7700 feet	8400 feet
Fathoms												
−1 500												
−1 200												
− 900												
− 600												
− 300												
Feet												
0												
500												
1 000	0											
1 500	0	0										
2 000	0	0										
2 500	0	0	0									
3 000	0	0	0	0								
3 500	0	0	0	0	0							
4 000	0	0	0	0	0							
4 500	0	0	0	0	0	0						
5 000	0	0	0	0	0	0	0					
6 000	0	0	0	0	0	0	0	−1				
7 000	0	0	0	0	0	0	0	−1	−1	−1		
8 000	0	0	0	0	−1	−1	−1	−1	−1	−1	−2	−2
9 000	0	0	0	−1	−1	−1	−1	−1	−1	−1	−2	−2
10 000	0	0	0	−1	−1	−1	−1	−2	−2	−2	−2	−3
11 000	0	0	−1	−1	−1	−1	−2	−2	−2	−2	−3	−3
12 000	0	0	−1	−1	−1	−1	−2	−2	−2	−2	−3	−3
13 000	0	0	−1	−1	−1	−2	−2	−2	−2	−3	−3	−3
14 000	0	0	−1	−1	−1	−2	−2	−2	−3	−3	−3	−4
15 000	0	0	−1	−2	−2	−2	−2	−3	−3	−4	−4	−4

The distance from the station to the middle of this zone is 78.9 km (= 49.0 miles) and the curvature is 1600 feet.

Zone O.

[Inner radius, 99 000 meters; outer radius, 166 700 meters. Twenty-eight compartments.]

Correction for — (Topography, Compensation, Topography and compensation); Correction for elevation of station — (At same elevation as compartment; Above compartment; Below compartment).

Above compartment

Mean elevation of compartment	Topography	Compensation	Topography and compensation	At same elevation as compartment	800 feet	1600 feet	2400 feet	3200 feet	4000 feet	4800 feet	5600 feet	6400 feet	7200 feet	8000 feet	8800 feet	9600 feet
Fathoms																
−1 800	0	+12	+12	0												
−1 500	0	+10	+10	0	0											
−1 200	0	+8	+8	0	0	0	0									
− 900	0	+6	+6	0	0	0	0	0	0							
− 600	0	+4	+4	0	0	0	0	0	0	0	0					
− 300	0	+2	+2	0	0	0	0	0	0	0	0	0	0			
Feet																
0	0	0	0	0	0	0	0	0	0	0	0	0	0	0	0	0
500	0	−1	−1	0	0	0	0	0	0	0	0	0	0	0	0	0
1 000	0	−2	−2	0	0	0	0	0	0	0	0	0	0	0	0	0
1 500	0	−3	−3	0	0	0	0	0	0	0	0	0	0	0	0	0
2 000	0	−4	−4	0	0	0	0	0	0	0	0	0	0	0	0	0
2 500	0	−4	−4	0	0	0	0	0	0	0	0	0	0	0	0	0
3 000	0	−5	−5	0	0	0	0	0	0	0	0	0	0	0	0	0
3 500	0	−6	−6	0	0	0	0	0	0	0	0	0	0	0	0	0
4 000	0	−7	−7	0	0	0	0	0	0	0	0	0	0	0	0	0
5 000	0	−9	−9	0	0	0	0	0	0	0	0	0	0	+1	+1	+1
6 000	0	−10	−10	0	0	0	0	0	0	0	0	+1	+1	+1	+1	+1
7 000	0	−12	−12	0	0	0	0	0	0	+1	+1	+1	+1	+1	+1	+1
8 000	0	−14	−14	0	0	0	0	+1	+1	+1	+1	+1	+1	+1	+1	+1
9 000	+1	−16	−15	0	0	+1	+1	+1	+1	+1	+1	+1	+1	+1	+1	+1
10 000	+1	−18	−17	0	+1	+1	+1	+1	+1	+1	+1	+1	+1	+1	+1	+1
11 000	+1	−20	−19	0	+1	+1	+1	+1	+1	+1	+1	+1	+1	+1	+1	+1
12 000	+1	−21	−20	0	+1	+1	+1	+1	+1	+1	+1	+1	+1	+1	+1	+1
13 000	+1	−23	−22	+1	+1	+1	+1	+1	+1	+1	+1	+1	+1	+1	+2	+2
14 000	+2	−25	−23	+1	+1	+1	+1	+1	+1	+1	+1	+1	+2	+2	+2	+2
15 000	+2	−27	−25	+1	+1	+1	+1	+1	+1	+1	+1	+2	+2	+2	+2	+2

Below compartment

Mean elevation of compartment	800 feet	1600 feet	2400 feet	3200 feet	4000 feet	4800 feet	5600 feet	6400 feet	7200 feet	8000 feet	8800 feet	9600 feet
Fathoms												
−1 800												
−1 500												
−1 200												
− 900												
− 600												
− 300												
Feet												
0												
500												
1 000	0											
1 500	0	0										
2 000	0	0										
2 500	0	0	0									
3 000	0	0	0									
3 500	0	0	0	0								
4 000	0	0	0	0	0							
5 000	0	0	0	0	0	0						
6 000	0	0	0	0	0	0	0					
7 000	0	0	0	0	0	0	0	0				
8 000	0	0	0	0	0	0	0	0	0			
9 000	0	0	0	0	0	0	0	0	0	0		
10 000	0	0	0	0	0	0	0	0	0	0	0	−1
11 000	0	0	0	0	0	0	0	0	0	0	0	−1
12 000	0	0	0	0	0	0	0	0	0	0	0	−1
13 000	0	0	0	0	0	0	0	0	0	0	−1	−1
14 000	0	0	0	0	0	0	0	0	0	−1	−1	−1
15 000	0	0	0	0	0	0	0	0	−1	−1	−1	−1

The distance from the station to the middle of this zone is 132.8 km (=82.5 miles) and the curvature is 4500 feet.

REDUCTION TABLES FOR NUMBERED ZONES.

Zone 18.

[Unit of elevation 100 feet (27.1 fathoms for depths). $\theta = 1°\ 41'\ 13''$ to $1°\ 29'\ 58''$. One compartment.]

Correction as read from map	Correction for departure from proportionality	Correction for elevation of station at—			Correction as read from map	Correction for departure from proportionality	Correction for elevation of station at—		
		5 000 feet	10 000 feet	15 000 feet			5 000 feet	10 000 feet	15 000 feet
+150	+1	−2	−5	−7	0	0	0	0	0
+125	+1	−2	−4	−6	− 25	0	0	+1	+1
+100	+1	−2	−3	−5	− 50	0	+1	+2	+2
+ 75	0	−1	−2	−3	− 75	0	+1	+2	+3
+ 50	0	−1	−2	−2	−100	0	+2	+3	+5
+ 25	0	0	−1	−1					

Zone 17.

[Unit of elevation 100 feet (27.1 fathoms for depths). $\theta = 1°\ 54'\ 52''$ to $1°\ 41'\ 13''$. One compartment.]

Correction as read from map	Correction for departure from proportionality	Correction for elevation of station at—			Correction as read from map	Correction for departure from proportionality	Correction for elevation of station at—		
		5 000 feet	10 000 feet	15 000 feet			5 000 feet	10 000 feet	15 000 feet
+150	+3	−2	−4	−6	0	0	0	0	0
+125	+2	−2	−3	−5	− 25	0	+1	+1	+1
+100	+1	−1	−3	−4	− 50	0	+1	+1	+2
+ 75	+1	−1	−2	−3	− 75	+1	+1	+2	+3
+ 50	0	−1	−1	−2	−100	+1	+1	+3	+4
+ 25	0	−1	−1	−1					

Zone 16.

[Unit of elevation 100 feet (27.1 fathoms for depths). $\theta = 2°\ 11'\ 53''$ to $1°\ 54'\ 52''$. One compartment.]

Correction as read from map	Correction for departure from proportionality	Correction for elevation of station at—			Correction as read from map	Correction for departure from proportionality	Correction for elevation of station at—		
		5 000 feet	10 000 feet	15 000 feet			5 000 feet	10 000 feet	15 000 feet
+150	+4	−2	−3	−5	0	0	0	0	0
+125	+3	−1	−3	−4	− 25	0	0	+1	+1
+100	+2	−1	−2	−3	− 50	0	+1	+1	+2
+ 75	+1	−1	−1	−2	− 75	+1	+1	+1	+2
+ 50	0	−1	−1	−2	−100	+1	+1	+2	+3
+ 25	0	0	−1	−1					

Zone 15.

[Unit of elevation 100 feet (27.1 fathoms for depths). $\theta = 2°\ 33'\ 46''$ to $2°\ 11'\ 53''$. One compartment.]

Correction as read from map	Correction for departure from proportionality	Correction for elevation of station at—			Correction as read from map	Correction for departure from proportionality	Correction for elevation of station at—		
		5 000 feet	10 000 feet	15 000 feet			5 000 feet	10 000 feet	15 000 feet
+150	+5	−1	−3	−4	0	0	0	0	0
+125	+4	−1	−2	−3	− 25	0	0	0	+1
+100	+2	−1	−2	−3	− 50	0	0	+1	+1
+ 75	+1	−1	−1	−2	− 75	+1	+1	+1	+2
+ 50	+1	0	−1	−1	−100	+1	+1	+2	+3
+ 25	0	0	0	−1					

Zone 14.

[Unit of elevation 100 feet (27.1 fathoms for depths). $\theta = 3°\ 03'\ 05''$ to $2°\ 33'\ 46''$. One compartment.]

Correction as read from map	Correction for departure from proportionality	Correction for elevation of station at—			Correction as read from map	Correction for departure from proportionality	Correction for elevation of station at—		
		5 000 feet	10 000 feet	15 000 feet			5 000 feet	10 000 feet	15 000 feet
+150	+6	−1	−2	−3	0	0	0	0	0
+125	+4	−1	−2	−3	− 25	0	0	0	0
+100	+3	−1	−1	−2	− 50	0	0	+1	+1
+ 75	+2	−1	−1	−2	− 75	+1	0	+1	+1
+ 50	+1	0	−1	−1	−100	+2	+1	+1	+2
+ 25	0	0	0	0					

Zone 13.

[Unit of elevation 1000 feet (271 fathoms for depths). $\theta = 4° 19' 13''$ to $3° 03' 05''$. Sixteen compartments.]

No correction for elevation of station. No correction for departure from proportionality.

Zone 12.

[Unit of elevation 1000 feet (271 fathoms for depths). $\theta = 5° 46' 34''$ to $4° 19' 13''$. Ten compartments.]

No correction for elevation of station. No correction for departure from proportionality.

Zone 11.

[Unit of elevation 1000 feet (271 fathoms for depths). $\theta = 7° 51' 30''$ to $5° 46' 34''$. Eight compartments.]

No correction for elevation of station. No correction for departure from proportionality.

Zone 10.

[Unit of elevation 1000 feet (271 fathoms for depths). $\theta = 10° 44'$ to $7° 51' 30''$. Six compartments.]

No correction for elevation of station. No correction for departure from proportionality.

Zone 9.

[Unit of elevation 1000 feet (271 fathoms for depths). $\theta = 14° 09'$ to $10° 44'$. Four compartments.]

No correction for elevation of station. No correction for departure from proportionality.

Zone 8.

[Unit of elevation 1000 feet (271 fathoms for depths). $\theta = 20° 41'$ to $14° 09'$. Four compartments.]

No correction for elevation of station. No correction for departure from proportionality.

Zone 7.

[Unit of elevation 1000 feet (271 fathoms for depths). $\theta = 26° 41'$ to $20° 41'$. Two compartments.]

No correction for elevation of station. No correction for departure from proportionality.

Zone 6.

[Unit of elevation 10 000 feet (2710 fathoms for depths). $\theta = 35° 58'$ to $26° 41'$. Eighteen compartments.]

No correction for elevation of station. No correction for departure from proportionality.

Zone 5.

[Unit of elevation 10 000 feet (2710 fathoms for depths). $\theta = 51° 04'$ to $35° 58'$. Sixteen compartments.]

No correction for elevation of station. No correction for departure from proportionality.

Zone 4.

[Unit of elevation 10 000 feet (2710 fathoms for depths). $\theta = 72° 13'$ to $51° 04'$. Twelve compartments.]

No correction for elevation of station. No correction for departure from proportionality.

Zone 3.

[Unit of elevation 10 000 feet (2710 fathoms for depths). $\theta = 105° 48'$ to $72° 13'$. Ten compartments.]

No correction for elevation of station. No correction for departure from proportionality.

Zone 2.

[Unit of elevation 10 000 feet (2710 fathoms for depths).   θ=150° 56′ to 105° 48′.   Six compartments.]

No correction for elevation of station.   No correction for departure from proportionality.

Zone 1.

[Unit of elevation 10 000 feet (2710 fathoms for depths).   θ=180° to 150° 56′.   One compartment only.]

No correction for elevation of station.   No correction for departure from proportionality.

SPECIAL REDUCTION TABLES FOR SEA STATIONS.

[Corrections in dynes in units of the fourth decimal place.   Station at sea level.]

Depth	Zones														
Fathoms	A	B	C	D	E	F	G	H	I	J	K	L	M	N	O
5 000	−1	−11	−27	−39	−53	−55	−48	−40	−40	−34	−18	−3	+41	+51	+32
4 800	−1	−11	−27	−39	−53	−55	−47	−39	−38	−32	−17	−2	+41	+49	+31
4 600	−1	−11	−27	−39	−53	−54	−46	−37	−36	−29	−15	−1	+40	+47	+29
4 400	−1	−11	−27	−38	−53	−54	−45	−36	−34	−27	−14	−1	+40	+45	+28
4 200	−1	−11	−27	−38	−53	−53	−44	−34	−32	−25	−12	0	+39	+44	+27
4 000	−1	−11	−27	−38	−52	−52	−43	−33	−30	−23	−11	+1	+39	+42	+26
3 800	−1	−11	−27	−38	−51	−51	−42	−31	−28	−21	− 9	+1	+38	+40	+24
3 600	−1	−11	−27	−38	−51	−50	−41	−29	−26	−19	− 8	+2	+37	+38	+23
3 400	−1	−11	−26	−37	−50	−49	−39	−28	−24	−17	− 7	+2	+36	+36	+22
3 200	−1	−11	−26	−37	−49	−48	−38	−26	−22	−15	− 5	+3	+35	+34	+21
3 000	−1	−11	−26	−37	−48	−46	−36	−24	−20	−13	− 4	+3	+33	+32	+19
2 800	−1	−11	−26	−37	−47	−44	−34	−23	−18	−11	− 3	+4	+32	+30	+18
2 600	−1	−11	−26	−36	−46	−43	−32	−21	−16	−10	− 2	+4	+30	+28	+17
2 400	−1	−11	−26	−36	−44	−41	−30	−20	−14	− 8	− 1	+4	+28	+26	+15
2 200	−1	−11	−26	−35	−43	−39	−27	−17	−12	− 6	− 1	+4	+26	+24	+14
2 000	−1	−10	−26	−35	−42	−37	−25	−15	−11	− 5	0	+4	+25	+22	+12
1 800	−1	−10	−26	−34	−41	−34	−22	−13	− 9	− 4	0	+4	+23	+20	+12
1 600	−1	−10	−25	−34	−40	−32	−19	−10	− 7	− 2	+ 1	+4	+20	+18	+10
1 400	−1	−10	−25	−34	−38	−28	−16	− 9	− 5	− 2	+ 1	+4	+19	+16	+ 9
1 200	−1	−10	−25	−33	−35	−25	−13	− 7	− 3	− 1	+ 1	+3	+17	+14	+ 8
1 000	−1	−10	−25	−31	−31	−20	−10	− 5	− 2	0	+ 1	+2	+14	+12	+ 6
800	−1	−10	−25	−30	−27	−15	− 7	− 3	− 1	0	+ 1	+2	+11	+ 9	+ 5
600	−1	−10	−23	−26	*−21	−10	− 4	− 1	− 1	+ 1	+ 1	+2	+ 9	+ 7	+ 4
400	−1	−10	−22	−21	*−13	*− 5	− 2	− 1	0	+ 1	+ 1	+1	+ 6	+ 5	+ 2
200	−1	*−10	*−17	*−11	*− 4	*− 1	0	0	0	+ 1	+ 1	+1	+ 3	+ 2	+ 1
0	0	*0	*0	*0	*0	*0	0	0	0	0	0	0	0	0	0

* Use table following for these values on account of large second difference.

Supplementary table for use in connection with gravity stations at sea.

[Correction in dynes in units of the fourth decimal place.   Station at sea level.]

Depth	Zone				
Fathoms	B	C	D	E	F
800		−25		−27	
750		−24		−26	
700		−24		−24	
650		−24		−22	
600		−23	−26	−21	−10
550		−23	−26	−19	− 9
500		−23	−25	−17	− 7
450		−23	−23	−15	− 6
400		−22	−21	−13	− 5
350		−21	−19	−11	− 4
300		−20	−17	− 9	− 3
250		−19	−14	− 6	− 2
200	−10	−17	−11	− 4	− 1
150	−10	−15	− 7	− 2	− 1
100	− 9	−11	− 4	− 1	0
75	− 8	− 9	− 2	− 1	0
50	− 7	− 5	− 1	− 1	0
25	− 5	− 1	− 1	0	0
10	− 2	0	0	0	0
0	0	0	0	0	0

USE OF TEMPLATES.

For each scale of map or chart to be used in the computations there was prepared a sheet of transparent celluloid with the circles and radial lines which define the limits of the zones and compartments drawn to the same scale.

Such a template is shown in illustration No. 10*a* as used for maps on a scale of 1/10000. The zones are marked with their designating letters, and the scale of the template is ordinarily marked on each.   No attempt has been made to reproduce the illustration to the proper scale.

Each template consists of a sheet similar to that indicated in illustration No. 10*a* carrying lines bounding the compartments which lie on one side of the reference line.   By turning the template 180° in azimuth on a map it serves also to fix the position of the remaining compartments.   While in use the template is placed on a map with the center of the circles at the station and with the reference line lying in the meridian.   As a convenient designation the compartments in any zone are numbered in the clockwise direction commencing with the first which is to the eastward of north from the station.

Illustration No. 10*b* shows a template such as was used on maps on a scale of 1/6013500. This necessarily shows more distant zones than illustration No. 10*a*.   The dotted radial lines in zones 14 to 18 are not compartment boundaries.   Each of these zones has one compartment only.   They are lines dividing each of the zones into ten equal parts, as it was found convenient in estimating the mean elevation for such large zones to make separate estimates for each part rather than to make an estimate at once for the whole compartment or zone.   For the same purpose dotted lines are shown in zone 7 separating each of its two compartments into five equal parts.

By the use of these transparent (celluloid) templates the many circles and radial lines fixing the limits of the zones and compartments on a given map for any station were superposed on the map by the mere process of laying the template on the map in the proper position. The use of the templates saved a very large amount of labor which would otherwise have been necessary in drawing the many zones and compartments on several hundred maps.   It also left the maps without damage or defacement.

In computing the correction for topography and isostatic compensation for a given station the computer places the appropriate template in the proper position on the best contour map available. He then estimates the mean elevation of the surface in each compartment from the contour lines on the map, seen through the template, and at once takes out from the reduction tables the two corrections for that compartment and records them in the proper places on the computation forms. As he has the reduction tables constantly before him he is continually guided as to the accuracy with which the estimate of mean elevations must be made in order to secure the corrections with the required degree of accuracy. As a rule this estimate

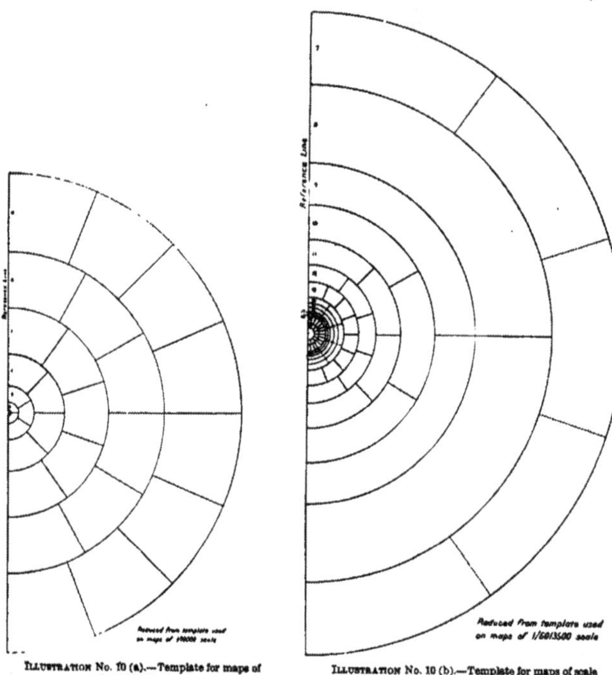

ILLUSTRATION No. 10 (a).—Template for maps of scale 1/10000 (reduced).

ILLUSTRATION No. 10 (b).—Template for maps of scale 1/6013500 (reduced).

may be made very quickly, for as indicated in the reduction tables, an approximate elevation of a compartment is sufficient. This is especially true in the numbered zones 13 to 1, for which the unit elevations are either 1000 or 10 000 feet.

EXAMPLES OF COMPUTATIONS OF CORRECTIONS.

The following table is a sample of the computations, and in it are given the values (in units of the fourth decimal place in dynes) of the correction for topography and isostatic compensation for each compartment of zones A to 1 at the San Francisco gravity station. This station is near the open coast, is 85 miles from the 1000-fathom line, and is only 375 feet above sea level.

San Francisco, Cal., gravity station No. 54.

[ϕ=37° 47′ 22″. λ=122° 25′ 40″. Elevation=375 feet.]

A	B	C	D	E	F	G	H	I	J	K	L	M	N	O
+2 0	+13 −1	+8 0	+1 +1	0 0	0 0	0 0	0 0	0 0	0 0	0 0	0 0	0 0	−2 0	−1 0
	+13 −1	+9 0	+1 +1	+1 0	0 0	0 0	0 0	0 0	0 0	0 0	0 0	0 0	0 0	0 0
	+13 −1	+9 0	+2 +1	0 0	0 0	0 0	0 0	0 0	0 0	0 0	0 0	−4 0	0 0	0 0
	+13 −1	+9 0	+2 +1	0 0	0 0	0 0	0 0	0 0	0 0	0 0	−1 0	−4 0	0 0	0 0
			+2 +1	0 0	0 0	0 0	0 0	0 0	0 0	0 0	−1 0	−1 0	−2 0	0 0
			+1 +1	0 0	0 0	0 0	0 0	0 0	0 0	0 0	−1 0	0 0	−3 0	−1 0
				0 0	0 0	0 0	0 0	0 0	0 0	0 0	0 0	0 0	−3 0	−1 0
				0 0	0 0	0 0	0 0	0 0	0 0	0 0	−1 0	−3 0	−1 0	0 0
					0 0	0 0	0 0	0 0	0 0	0 0	0 0	0 0	0 0	0 0
					0 0	0 0	0 0	0 0	0 0	0 0	0 0	0 0	+2 0	−2 0
					0 0	0 0	0 0	0 0	−1 0	0 0	0 0	0 0	+2 0	−2 0
						0 0	0 0	0 0	0 0	0 0	0 0	0 0	+10 0	0 0
						0 0	0 0	0 0	0 0	0 0	0 0	0 0	+10 0	0 0
						0 0	0 0	0 0	0 0	0 0	0 0	0 0	+4 0	0 0
						0 0	0 0	0 0	0 0	0 0	0 0	0 0	+1 0	0 0
							0 0	0 0	0 0	0 0	−1 0	−2 0	−1 0	+2 0
							0 0	0 0	−1 0	0 0	0 0	0 0	0 0	+8 0
							0 0	0 0	0 0	0 0	0 0	0 0	−2 0	+11 0
							0 0	0 0	0 0	0 0	0 0	0 0		+12 0
							0 0	0 0	0 0	0 0	0 0			+13 0
								0 0	0 0	0 0	0 0			+13 0
								0 0		0 0	0 0			+13 0
								0 0		0 0	0 0			+13 0
								0 0		0 0	0 0			+12 0
								0 0		−1 0	−1 0			+9 0
								0 0		0 0	0 0			+6 0
										0 0	−1 0			+1 0
										0 0	0 0			−2 0
										0 0	0 0			−3 0
											0 0			−2 0
+2 0	+52 −4	+35 0	+9 +6	+1 0	0 0	0 0	0 0	0 0	−2 0	−1 0	−7 0	−14 0	+15 0	+99 0
+2	+48	+35	+15	+1	0	0	0	0	−2	−1	−7	−14	+15	+99

18	17	16	15	14	13	12	11	10	9	8	7	6	5	4	3	2	1
−4 0	−7 0	−12 0	−16 0	−21 0	−5	−6	−5	−5	−7	−2	0	0	0	0	0	0	0
+28 0	+28 0	+32 0	+36 0	+38 0	−5	−6	−6	−6	−2	−2	+1	0	0	0	0	0	+1
					−6	−6	−4	−1	+2	+3	0	0	0	+1	0	0	
					−6	−3	0	+4	+10	+9	+9	0	0	+1	0	+1	
					−7	+5	+5	+8	0	0		0	0	0	0	0	
					−3	+9	+8	+10	+7	+7		0	0	+1	0	+1	
					0	+11	+10	0				0	+1	0	0	+1	
					−2	+11	+9	+4				0	0	0	+1	+1	
					+5	+7	0					0	0	+1	+1	0	
					+8	−1	+4					0	0	+1	+1	0	
					+9	+2						0	+1	+1	+1		
					+10							0	+1	+1	+1		
					+10							0	+1	+1	0		
					+9							0	+1	0	0		
					+8							+1	+1	0			
					+4							+1	+1	0			
					−4							+1	+1	0			
					0							+1	+1				
												+1	0				
												+1	0				
												+1					
												+1					
												+1					
												0					
												0					
												0					
												0					
+24 0	+21 0	+20 0	+19 0	+17 0	+25	+23	+21	+14	+10	+15	+10	+9	+9	+8	+5	+4	+1
+24	+21	+20	+19	+17													

Sum of all zones = +446.

At the top of the table are given the latitude, longitude, and elevation of the station. In actual practice the zones may be arranged in any convenient manner on a single sheet. Here they are placed in such a way as to show them in as compact a form as possible.

The headings of the several columns indicate the zones by letter or number, it being understood that the zones are in the order of their distances from the station, namely, A to O, and 18 to 1, the zone A being at the station with its inner radius zero.

In a zone having more than one compartment, the compartments are numbered clockwise, the first one being to the north of the station and just to the east of the meridian passing through the station. Having this arrangement of compartments in mind, one can readily see in the table for any station the effect of the different prominent topographic features. This is noticeable in zone O for both the San Francisco and Pikes Peak gravity stations.

At San Francisco for the first 13 compartments of zone O the corrections are all zero or negative. These are all land compartments. In compartment 14, nearly due south from the station, a positive correction, due to the ocean, first appears. In compartments 15 to 25, all to the westward of the station, the corrections are all positive, showing the influence of the deep waters of the Pacific. Compartments 26 to 28 are land compartments, showing the influence of the Coast Range to the northwestward of San Francisco. The similar influence of the part of the Coast Range to the southeastward of San Francisco lying within this zone is shown in compartments 10 and 11.

It will be noticed that there is a double column for each of the zones B to O. The first column gives the effect .on the intensity of gravity at the station, due to the topography and the isostatic compensation of the several compartments based upon the assumption that the station is, in each case, at the same elevation as the compartment. The mean elevation of the compartment is obtained from the map or maps used. Entering the table for the particular zone with this elevation, this correction is obtained from the fourth column, which is headed "Correction for topography and compensation." In the second column for zones B to O is given the effect of the intensity of gravity due to the elevation of the station above or below the average elevation of each compartment. These quantities are given in the tables under the headings "Correction for elevation of station above compartment" and "Correction for elevation of station below compartment."

In taking out the second correction it must be kept in mind, as already noted on pages 22 and 29, that it does not become zero in zones M, N, and O when the station is at the same elevation as the compartment, but, instead, has the values shown in the special column in the reduction tables for these zones. For zones B to L the second correction is zero when the station is at the same elevation as the compartment.

Two columns are given for each zone 18 to 14, the first one showing the correction as read from the map and given in the first columns of the reduction tables for those zones, while the second column contains the algebraic sum of the corrections for the departure from proportionality and for the elevation of the station above sea level.

For each of the zones 13 to 1, there is only one column of figures, which are the corrections for the compartments as read from the map, each compartment of zones 13 to 7 having a correction of 0.0001 dyne for each 1000 feet in elevation (271 fathoms for depth), and zones 6 to 1 having a correction of 0.0001 dyne for each 10 000 feet of elevation (2710 fathoms for depth).

The algebraic sums for each column is given at the foot of the column and immediately below these separate sums is given the algebraic sum for the zone. The sum for all zones is +446 in the units used in the computation or +0.0446 dynes. This is the correction at San Francisco for the topography of the entire earth and its compensation.

It was found at times to be desirable to treat in two parts the corrections for a compartment which contained both land and water areas. The corrections for land and water for the compartments treated in this way are connected in the table by brackets, the first number being for the land portion and the second for the water portion of the compartment in question. In determining the correction for any portion of a compartment the table is entered with the elevation of that portion as the argument as if it were the elevation of the whole compartment, but the correction entered in the computations is only that proportion of the total correction which the area of the portion of the compartment bears to its total area.

The elevations close to the gravity station at San Francisco are low and in no case inside of zone L is the height of a single compartment more than 700 feet above sea level. In zone L one compartment to the eastward of San Francisco, in the Coast Range, has an average elevation of about 800 feet. Zone L is just beyond the change of sign due to distance (see p. 65), and therefore the correction for that compartment is not over 0.0001 dyne. In zone M there are several compartments near the compartments of zone L in the Coast Range, already referred to, with elevations of about 1000 feet, each of which causes corrections of -0.0004 dyne (see third and fourth numbers in the column for zone M). In zone N there are two compartments h'aving depths of about 900 fathoms, which cause corrections of $+0.0010$ dyne. The land compartments in this zone do not have elevations above 1000 feet. A portion of zone O extends well beyond the 1000-fathom line, which causes corrections as large as $+0.0013$ dyne for several water compartments.

The corrections for the land and water portions of each of the zones 18 to 14 are given separately, the correction being minus for the land and plus for the water. Most of the water sections of these zones are far far out in the Pacific Ocean. Each of these zones has only one compartment, but for convenience in reading elevations and depths from the maps, each zone is divided into 10 parts and for each part the correction is taken from the reduction tables as one-tenth of the value given for the whole zone for an elevation equal to that of the part in question. The table was entered only once to obtain for the zone the correction for the elevation of the station above sea level. For each of the zones 18 to 14 at San Francisco the algebraic sum of the corrections for departure from proportionality and for elevation of station is zero.

Each of the zones 13 to 1 has only one column of figures in the table, as there are no corrections for elevation of station nor for departure from proportionality. The total correction for each of these zones is plus, showing that the effect of the water compartments predominates. There was no interpolation of values in any of the zones for the gravity station at San Francisco. All values were computed directly from the maps and charts.

The following table gives in detail the computation of the effect of topography and its isostatic compensation at the gravity station Pikes Peak, which is a mountain station far from the ocean. The station is much above the general elevation of the surrounding country.

Pikes Peak, Colo., Gravity Station No. 43.

[ϕ=38° 50′ 18″. λ=105° 02′ 00″.   Elevation=14 085 feet.]

A		B		C		D		E	
+2	0	+18	0	+42	−4	+57	−6	+70	−8
		+18	0	+42	−3	+57	−11	+70	−9
		+18	0	+42	0	+57	−8	+70	−11
		+18	0	+42	−4	+58	−3	+71	−4
						+58	−2	+71	−2
						+57	−4	+71	−3
								+72	0
								+70	−8
+2	0	+72	0	+168	−11	+344	−34	+565	−45
+2		+72		+157		+310		+520	

F		G		H		I		J	
+58	−2	+35	+6	+19	+7	+11	+9	+3	+10
+59	−2	+35	+6	+18	+8	+9	+11	+3	+10
+58	−2	+35	+6	+19	+7	+9	+10	+2	+10
+60	−1	+35	+6	+19	+7	+9	+10	+2	+10
+61	+1	+38	+5	+19	+7	+9	+10	+3	+9
+61	+1	+38	+5	+20	+7	+10	+10	+4	+9
+61	0	+40	+4	+22	+6	+12	+9	+7	+8
+62	+1	+38	+5	+22	+6	+15	+6	+6	+7
+63	+1	+39	+4	+25	+4	+14	+8	+5	+8
+61	0	+40	+4	+24	+5	+15	+6	+6	+8
		+41	+4	+23	+5	+15	+7	+5	+8
		+38	+5	+25	+5	+14	+7	+4	+8
				+26	+4	+13	+8	+3	+9
				+26	+3	+13	+8	+4	+8
				+23	+5	+12	+8	+4	+8
				+21	+6	+12	+9		
						+13	+8		
						+14	+8		
						+12	+9		
						+11	+9		
+605	−3	+452	+60	+351	+92	+242	+170	+65	+136
+602		+512		+443		+412		+201	

K		L		M		N		O	
−2	+6	−6	+3	−28	+7	−18	+2	−9	+1
−2	+5	−6	+4	−27	+7	−20	+2	−9	+1
−2	+6	−5	+4	−27	+7	−20	+2	−9	+1
−2	+6	−5	+5	−24	+7	−20	+2	−9	+1
−2	+6	−4	+5	−20	+6	−18	+2	−10	+1
−2	+6	−4	+5	−21	+7	−18	+2	−10	+1
−2	+7	−4	+4	−21	+6	−16	+2	−9	+1
−1	+6	−4	+4	−23	+7	−18	+2	−9	+1
−2	+6	−5	+4	−27	+6	−26	+2	−8	+1
−2	+6	−5	+4	−32	+6	−27	+2	−8	+1
−2	+6	−6	+4	−33	+5	−25	+2	−8	+1
−1	+5	−5	+4	−33	+6	−27	+2	−9	+1
−2	+6	−6	+4	−34	+7	−30	+2	−10	+1
−2	+6	−6	+3	−30	+6	−30	+2	−12	+1
−2	+6	−5	+4			−31	+2	−14	+1
−2	+5	−5	+4			−22	+2	−15	+1
−2	+6	−6	+4					−14	+1
−2	+5	−6	+4					−14	+1
−2	+6	−6	+4					−17	+1
−2	+6	−6	+4					−17	+1
		−6	+4					−19	+1
		−6	+4					−19	+1
		−6	+4					−19	+1
								−17	+1
								−17	+1
								−18	+1
								−17	+1
								−11	+1
−38	+117	−129	+97	−380	+90	−366	+32	−357	+28
+79		−32		−290		−334		−329	

18	17	16	15	14	13	12	11	10	9	8	7	6	5	4	3	2	1
−71 +3	−71 +3	−71 +3	−66 +2	−60 +1	....	....	....	....	....	....	....	....	....	....	....	....	....
−71 +3	−71 +3	−71 +3	−66 +2	−60 +1	*−85*	*−48*	*−30*	*−17*	*0*	*+9*	*+7*	*+9*	*+9*	*+8*	*+5*	*+5*	*+1*
−68	−68	−68	−64	−59													

Sum of all zones = +1871.

NOTE.—Values shown in italics were obtained by interpolation from gravity stations Nos. 42, 44, and 45, at Colorado Springs, Denver, and Gunnison, Colo., respectively.

The arrangement of this table is the same as that for the station at San Francisco, which was discussed in detail. The corrections for the zones A to 14, at Pikes Peak, were computed from the elevations read from maps. For zones 13 to 1 they were interpolated (in the manner explained later under the heading "Saving of time by interpolation") from stations Nos. 42, 44, and 45, which are at Colorado Springs, Denver, and Gunnison, Colo., respectively. The total value of the effect of the topography and its isostatic compensation as obtained by the interpolation is given in the table for each of the zones 13 to 1. The leaders shown in the columns for these zones indicate the number of compartments in each zone.

As Pikes Peak is an inland station, there are no water compartments within the computed zones A to 14.

As was the case in the table showing the corrections for the different zones at the San Francisco gravity station, zones B to 14 at Pikes Peak have two columns of figures each. In each zone the first column shows the effect of the topography and compensation with the station at the same elevation as the several compartments, while the second column of figures shows the corrections due to the elevation of the station above or below the compartment.

It is interesting to notice the change of sign at zone F of the correction for elevation of station (see p. 52), the change of sign due to distance between zones J and K, in the first column for these zones, also the change in the sign of the total correction between zones K and L.

Pikes Peak is a conical-shaped mountain, which accounts for the corrections for the several compartments of each of the near-by zones being of about the same size. The effect of the mountains to the westward is clearly shown in zones M, N, and O, but especially in zone O, the corrections being larger in the lower half of each column corresponding to compartments west of the station than in the upper half of the column in each of these zones.

CORRECTIONS FOR TOPOGRAPHY AND ISOSTATIC COMPENSATION, SEPARATE ZONES.

In the following table are given the total corrections for each zone, for topography and its isostatic compensation, to the intensity of gravity at each of the 89 gravity stations used in this investigation. There is also given the total correction for each station, this necessarily being the sum of the corrections for the separate zones. The values are given in units of the fourth decimal place in dynes.

The names and numbers of the stations are given in the headings of the table, while the letters or numbers of the zones are shown in the first column. The value for each zone at a station was obtained from the computations of the corrections for the separate compartments of the zones. Samples of such computations made at a station are given in tables on pages 49 and 52 for the gravity stations at San Francisco and on Pikes Peak.

The figures in italics represent the accepted interpolated values for the correction for topography and its compensation as explained on pages 58–60. The other figures are the values for the zones for which the corrections were obtained directly from maps and the reduction tables.

Correction for topography and isostatic compensation, separate zones

Zone	Key West, No. 1	West Palm Beach, No. 2	Punta Gorda, No. 3	Apalachicola, No. 4	New Orleans, No. 5	Rayville, No. 6	Galveston, No. 7	Point Isabel, No. 8	Laredo, No. 9	Austin Capitol, No. 10
A	+ 1	+ 2	+ 1	+ 2	+ 1	+ 2	+ 2	+ 2	+ 2	+ 2
B	0	0	0	0	0	+20	0	+ 4	+ 56	+56
C	− 1	0	0	0	0	+ 4	0	0	+ 50	+64
D	0	0	0	0	0	+ 6	0	0	+ 21	+34
E	0	0	0	0	0	0	0	0	+ 8	+15
F	0	0	0	0	0	0	0	0	0	+ 2
G	0	0	0	0	0	0	0	0	0	0
H	0	0	0	0	0	0	0	0	0	0
I	0	0	0	0	0	0	0	0	0	0
J	0	0	0	0	0	0	0	0	0	−14
K	0	0	0	0	0	0	0	0	− 4	−18
L	0	+ 5	0	0	0	0	0	0	−10	−22
M	+ 14	+ 20	0	0	0	0	0	0	−24	−41
N	+ 42	+ 24	0	0	0	0	0	− 1	−26	−43
O	+ 55	+ 16	0	+ 6	0	0	0	+ 27	−21	−44
18	+ 8	+ 4	0	+ 2	+ 2	− 1	0	+ 10	− 5	− 8
17	+ 4	+ 5	+ 1	+ 3	+ 2	− 1	+ 2	+ 12	− 6	− 8
16	+ 3	+ 5	+ 2	+ 4	+ 5	− 1	+ 3	+ 13	− 7	− 7
15	+ 5	+ 5	+ 6	+ 9	+ 7	− 2	+ 4	+ 15	−10	− 7
14	+ 8	+ 9	+ 10	+ 11	+ 11	− 3	+ 6	+ 14	− 8	− 7
13	+ 38	+ 33	+ 30	+ 17	+ 24	+ 5	+ 6	+ 12	−21	−12
12	+ 38	+ 39	+ 31	+ 11	+ 22	+ 5	+ 4	− 1	−10	− 9
11	+ 42	+ 45	+ 33	+ 9	+ 7	0	− 2	− 9	−12	− 7
10	+ 25	+ 27	+ 22	+ 14	+ 3	− 1	− 5	− 5	− 4	−11
9	+ 15	+ 15	+ 14	+ 12	− 2	− 3	+ 1	+ 5	+ 4	+ 1
8	+ 15	+ 15	+ 13	+ 10	+ 5	+ 3	+ 7	+ 9	+10	+ 7
7	+ 5	+ 5	+ 5	+ 6	+ 7	+ 8	+ 8	+ 9	+ 9	+ 9
6	+ 6	+ 5	+ 6	+ 8	+ 10	+ 9	+ 10	+ 10	+10	+10
5	+ 10	+ 10	+ 10	+ 10	+ 10	+ 11	+ 10	+ 10	+10	+10
4	+ 8	+ 8	+ 8	+ 7	+ 8	+ 7	+ 9	+ 9	+ 9	+ 9
3	+ 6	+ 6	+ 6	+ 6	+ 6	+ 5	+ 6	+ 6	+ 6	+ 6
2	+ 2	+ 2	+ 2	+ 3	+ 3	+ 3	+ 2	+ 2	+ 2	+ 2
1	+ 1	+ 1	+ 1	+ 1	+ 1	+ 1	+ 1	+ 1	+ 1	+ 1
Total	+322	+306	+201	+151	+132	+77	+74	+154	+30	−30

Zone	Austin, University, No. 11	McAlester, No. 12	Little Rock, No. 13	Columbia, No. 14	Atlanta, No. 15	McCormick, No. 16	Charleston, No. 17	Beaufort, No. 18	Charlottesville, No. 19	Deer Park, No. 20
A	+ 2	+ 2	+ 2	+ 2	+ 2	+ 2	+ 2	+ 1	+ 2	+ 2
B	+56	+60	+48	+60	+ 64	+ 56	+ 4	0	+56	+ 68
C	+72	+87	+31	+78	+104	+ 64	0	0	+62	+144
D	+40	+52	+12	+48	+ 90	+ 30	0	0	+33	+209
E	+16	+21	+ 5	+19	+ 40	+ 13	0	0	+11	+178
F	+ 6	+10	0	+ 7	+ 19	0	0	0	+ 3	+ 91
G	0	0	0	0	0	0	0	0	0	+ 40
H	0	0	0	0	0	0	0	0	0	+ 20
I	0	0	0	0	0	0	0	0	0	0
J	−14	−13	0	−12	− 16	− 2	0	0	− 7	− 16
K	−18	−16	− 1	−16	− 20	− 5	0	0	−11	− 36
L	−22	−22	0	−17	− 24	− 7	0	0	−21	− 59
M	−41	−46	−20	−34	− 50	− 28	0	0	−52	− 97
N	−43	−35	−30	−39	− 44	− 31	− 1	+ 4	−46	− 79
O	−44	−40	−29	−42	− 49	− 37	+ 2	+ 45	−52	− 72
18	− 8	− 8	− 5	− 7	− 9	− 7	+ 2	+ 14	−10	− 11
17	− 8	− 8	− 5	− 7	− 10	− 8	+ 2	+ 16	− 9	− 10
16	− 7	− 9	− 5	− 6	− 9	− 8	+ 2	+ 20	− 8	− 10
15	− 7	− 9	− 5	− 6	− 7	− 3	+ 3	+ 27	− 7	− 8
14	− 7	− 9	− 5	− 7	− 6	− 3	+ 4	+ 34	− 7	− 8
13	−12	−15	− 8	−10	− 7	− 1	+ 12	+ 52	−10	− 11
12	− 9	−13	− 7	− 5	− 1	+ 7	+ 21	+ 36	+ 8	+ 2
11	− 7	−12	− 5	0	+ 6	+ 13	+ 24	+ 29	+13	+ 7
10	−11	−12	− 2	+ 6	+ 14	+ 17	+ 21	+ 19	+18	+ 13
9	+ 1	− 4	− 5	+ 3	+ 9	+ 10	+ 12	+ 14	+12	+ 10
8	+ 7	+ 2	+ 2	+ 4	+ 6	+ 8	+ 12	+ 14	+11	+ 10
7	+ 9	+ 8	+ 8	+ 6	+ 6	+ 6	+ 5	+ 5	+ 5	+ 5
6	+10	+ 9	+ 9	+ 7	+ 7	+ 7	+ 6	+ 6	+ 6	+ 6
5	+10	+11	+11	+10	+ 10	+ 10	+ 9	+ 8	+ 8	+ 8
4	+ 9	+ 8	+ 7	+ 7	+ 7	+ 7	+ 7	+ 7	+ 7	+ 7
3	+ 6	+ 5	+ 5	+ 6	+ 6	+ 6	+ 6	+ 6	+ 6	+ 6
2	+ 2	+ 3	+ 3	+ 3	+ 3	+ 3	+ 3	+ 3	+ 3	+ 3
1	+ 1	+ 1	+ 1	+ 1	+ 1	+ 1	+ 1	+ 1	+ 1	+ 1
Total	− 11	+ 8	+12	+59	+142	+120	+159	+361	+25	+413

Correction for topography and isostatic compensation, separate zones—Continued.

Zone	Washington, C. & G. S. Office, No. 21	Washington, Smithsonian Institution, No. 22	Baltimore, No. 23	Philadelphia, No. 24	Princeton, No. 25	Hoboken, No. 26	New York, No. 27	Worcester, No. 28	Boston, No. 29	Cambridge, No. 30
A	+ 2	+ 2	+ 2	+ 2	+ 2	+ 2	+ 2	+ 2	+ 2	+ 2
B	+12	+ 8	+24	+12	+ 40	+ 8	+ 27	+ 56	+ 16	+ 12
C	+ 2	0	+ 4	+ 4	+ 16	0	+ 7	+ 64	+ 4	0
D	0	0	+ 6	0	+ 6	0	+ 2	+ 31	+ 1	0
E	0	0	0	0	0	0	0	+ 11	0	0
F	0	0	0	0	0	0	0	+ 7	0	0
G	0	0	0	0	0	0	0	0	0	0
H	0	0	0	0	0	0	0	0	0	0
I	0	0	0	0	0	0	0	0	0	0
J	0	0	- 1	0	0	0	0	- 10	0	- 2
K	0	0	- 2	0	0	0	0	- 13	0	- 3
L	0	0	- 3	0	0	0	0	- 14	0	- 3
M	-12	-12	-20	- 6	- 11	-12	- 12	- 27	- 4	- 9
N	-17	-17	-16	-10	- 16	-18	- 18	- 25	- 12	- 15
O	-23	-23	-20	-19	- 22	-25	- 26	- 28	- 10	- 14
18	- 5	- 5	- 6	- 3	- 4	- 6	- 6	- 2	- 2	- 2
17	- 8	- 8	- 7	- 6	- 6	- 5	- 5	- 3	- 1	- 1
16	- 9	- 9	- 9	- 6	- 5	- 3	- 3	- 4	- 1	- 2
15	- 8	- 8	- 8	- 3	- 1	+ 1	+ 1	- 2	- 2	- 2
14	- 4	- 4	- 3	0	+ 1	+ 3	+ 3	- 2	- 2	- 2
13	+ 3	+ 3	+ 7	+12	+ 13	+14	+ 14	+ 9	+ 11	+ 10
12	+13	+13	+14	+19	+ 20	+22	+ 22	+ 24	+ 26	+ 25
11	+18	+18	+19	+21	+ 21	+21	+ 21	+ 23	+ 25	+ 25
10	+17	+17	+17	+16	+ 16	+16	+ 16	+ 17	+ 18	+ 18
9	+11	+11	+10	+11	+ 11	+11	+ 11	+ 12	+ 12	+ 12
8	+12	+12	+13	+14	+ 14	+15	+ 15	+ 17	+ 17	+ 17
7	+ 6	+ 6	+ 6	+ 6	+ 6	+ 6	+ 6	+ 6	+ 6	+ 6
6	+ 6	+ 6	+ 6	+ 6	+ 6	+ 6	+ 6	+ 6	+ 6	+ 6
5	+ 7	+ 7	+ 7	+ 6	+ 6	+ 6	+ 6	+ 6	+ 6	+ 6
4	+ 6	+ 6	+ 6	+ 6	+ 6	+ 6	+ 6	+ 6	+ 6	+ 6
3	+ 6	+ 6	+ 6	+ 6	+ 6	+ 6	+ 6	+ 6	+ 6	+ 6
2	+ 4	+ 4	+ 4	+ 4	+ 4	+ 4	+ 4	+ 4	+ 4	+ 4
1	+ 1	+ 1	+ 1	+ 1	+ 1	+ 1	+ 1	+ 1	+ 1	+ 1
Total	+40	+34	+57	+93	+130	+79	+106	+178	+133	+101

Zone	Calais, No. 31	Ithaca, No. 32	Cleveland, No. 33	Cincinnati, No. 34	Terre Haute, No. 35	Chicago, No. 36	Madison, No. 37	St. Louis No. 38	Kansas City, No. 39	Ellsworth, No. 40
A	+ 2	+ 2	+ 2	+ 2	+ 2	+ 2	+ 2	+ 2	+ 2	+ 2
B	+ 25	+60	+58	+60	+56	+56	+62	+56	+64	+ 68
C	+ 4	+88	+78	+84	+60	+72	+95	+60	+97	+124
D	+ 4	+59	+48	+57	+28	+42	+70	+30	+72	+140
E	0	+27	+20	+22	+12	+16	+30	+13	+30	+ 82
F	0	+ 6	+10	0	+ 2	+ 4	+10	0	+16	+ 40
G	0	0	0	0	0	0	0	0	0	+ 12
H	0	0	0	0	0	0	0	0	0	0
I	0	0	0	0	0	0	0	0	0	0
J	0	-16	-16	-11	- 8	- 7	-16	- 3	-16	- 16
K	0	-20	-20	-17	-10	- 9	-20	-12	-20	- 20
L	0	-32	-24	-20	-12	-11	-24	-13	-24	- 47
M	- 5	-50	-42	-42	-30	-22	-57	-28	-53	- 87
N	- 4	-56	-41	-50	-37	-26	-48	-32	-47	- 85
O	- 15	-58	-45	-48	-35	-23	-49	-33	-55	- 95
18	- 3	- 8	- 9	- 8	- 6	- 6	- 7	- 5	-10	- 19
17	- 3	- 8	-10	- 8	- 6	- 6	- 7	- 5	-10	- 19
16	- 3	- 7	-10	- 8	- 6	- 7	- 8	- 5	-10	- 19
15	- 4	- 7	-11	- 8	- 6	- 8	- 8	- 7	-11	- 19
14	- 3	- 7	-11	- 8	- 7	- 9	- 9	- 9	-11	- 20
13	- 3	- 6	-18	-15	-16	-16	-16	-16	-20	- 44
12	+ 9	+ 7	-10	- 8	- 9	-10	-10	-10	-13	- 26
11	+ 18	+ 8	- 5	- 3	- 7	- 4	- 3	- 9	-14	- 19
10	+ 18	+11	+ 4	+ 4	- 2	- 1	- 2	- 5	-14	- 15
9	+ 13	+ 8	+ 5	+ 4	+ 1	+ 1	0	- 2	- 8	- 4
8	+ 16	+12	+ 8	+ 6	+ 4	+ 6	+ 6	+ 2	- 1	+ 3
7	+ 6	+ 6	+ 6	+ 6	+ 7	+ 7	+ 7	+ 7	+ 8	+ 7
6	+ 6	+ 6	+ 7	+ 7	+ 8	+ 8	+ 8	+ 8	+ 9	+ 9
5	+ 5	+ 7	+ 8	+ 9	+ 9	+ 9	+ 9	+10	+11	+ 10
4	+ 6	+ 6	+ 7	+ 7	+ 7	+ 7	+ 7	+ 7	+ 7	+ 8
3	+ 6	+ 6	+ 5	+ 5	+ 5	+ 5	+ 5	+ 5	+ 5	+ 5
2	+ 5	+ 4	+ 3	+ 3	+ 3	+ 3	+ 3	+ 3	+ 3	+ 3
1	+ 1	+ 1	+ 1	+ 1	+ 1	+ 1	+ 1	+ 1	+ 1	+ 1
Total	+101	+49	- 2	+23	+ 6	+74	+31	+10	-12	- 40

Correction for topography and isostatic compensation, separate zones—Continued.

Zone	Wallace, No. 41	Colorado Springs, No. 42	Pikes Peak, No. 43	Denver, No. 44	Gunnison, No. 45	Grand Junction, No. 46	Green River, No. 47	Pleasant Valley Junction, No. 48	Salt Lake City, No. 49	Grand Canyon, Wyo., No. 50
A	+ 2	+ 2	+ 2	+ 2	+ 2	+ 2	+ 2	+ 2	+ 2	+ 2
B	+ 68	+ 68	+ 72	+ 68	+ 68	+ 68	+ 68	+ 68	+ 68	+ 68
C	+152	+160	+ 157	+160	+164	+160	+156	+160	+156	+164
D	+246	+306	+ 310	+300	+324	+282	+270	+318	+276	+327
E	+248	+408	+ 520	+384	+472	+336	+302	+451	+325	+473
F	+140	+331	+ 602	+290	+430	+239	+199	+399	+216	+429
G	+ 72	+192	+ 512	+168	+285	+120	+ 97	+254	+109	+288
H	+ 32	+127	+ 443	+ 98	+202	+ 66	+ 56	+174	+ 59	+199
I	+ 20	+ 78	+ 412	+ 60	+130	+ 33	+ 27	+101	+ 19	+132
J	- 16	- 11	+ 201	0	+ 22	- 7	- 16	+ 4	- 18	+ 25
K	- 40	- 71	+ 79	- 40	- 56	- 65	- 51	- 49	- 73	- 39
L	- 72	-147	- 32	- 98	-168	-132	-101	-142	-121	-125
M	-211	-369	- 290	-362	-526	-391	-329	-378	-336	-420
N	-192	-342	- 334	-376	-462	-374	-295	-343	-316	-389
O	-169	-339	- 329	-346	-409	-349	-324	-315	-299	-308
18	- 36	- 68	- 68	- 68	- 76	- 74	- 65	- 59	- 65	- 57
17	- 36	- 69	- 68	- 67	- 74	- 73	- 70	- 61	- 64	- 60
16	- 36	- 69	- 68	- 67	- 68	- 72	- 67	- 63	- 63	- 61
15	- 37	- 68	- 64	- 64	- 64	- 66	- 68	- 64	- 65	- 60
14	- 39	- 62	- 59	- 63	- 62	- 65	- 69	- 65	- 65	- 54
13	- 69	- 81	- 83	- 84	- 97	-101	-108	-104	-107	- 86
12	- 38	- 48	- 48	- 48	- 52	- 55	- 59	- 58	- 62	- 51
11	- 25	- 30	- 30	- 30	- 33	- 34	- 35	- 35	- 36	- 38
10	- 16	- 17	- 17	- 17	- 18	- 15	- 12	- 14	- 12	- 22
9	- 2	0	0	0	+ 2	+ 3	+ 4	+ 4	+ 5	- 1
8	+ 6	+ 9	+ 9	+ 9	+ 11	+ 11	+ 11	+ 11	+ 11	+ 9
7	+ 7	+ 7	+ 7	+ 7	+ 7	+ 7	+ 8	+ 7	+ 7	+ 6
6	+ 9	+ 9	+ 9	+ 9	+ 9	+ 9	+ 9	+ 9	+ 9	+ 8
5	+ 10	+ 9	+ 9	+ 10	+ 9	+ 9	+ 9	+ 9	+ 9	+ 8
4	+ 8	+ 8	+ 8	+ 8	+ 8	+ 8	+ 8	+ 8	+ 8	+ 7
3	+ 5	+ 5	+ 5	+ 5	+ 5	+ 5	+ 5	+ 5	+ 5	+ 4
2	+ 3	+ 3	+ 3	+ 3	+ 3	+ 3	+ 3	+ 3	+ 3	+ 3
1	+ 1	+ 1	+ 1	+ 1	+ 1	+ 1	+ 1	+ 1	+ 1	+ 1
Total	- 5	- 68	+1871	-148	- 11	-511	-434	+238	-414	+382

Zones	Norris Geyser Basin, No. 51	Lower Geyser Basin, No. 52	Seattle, University, No. 53	San Francisco, No. 54	Mount Hamilton, No. 55	Seattle High School, No. 56	Iron River, No. 57	Ely, No. 58	Pembina, No. 59	Mitchell, No. 60
A	+ 2	+ 2	+ 2	+ 2	+ 2	+ 2	+ 2	+ 2	+ 2	+ 2
B	+ 68	+ 68	+ 33	+ 48	+ 68	+ 44	+ 64	+ 64	+60	+ 64
C	+164	+160	+ 12	+ 35	+ 156	+ 18	+124	+124	+88	+116
D	+324	+318	+ 6	+ 15	+ 240	+ 10	+138	+138	+60	+123
E	+464	+459	+ 1	+ 1	+ 274	+ 8	+ 80	+ 80	+24	+ 65
F	+411	+403	0	0	+ 184	0	+ 40	+ 30	+10	+ 30
G	+264	+254	0	0	+ 92	0	+ 12	+ 12	0	+ 12
H	+184	+176	0	0	+ 53	0	0	0	0	0
I	+115	+107	0	0	+ 33	0	0	0	0	0
J	+ 17	+ 12	0	- 2	+ 7	0	- 16	- 16	-16	- 16
K	- 46	- 41	0	- 1	- 8	0	- 20	- 20	-20	- 20
L	-124	-126	- 1	- 7	- 18	- 1	- 42	- 33	-24	- 28
M	-409	-406	- 19	- 14	- 24	- 19	- 84	- 85	-52	- 78
N	-381	-379	- 95	+ 15	- 16	- 95	- 63	- 69	-52	- 80
O	-303	-299	- 90	+ 99	0	- 89	- 50	- 67	-62	- 89
18	- 56	- 55	- 14	+ 24	+ 2	- 14	- 6	- 12	-13	- 18
17	- 59	- 58	- 11	+ 21	- 2	- 11	- 6	- 12	-13	- 18
16	- 60	- 59	- 10	+ 20	0	- 10	- 6	- 12	-13	- 18
15	- 59	- 58	- 10	+ 19	+ 2	- 10	- 7	- 12	-13	- 19
14	- 53	- 52	- 11	+ 17	+ 8	- 11	- 7	- 11	-14	- 19
13	- 84	- 83	- 21	+ 25	+ 22	- 21	- 18	- 16	-25	- 31
12	- 51	- 49	- 18	+ 23	+ 19	- 18	- 12	- 13	-14	- 21
11	- 38	- 37	- 8	+ 21	+ 20	- 8	- 9	- 11	-13	- 24
10	- 22	- 24	0	+ 14	+ 15	0	- 7	- 10	-15	- 16
9	- 1	- 1	+ 4	+ 10	+ 10	+ 4	- 2	- 5	- 8	- 10
8	+ 9	+ 9	+ 10	+ 15	+ 15	+ 10	+ 2	- 1	- 5	- 5
7	+ 6	+ 6	+ 6	+ 10	+ 10	+ 6	+ 5	+ 5	+ 4	+ 6
6	+ 8	+ 8	+ 7	+ 9	+ 9	+ 7	+ 8	+ 9	+10	+ 9
5	+ 8	+ 8	+ 8	+ 9	+ 9	+ 8	+ 8	+ 9	+10	+ 11
4	+ 7	+ 7	+ 7	+ 8	+ 8	+ 7	+ 6	+ 6	+ 7	+ 7
3	+ 4	+ 4	+ 3	+ 5	+ 5	+ 3	+ 4	+ 4	+ 3	+ 4
2	+ 3	+ 3	+ 3	+ 4	+ 4	+ 3	+ 4	+ 4	+ 4	+ 3
1	+ 1	+ 1	+ 1	+ 1	+ 1	+ 1	+ 1	+ 1	+ 1	+ 1
Total	+313	+281	-205	+446	+1200	-181	+143	+ 83	-89	- 57

Correction for topography and isostatic compensation, separate zones—Continued.

Zones	Sweetwater, No. 61	Kerrville, No. 62	El Paso, No. 63	Nogales, No. 64	Yuma, No. 65	Compton, No. 66	Goldfield, No. 67	Yavapai, No. 68	Grand Canyon, Ariz., No. 69	Gallup, No. 70
A	+ 2	+ 2	+ 2	+ 2	+ 2	+ 2	+ 2	+ 2	+ 2	+ 2
B	+ 68	+ 68	+ 68	+ 68	+ 36	+ 16	+ 68	+ 68	+ 68	+ 68
C	+136	+128	+156	+156	+ 12	+ 4	+160	+122	+148	+160
D	+191	+151	+262	+264	+ 6	0	+295	+261	+185	+312
E	+148	+ 92	+284	+288	0	0	+394	+379	+174	+424
F	+ 69	+ 45	+177	+183	0	0	+308	+324	+ 82	+370
G	+ 25	+ 20	+ 86	+ 93	0	0	+171	+227	+ 21	+218
H	+ 16	+ 16	+ 45	+ 48	0	0	+115	+152	- 12	+143
I	0	0	+ 20	+ 20	0	0	+ 61	+109	- 41	+ 88
J	- 16	- 16	- 16	- 16	0	0	- 11	+ 25	- 46	+ 4
K	- 24	- 20	- 40	- 40	- 6	0	- 40	- 26	-112	- 45
L	- 54	- 48	- 72	- 72	- 12	- 5	- 96	-107	-154	-121
M	-123	-107	-226	-162	- 28	- 25	-313	-294	-357	-383
N	-100	- 76	-210	-150	- 25	- 50	-277	-289	-299	-343
O	-107	- 64	-221	-148	- 48	- 60	-301	-256	-256	-312
18	- 24	- 12	- 46	- 30	- 17	- 10	- 61	- 56	- 56	- 63
17	- 22	- 12	- 45	- 24	- 17	- 8	- 56	- 53	- 53	- 63
16	- 21	- 11	- 44	- 24	- 18	0	- 51	- 48	- 48	- 65
15	- 22	- 13	- 48	- 28	- 18	+ 6	- 41	- 48	- 48	- 69
14	- 22	- 12	- 49	- 28	- 20	+ 7	- 40	- 50	- 50	- 68
13	- 38	- 23	- 75	- 49	- 15	+ 18	- 61	- 81	- 81	- 91
12	- 21	- 13	- 32	- 27	- 9	+ 14	- 20	- 56	- 56	- 47
11	- 14	- 11	- 23	- 12	+ 3	+ 9	- 4	- 25	- 25	- 32
10	- 11	- 8	- 7	0	+ 3	+ 13	+ 5	- 4	- 4	- 9
9	+ 2	+ 2	+ 3	+ 6	+ 10	+ 11	+ 8	+ 6	+ 6	+ 4
8	+ 8	+ 8	+ 14	+ 15	+ 16	+ 16	+ 12	+ 12	+ 8	+ 12
7	+ 9	+ 9	+ 5	+ 8	+ 10	+ 11	+ 9	+ 8	+ 9	+ 7
6	+ 10	+ 10	+ 10	+ 9	+ 9	+ 9	+ 9	+ 9	+ 9	+ 9
5	+ 10	+ 10	+ 10	+ 9	+ 9	+ 9	+ 9	+ 9	+ 9	+ 9
4	+ 9	+ 9	+ 9	+ 8	+ 8	+ 8	+ 8	+ 8	+ 8	+ 8
3	+ 6	+ 6	+ 6	+ 5	+ 5	+ 5	+ 5	+ 5	+ 5	+ 5
2	+ 2	+ 2	+ 3	+ 4	+ 4	+ 4	+ 4	+ 3	+ 3	+ 3
1	+ 1	+ 1	+ 1	+ 1	+ 1	+ 1	+ 1	+ 1	+ 1	+ 1
Total	+ 92	+133	+ 7	+377	-102	+ 5	+272	+337	-957	+141

Zones	Las Vegas, No. 71	Shamrock, No. 72	Denison, No. 73	Minneapolis, No. 74	Lead, No. 75	Bismarck, No. 76	Hinsdale, No. 77	Sandpoint, No. 78	Boise, No. 79	Astoria, No. 80
A	+ 2	+ 2	+ 2	+ 2	+ 2	+ 2	+ 2	+ 2	+ 2	+ 1
B	+ 68	+ 68	+60	+60	+ 64	+ 68	+ 68	+ 68	+ 68	0
C	+160	+140	+84	+92	+160	+128	+140	+136	+148	0
D	+312	+198	+54	+64	+294	+156	+190	+186	+222	- 5
E	+424	+160	+24	+24	+378	+98	+147	+140	+193	- 1
F	+361	+ 80	+10	+10	+276	+ 44	+ 70	+ 63	+101	0
G	+217	+ 36	0	0	+158	+ 18	+ 26	+ 24	+ 48	0
H	+137	+ 16	0	0	+ 99	+ 6	+ 1	+ 10	+ 25	0
I	+ 88	0	0	0	+ 43	0	0	- 5	- 2	0
J	+ 6	- 16	-16	-16	- 3	- 16	- 16	- 16	- 14	0
K	- 42	- 27	-20	-20	- 35	- 20	- 25	- 43	- 55	0
L	-128	- 52	-24	-24	- 88	- 48	- 54	- 71	- 85	- 4
M	-377	-128	-37	-56	-233	-112	-149	-227	-223	- 23
N	-329	-115	-42	-48	-199	- 96	-145	-204	-227	+ 4
O	-297	-122	-45	-56	-174	-105	-135	-205	-233	+ 29
18	- 62	- 24	- 9	-12	- 36	- 20	- 31	- 42	- 53	+ 3
17	- 62	- 24	- 9	-12	- 37	- 20	- 31	- 42	- 56	0
16	- 62	- 24	- 9	-12	- 37	- 19	- 31	- 40	- 56	+ 3
15	- 59	- 24	- 9	-13	- 39	- 20	- 32	- 40	- 54	+ 5
14	- 61	- 25	- 9	-13	- 40	- 20	- 33	- 40	- 52	+ 3
13	- 89	- 44	-20	-21	- 61	- 38	- 66	- 70	- 80	0
12	- 43	- 25	-15	-15	- 35	- 26	- 40	- 39	- 57	- 1
11	- 26	- 17	-11	-12	- 30	- 23	- 30	- 21	- 24	+ 3
10	- 18	- 14	-12	- 9	- 19	- 17	- 21	- 11	- 8	+ 6
9	- 1	- 1	- 3	- 5	- 6	- 10	- 13	0	+ 2	+ 6
8	+ 9	+ 6	+ 3	0	+ 1	- 3	+ 2	+ 7	+ 9	+ 11
7	+ 7	+ 8	+ 8	+ 6	+ 6	+ 5	+ 5	+ 6	+ 7	+ 7
6	+ 9	+ 10	+19	+ 9	+ 9	+ 9	+ 10	+ 8	+ 8	+ 7
5	+ 10	+ 10	+11	+10	+ 10	+ 10	+ 9	+ 8	+ 8	+ 8
4	+ 8	+ 9	+ 8	+ 6	+ 7	+ 7	+ 7	+ 7	+ 7	+ 7
3	+ 5	+ 6	+ 5	+ 4	+ 4	+ 4	+ 3	+ 3	+ 4	+ 3
2	+ 3	+ 2	+ 4	+ 4	+ 3	+ 3	+ 4	+ 3	+ 3	+ 3
1	+ 1	+ 1	+ 1	+ 1	+ 1	+ 1	+ 1	+ 1	+ 1	+ 1
Total	+171	+ 70	- 6	-52	+443	- 54	-167	-444	-423	+76

Correction for topography and isostatic compensation, separate zones—Continued.

Zones	Sisson, No. 81	Rock Springs, No 82	Paxton, No. 83	Washington, Bureau of Standards, No. 84	North Hero, No. 85	Lake Placid, No. 86	Potsdam, No. 87	Wilson, No. 88	Alpena, No. 89
A	+ 2	+ 2	+ 2	+ 2	+ 2	+ 2	+ 2	+ 2	+ 2
B	+ 68	+ 68	+ 68	+ 48	+24	+ 68	+56	+48	+56
C	+151	+160	+152	+ 32	+ 4	+136	+52	+28	+68
D	+253	+309	+240	+ 16	+ 6	+170	+22	+12	+42
E	+256	+417	+228	+ 8	0	+116	+ 8	+ 8	+16
F	+159	+350	+130	0	0	+ 52	0	0	0
G	+ 72	+210	+ 60	0	0	+ 25	0	0	0
H	+ 32	+129	+ 32	0	0	+ 15	0	0	0
I	− 5	+ 86	0	0	0	− 9	0	0	0
J	− 32	+ 9	− 16	− 1	0	− 16	−13	0	−16
K	− 78	− 40	− 40	− 1	0	− 34	−17	0	−20
L	−103	−120	− 72	− 2	− 3	− 50	−18	− 8	−24
M	−241	−350	−183	− 15	−32	− 75	−40	−20	−35
N	−205	−363	−170	− 19	−44	− 52	−47	−33	−36
O	−174	−371	−155	− 25	−48	− 41	−42	−46	−34
18	− 29	− 73	− 33	− 5	−10	− 10	− 8	− 9	− 7
17	− 25	− 71	− 34	− 8	−10	− 9	− 8	−10	− 7
16	− 21	− 71	− 33	− 9	−11	− 9	− 9	− 9	− 7
15	− 17	− 73	− 33	− 8	− 7	− 8	− 8	−10	− 7
14	− 7	− 67	− 33	− 4	− 7	− 7	− 9	−10	− 8
13	− 2	− 99	− 59	+ 2	−16	− 13	−16	−13	−15
12	+ 8	− 55	− 33	+ 13	− 6	− 3	− 5	− 3	−10
11	+ 12	− 38	− 26	+ 18	+ 3	+ 4	+ 1	− 1	− 5
10	+ 9	− 16	− 17	+ 17	+11	+ 11	+ 8	+ 5	− 1
9	+ 8	+ 2	− 4	+ 11	+10	+ 9	+ 7	+ 5	+ 1
8	+ 13	+ 10	+ 3	+ 12	+11	+ 11	+11	+10	+ 6
7	+ 9	+ 7	+ 7	+ 6	+ 6	+ 6	+ 7	+ 7	+ 6
6	+ 8	+ 9	+ 9	+ 6	+ 6	+ 6	+ 6	+ 6	+ 7
5	+ 9	+ 9	+ 10	+ 7	+ 7	+ 7	+ 6	+ 6	+ 7
4	+ 8	+ 8	+ 8	+ 6	+ 6	+ 6	+ 5	+ 5	+ 5
3	+ 4	+ 5	+ 5	+ 6	+ 6	+ 6	+ 6	+ 6	+ 5
2	+ 4	+ 3	+ 3	+ 4	+ 5	+ 5	+ 5	+ 5	+ 5
1	+ 1	+ 1	+ 1	+ 1	+ 1	+ 1	+ 1	+ 1	+ 1
Total	+147	− 13	+ 17	+118	−86	+320	−37	−18	− 5

INTERPOLATION FOR OUTER ZONES.[*]

To compute the effect of topography and its isostatic compensation upon the intensity of gravity for all zones at all stations by the methods thus far described would be an unnecessary waste of time. Each figure in the table on pp. 54–58 is the value of the effect, on the intensity of gravity, of the topography and compensation of an entire zone. A comparison of the values for similar zones at any two stations comparatively near each other shows that the effect produced by corresponding zones tend to be more nearly the same for the two stations the larger the zone considered. If the comparison be extended to include several stations in a group it becomes evident that it is possible to obtain with considerable accuracy the effect for any large zone, for a station near the center of the group, by interpolation from the computed effects for that zone at surrounding stations near it.

For instance, the two values of each of zones 5 to 1 and zone 7 at Point Isabel (station No. 8) and at Kerrville (station No. 62) are identical, while the two values of each of zones 6 and 8 differ by only 0.0001 dyne. All the zones were computed at each of these two stations which are 476 kilometers (296 miles) apart.

[*] Pp. 36 to 45 of The Figure of the Earth and Isostasy from Measurements in the United States, by John F. Hayford, contain in detail a description of the interpolation for outer zones of the effect of topography and its isostatic compensation upon the deflections of the plumb line.

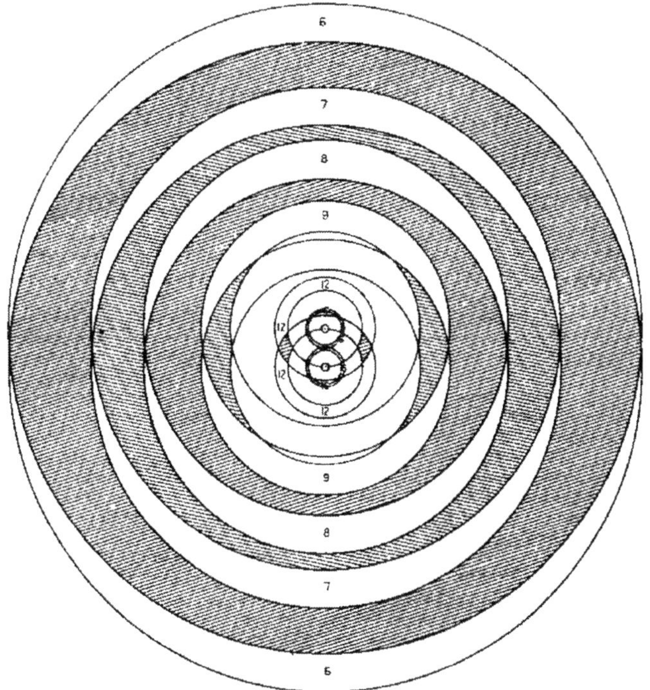

Showing overlapping of zones at two near stations.

The distance between centers is 296 statute miles, the same as that between Pt. Isabel and Kerrville, two stations which are referred to in the text under "Interpolation"

Scale   Degrees

PRINTED BY THE U. S. GEOLOGICAL SURVEY

The values of the effect of topography and its isostatic compensation for the separate zones for Point Isabel and Kerrville are shown in the following table:

Comparison of separate zones at two close stations.

Zone	Point Isabel, No. 8	Kerrville, No. 62*	Zone	Point Isabel, No. 8	Kerrville, No. 62*	Zone	Point Isabel, No. 8	Kerrville, No. 62*
A	+2	+2	L	0	− 48	11	− 9	−13
B	+4	+ 68	M	0	−107	10	− 5	− 8
C	0	+128	N	− 1	− 76	9	+ 5	+ 1
D	0	+151	O	+27	− 64	8	+ 9	+ 7
E	0	+ 92	18	+10	− 12	7	+ 9	+ 9
F	0	+ 45	17	+12	− 12	6	+10	+11
G	0	+ 20	16	+13	− 11	5	+10	+10
H	0	+ 16	15	+15	− 10	4	+ 9	+ 9
I	0	0	14	+14	− 11	3	+ 6	+ 6
J	0	− 16	13	+12	− 20	2	+ 2	+ 2
K	0	− 20	12	− 1	− 13	1	+ 1	+ 1

* The values for Kerrville in the table on p. 57 were interpolated for zones 15 to 1. The values for those zones in the table above were directly computed for the purpose of comparison with directly computed values at Point Isabel.

For zone 12 and smaller zones (meaning zones with smaller outer radii) there is no resemblance between the computed effects for the two stations of topography and its compensation. For zone 12 and larger zones there is no contradiction in signs. Zone 17 and smaller zones for these stations do not intersect and consequently have no area in common. Zones 16 to 10 overlap, but the percentage of area common to any two zones of the same number is very small. The overlapping becomes marked in zone 9, and in zone 8 the overlapping is approximately half of the zones. For the still larger zones, 7 to 1, the amount of overlapping increases rapidly and it is practically complete for the last five zones.

In the table above, which shows the values for the separate zones for stations Point Isabel and Kerrville, it will be noticed that where corresponding zones have a large percentage of overlapping the values at the two stations for that zone agree and that for corresponding zones which have little or no area in common there is no similarity in their values.

Illustration No. 11 shows graphically some of the above statements. The two centers are 476 kilometers (296 statute miles) apart, this being the distance between the two stations Point Isabel and Kerrville. It will be noticed that zone 16 is the first to overlap, that the percentage of overlapping is small until zone 9 is reached, and that the percentage of overlapping rapidly increases with the larger zones.

In general, for corresponding successively larger zones for any two given stations, the resemblance of values must tend to increase, for the larger the zones the greater is the percentage of overlapping of the two corresponding zones and the more insignificant becomes the fixed distance between the centers of the two stations, in comparison with the widths of the zones. It is obvious also that the same considerations show that the tendency to a more and more close resemblance with increasing size of zones exists for all the stations of a group; hence, if the effect of topography and compensation on the intensity of gravity for successive zones for a station be interpolated from the values for the corresponding zones at the stations surrounding it, these interpolated values will tend to agree with directly computed values, for the station in question, more closely as the zones are successively larger.

These ideas were, at first, a matter of pure theory, though the truth of similar ideas was established in the investigations connected with "The Figure of the Earth and Isostasy from Measurements in the United States." These ideas have, however, been thoroughly tested and proved to be correct in the present investigation. Under the heading "Discussion of errors" will be given a statement regarding the nature and extent of the tests applied.

A concrete example of interpolation is shown graphically in illustration No. 12, where it is proposed to obtain values by interpolation for station No. 71, Las Vegas, N. Mex., from stations

Nos. 41, 63, and 70 (Wallace, Kans.; El Paso, Tex.; and Gallup, N. Mex., respectively). These four stations are also indicated in the illustration by letters to make it easier to refer to them in the text.

For zones 18 to 7, at station No. 71, the effect of topography and compensation was computed directly and was also interpolated (by the method to be explained later) from the three values for corresponding zones at the three surrounding stations Nos. 63, 70, and 41. The following table shows the computed and interpolated values and their difference:

Station No. 71.

Zone	Computed values	Interpolated values	Computed minus interpolated	Zone	Computed values	Interpolated values	Computed minus interpolated
	Dynes	*Dynes*	*Dynes*		*Dynes*	*Dynes*	*Dynes*
18	−0.0062	−0.0046	−0.0016	12	−0.0043	−0.0033	−0.0010
17	− .0062	− .0046	− .0016	11	− .0026	− .0026	.0000
16	− .0062	− .0046	− .0016	10	− .0018	− .0011	− .0007
15	− .0059	− .0049	− .0010	9	− .0001	+ .0001	− .0002
14	− .0061	− .0049	− .0012	8	+ .0009	+ .0010	− .0001
13	− .0089	− .0077	− .0012	7	+ .0007	+ .0006	+ .0001

According to the evidence given by zones 9, 8, and 7, it was decided, in accordance with certain criteria given later, that it would be safe to stop the direct computation at zone 7 proceeding outward, and to accept the interpolated values for zones 6 to 1 as sufficiently close to the truth.

METHOD OF INTERPOLATING FOR OUTER ZONES.

The purpose of obtaining the values for certain zones by interpolation is to save time in making the computations and, necessarily, the greater the number of zones for which the interpolation is made the greater is the saving accomplished. On the other hand, if the amount of interpolation is made too great the accuracy will fall below that desired. It was necessary, therefore, to fix the amount and method of interpolation carefully in order to save as much time as possible and yet hold the accuracy to the required standard. The following method of interpolation and criteria for determining when interpolations should be made, were adopted and used after having been tested during the computations for the first few stations. It will be noticed that they are very similar to the methods and criteria used in "The Figure of the Earth and Isostasy from Measurements in the United States" for determining when interpolations should be made in obtaining the topographic deflections of the vertical. The degree of accuracy secured will be indicated in connection with the "Discussion of errors."

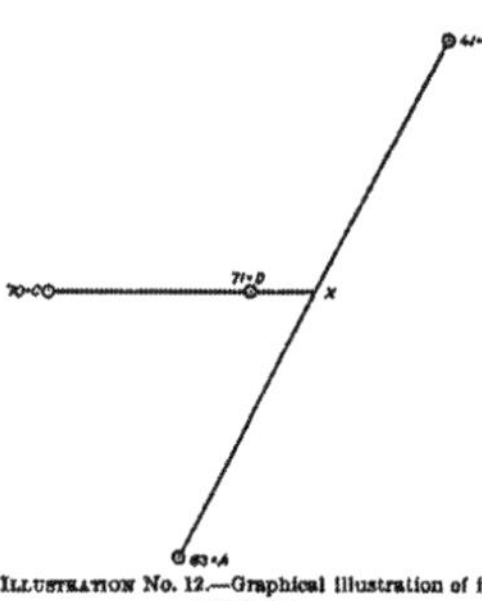

ILLUSTRATION No. 12.—Graphical illustration of interpolation.

The decision having been made to interpolate the corrections for some of the zones for station No. 71 from the corresponding values of the three stations Nos. 63, 41, and 70, such a figure as that shown in illustration No. 12 was drawn upon a map on which the gravity stations had been plotted in their proper relative positions. Let the three stations from which the interpolation is to be made be called, in general, A, B, and C. In this case they are, respectively, No. 63, No. 41, and No. 70. Let the station for which the interpolation is to be made be called D (in this case No. 71). The figure, such as is indicated in illustration No. 12, is drawn in each case by first connecting two of the stations, A and B, by a straight line and then drawing the straight line C D until it intersects A B in X. A linear interpolation is first made between A and B (stations Nos. 63 and 41 in this case) to obtain a value corresponding to X for each zone, and then a second linear interpolation between X and C to obtain the required value for each zone at D.

This process may be called interpolation along a plane. If the three values at A, B, and C were represented graphically by ordinates above a reference plane in which A, B, and C were located in their proper relative positions, and if a plane were passed through the three points in space fixed by these ordinates, then the interpolated value for D is represented by the ordinate at D limited by this plane.

The numerical work of the interpolation for station No. 71 is shown in the following table:

The factor 0.516 is the ratio $\frac{AX}{AB}$; the factor 0.243 is the ratio $\frac{XD}{XC}$. These may, for convenience, be called interpolation factors.

The decision may be made arbitrarily as to which two of the three stations shall be called A and B, and shall be utilized first by making a linear interpolation directly between them. Except for the effects of inaccuracy in scaling interpolation factors from the map, and inaccuracies in numerical work, the final results will be independent of the choice among three possible decisions. The effects of the small unavoidable inaccuracies in the scaling of interpolation factors will, in general, be smaller the nearer the angle C X A approaches to a right angle. Hence, it is advisable to choose among three possible decisions so as to make C X A as nearly as possible a right angle.

Interpolation of corrections due to topography and compensation at gravity station No. 71, Las Vegas, N. Mex.

Zone	Station No. 63	Station No. 41	Difference 41—63	Difference × 0.516	Station X No. 63 + (difference × 0.516)	Station 70	Difference No. 70—X	Difference × 0.243	Station 71. No. 70 + (difference × 0.243)
9	+ 3	− 2	−5	−3	0	+ 4	+4	+1	+ 1
8	+14	+ 6	−8	−4	+10	+12	+2	0	+10
7	+ 5	+ 7	+2	+1	+ 6	+ 7	+1	0	+ 6
6	+10	+ 9·	−1	−1	+ 9	+ 9	0	0	+ 9
5	+10	+10	0	0	+10	+ 9	−1	0	+10
4	+ 9	+ 8	−1	−1	+ 8	+ 8	0	0	+ 8
3	+ 6	+ 5	−1	−1	+ 5	+ 5	0	0	+ 5
2	+ 3	+ 3	0	0	+ 3	+ 3	0	0	+ 3
1	+ 1	+ 1	0	0	+ 1	+ 1	0	0	+ 1

In applying this method of interpolation the order of proceeding was, first, to compute the corrections completely for three or four stations at the edges of the area to be covered, so selected that all, or nearly all, of the remaining stations were included within the lines joining these stations. Then successive stations were selected for computation and for each in turn the computation was made complete up to the zone for which the adopted criteria, stated later, showed the interpolation to be safe. Then the interpolated values were depended upon for the remaining zones.

By inspection of the map on which the gravity stations were all plotted the order of computation was so selected as to insure, as far as possible, that each new station computed should be near the center of an area containing no stations for which the computation had already been made. The interpolation was then made (or attempted) from three stations among those already computed which lay nearest to it. The interpolations for the first few stations within a new region were thus in general made (or attempted) from stations at a considerable distance. Later interpolations were made from much nearer stations as the area became more thickly covered with stations for which the computations were already made.

In a few cases the point X in illustration No. 12 fell between D and C, and the last step of the interpolation was really an extrapolation. Similarly, in some cases the point X fell beyond A or beyond B, instead of falling between them, and the first interpolation factor became negative and really represented an extrapolation.

The same criteria of safety were applied to these cases as to the others in which only direct interpolations were involved. The cases of extrapolation most frequently occur at stations lying near the edge of the area covered by the investigation. The total number of such cases was small.

In the table of "Corrections for topography and isostatic compensation, separate zones," on pages 54–58, may be seen the extent of the agreement between values for corresponding zones at adjacent stations. This table also serves as an illustration of the amount of computation saved by interpolation. The interpolated values are shown in italics. For example, stations Nos. 1 to 11 are on or not very far from the Gulf of Mexico. Nos. 16 to 31 are on or close to the Atlantic coast. By consulting the table and illustration No. 13, which shows graphically the location of all the stations used in this investigation, other groups of adjacent stations may be found.

The following table will serve as an illustration of the degree of agreement between values for corresponding zones at adjacent stations and of the amount of computation saved by interpolation for the 89 stations used in this investigation. The stations are placed in the table in the order in which the computations were made. At stations Nos. 1, 31, 53, 8, 54, and 59 no interpolation was attempted.

Name of station	No. of station	Stations from which interpolation was made or attempted			Number of zones for which interpolation was accepted	Distance to nearest station from which interpolation was made or attempted	Inner radius of smallest zone for which the interpolation was accepted
						Kilometers	*Kilometers*
Key West, Fla.	1						
Calais, Me.	31						
Seattle, Wash. (university)	53						
Kansas City, Mo.	39	1	31	53	4	2020	5674
Madison, Wis.	37	31	53	39	11	625	642
Beaufort, N. C.	18	1	31	39	8	1245	1572
Cleveland, Ohio	33	18	31	37	7	665	2298
Boston, Mass.	29	18	33	31	7	445	2298
New York, N. Y.	27	29	18	33	13	298	340
Ithaca, N. Y.	32	29	33	27	13	280	340
Worcester, Mass.	28	29	27	32	15	62	245
Cambridge, Mass.	30	28	31	29	24	5	8
Baltimore, Md.	23	27	18	33	9	282	1194
Philadelphia, Pa.	24	27	23	32	17	140	188
Princeton, N. J.	25	24	27	32	19	62	99
Hoboken, N. J.	26	27	25	32	23	10	12
Atlanta, Ga.	15	18	1	39	7	718	2298
Charleston, S. C.	17	18	1	15	9	375	1194
Point Isabel, Tex.	8						
New Orleans, La.	5	15	8	1	5	685	3996
Apalachicola, Fla.	4	15	1	5	7	456	2298
West Palm Beach, Fla.	2	1	17	4	13	300	340
Punta Gorda, Fla.	3	2	1	4	15	202	245
Terre Haute, Ind.	35	33	39	15	*12	544	481
Cincinnati, Ohio	34	33	15	35	14	258	285
Charlottesville, Va.	19	18	34	23	8	217	1572
Deer Park, Md.	20	19	23	33	15	172	245
Washington, D. C. (Coast and Geodetic Survey Office)	21	23	19	20	17	60	188
Washington, D. C. (Smithsonian Institution)	22	21	19	20	27	1	2
McCormick, S. C.	16	15	17	19	15	192	245
Little Rock, Ark.	13	39	5	35	8	530	1572
Columbia, Tenn.	14	15	35	13	13	320	340
St. Louis, Mo.	38	35	14	39	14	262	285
Chicago, Ill.	36	35	33	37	15	210	245
McAlester, Okla.	12	39	8	13	10	318	873
San Francisco, Cal.	54						
Laredo, Tex.	9	8	54	13	7	280	2298
Austin, Tex. (university)	11	9	12	5	9	355	1194
Galveston, Tex.	7	11	8	5	13	303	340
Austin, Tex. (capitol)	10	11	8	7	24	1	8
Rayville, La.	6	5	7	13	13	260	340

* According to rule 1 the interpolation was accepted one zone too soon.

Name of station	No. of station	Stations from which interpolation was made or attempted			Number of zones for which interpolation was accepted	Distance to nearest station from which interpolation was made or attempted	Inner radius of smallest zone for which the interpolation was accepted
						Kilometers	*Kilometers*
Grand Canyon, Wyo.	50	53	54	37	6	980	2965
Gunnison, Colo.	45	50	54	9	7	747	2298
Wallace, Kans.	41	45	50	39	11	467	642
Ellsworth, Kans.	40	39	11	41	13	290	340
Denver, Colo.	44	41	50	45	10	210	873
Colorado Springs, Colo.	42	45	41	44	10	95	873
Pikes Peak, Colo.	43	42	45	44	13	18	340
Green River, Utah	47	45	54	50	7	283	2298
Salt Lake City, Utah	49	47	54	50	7	247	2298
Grand Junction, Colo.	46	45	50	47	15	138	245
Pleasant Valley Junction, Utah	48	46	47	49	13	120	340
Lower Geyser Basin, Wyo.	52	50	54	53	20	30	59
Norris Geyser Basin, Wyo.	51	50	52	53	19	17	99
Mt. Hamilton, Cal.	55	54	9	49	9	81	1194
Seattle, Wash. (high school)	56	53	54	51	24	3	8
Pembina, N. Dak.	59						
Iron River, Mich.	57	59	88	39	9	732	1194
Ely, Minn.	58	57	59	39	12	320	481
Mitchell, S. Dak.	60	39	44	59	7	590	2298
Sweetwater, Tex.	61	10	47	12	12	354	481
Kerrville, Tex.	62	9	61	10	15	138	244
El Paso, Tex.	63	9	55	41	6	840	2965
Compton, Cal.	66	55	9	49	6	497	2965
Yuma, Ariz.	65	66	63	47	6	353	2965
Nogales, Ariz.	64	65	63	47	7	382	2298
Goldfield, Nev.	67	55	65	49	7	390	2298
Yavapai, Ariz.	68	65	47	67	6	372	2965
Grand Canyon, Ariz.	69	68	67	47	16	3	213
Gallup, N. Mex.	70	63	47	65	10	407	873
Las Vegas, N. Mex.	71	63	41	70	6	310	2965
Shamrock, Tex.	72	61	40	71	12	307	481
Denison, Tex.	73	12	10	72	12	148	481
Minneapolis, Minn.	74	58	60	37	13	328	340
Lead, S. Dak.	75	60	50	44	12	468	481
Rock Springs, Wyo.	82	44	50	49	10	240	873
Sisson, Cal.	81	54	53	49	9	395	1194
Paxton, Nebr.	83	41	60	75	13	252	340
Hinsdale, Mont.	77	59	53	50	5	492	3996
Sandpoint, Idaho	78	77	53	52	8	440	1572
Bismarck, N. Dak.	76	60	77	59	12	363	481
Boise, Idaho	79	52	81	78	7	447	2298
Astoria, Oreg.	80	81	53	79	11	202	642
Washington, D. C. (Bureau of Standards)	84	21	20	23	24	8	8
North Hero, Vt.	85	32	*	29	13	331	340
Wilson, N. Y.	88	32	33	20	15	220	245
Potsdam, N. Y.	87	88	*	28	12	345	481
Lake Placid, N. Y.	86	87	85	27	15	82	245
Alpena, Mich.	89	88	57	36	11	420	642

* Fort Kent station.　All of the results for this station were not available for this investigation.

CRITERIA OF ACCEPTED INTERPOLATIONS.

The computation for any station commenced with the small inner zones and proceeded outward. The two rules used by the computers in deciding at what zone it was allowable to begin to accept the interpolated values and to accept them for all larger zones were as follows:

Rule 1.—Commence to accept interpolated values as final with the first zone for which such interpolation is allowable under rule 2, provided it is beyond the zone containing the nearest of the three stations from which the interpolation is made.

Rule 2.—Let 0.0005 dyne be the interpolation limit for any zone. Subject to rule 1, acceptance of the interpolation may begin with a given zone if each of the three zones next within it shows an agreement between the interpolated and computed values which is within the interpolation limit.

Rule 1 insures that the interpolation shall not be accepted for very small zones because of a chance agreement between interpolated and computed values when there is no reason for such agreement. It insures that the first zone for which the interpolation is accepted will be one which somewhat overlaps the corresponding zone at the nearest station.

Under rule 2, at any station, the maximum error made by accepting interpolated values would be in dynes, 0.0005 times the number of zones interpolated, if the error of interpolation $I-C$ (interpolated minus computed) always had the same sign. Experience showed, however, that the agreement between the interpolated and computed values (commencing with zones not smaller than those contemplated under rule 1) tend to be closer and closer for successive zones proceeding outward. Experience also showed that the various differences between interpolated and computed values, for several zones such as are interpolated under rule 1, include values having both plus and minus signs, and, therefore, the errors in the accepted interpolations tend to be eliminated from the final results for the station.

The difference between the computed and the interpolated values for each of the three zones next within the one for which the interpolation is accepted at any station is generally 0.0002 dyne or less. The average number of zones per station for which interpolated values were accepted is 11, therefore it is probable that the error at any station caused by accepting interpolated values is in general less than 0.0022 dyne.

An illustration of the application of rules 1 and 2 at station No. 71 is shown on page 60. Station No. 70 was the nearest of the three (70, 41, and 63) from which it was proposed to attempt an interpolation. Station 70 lies in zone 14, hence in so far as rule 1 is concerned, the interpolation might have commenced with zone 13, but the difference between the interpolated and computed values for zone 14 (-0.0012) was not within the interpolation limit (0.0005 dyne). Similarly for zones 13, 12, and 10 the differences between interpolated and computed values were outside the interpolation limit. For the three successive zones 9, 8, and 7, the agreement was within the interpolation limit and therefore under rule 2, the interpolated values were accepted for zones 6 to 1.

SAVING BY INTERPOLATION OF OUTER ZONES.

The following table indicates how much labor was saved by interpolation:

Zone	Outer radius of zone	Computations*	Zone	Outer radius of zone	Computations*
	Kilometers.			*Kilometers.*	
G	3.5	1	13	481	35
H	5.2	1	12	642	43
I	8.4	1	11	874	47
J	12.4	5	10	1 194	52
K	19	6	9	1 572	58
L	29	6	8	2 298	62
M	59	6	7	2 965	74
N	99	7	6	3 999	80
O	168	9	5	5 674	82
18	188	9	4	8 029	83
17	213	11	3	11 763	83
16	244	12	2	16 780	83
15	285	21	1	20 012	83
14	340	21			

* Number of computations out of the total of 89 in which the interpolated value was accepted for the zone specified.

There are only six stations for which no interpolations were accepted.

For more than one-half of the computations out of 89 the interpolation was accepted for zones 11 to 1 and thus no direct computation was made for any topography at a greater distance from the station than 642 kilometers (399 miles), this being the inner radius of zone 11.

Similarly, for more than one-third of the stations, 35 out of 89, the interpolation was accepted for zones 13 to 1 and no direct computation was made for any topography more than 340 kilometers (211 miles) from the station.

The interpolation was accepted for zone G (outer radius 3.5 kilometers or 2.2 miles) and for all larger zones at station No. 22, Washington, Smithsonian Institution, the nearest station from which the interpolation was made being No. 21, Washington, Coast and Geodetic Survey Office, distant only 1.46 kilometers.

The interpolation was accepted for 978 zones out of a total of 2937, or for very nearly one-third. The proportional part of the labor saved by interpolation is probably not so great as this, although the zones for which interpolation was accepted were, in general, much larger than those computed directly. The difficulty in reading elevations in the larger area is offset by the fact that for the outer zones only approximate elevations are necessary. The unit of elevation (see reduction tables) for zones beyond and including No. 13 is either 1000 or 10 000 feet. After allowing for the fact that it takes approximately the same time for a large (outer) zone as for a small (inner) zone and also for the fact that the interpolation itself takes some time, it is estimated that the scheme of interpolation saved about one-fourth of the time which would otherwise have been necessary to make direct computations of the vertical component of the topographic effect complete to the antipodes.

CHANGE OF SIGN DUE TO DISTANCE.

Sixty-eight of the 89 gravity stations shown in the tables on pages 54–58, are more than 100 kilometers from the sea coast.* For these stations, therefore, there are no oceanic compartments in any zone smaller than zone O, the inner radius of this zone being 99 kilometers (p. 18). Yet for each of these stations, except one,† although the corrections for topography and isostatic compensation for zone A and for a few other zones near the station is positive, the correction for zone L is negative and at many stations it is also negative for zones J and K. At each of these stations, therefore, if one considers the corrections for successive zones a change of sign from plus to minus, by passing through zero, is found before reaching zone L in every case except one, and in 42 cases among the 89 the minus sign is first found in zone J; that is, within less than 12 kilometers of the station. This change of sign of the effect, without any change from land to ocean, should be carefully noted and the reasons for it studied, for otherwise one's general conception of the relations between the topography and isostatic compensation surrounding the station, on the one hand, and the attraction of gravity at the station, on the other hand, is apt to be largely in error.

Let the reduction tables for zones A to O, pages 30–43, be examined to ascertain the reason for this change of sign, confining the examination to the portions of the tables which relate to land compartments, since land compartments only are concerned. For each zone from A to I inclusive the corrections for topography and isostatic compensation, as given in the fourth column of each table, are all positive; in zones J and K the corrections are negative for small mean elevations (in the upper part of the column) and positive for large mean elevations; and in zones L to O the corrections are all negative. Hence, according to these tables, it is clear that if the station is at about the same elevation as the surface of the ground in zones J and K the minus sign should ordinarily appear first in one of these zones.

If the station stands much above the surrounding country, the corrections in the tables for zones I to L for "Station above compartment" are large positive values and, therefore, tend to make the change to a minus sign occur later than would otherwise be the case. For example, in the extreme case the correction is +0.0201 dyne for zone J, −0.0079 for zone K and −0.0032 for zone L at station No. 43, Pikes Peak, Colo. (p. 52), a station on a high mountain summit. There is no other station among the 89 having a positive correction for zone J greater than 0.0025. The correction for "Station above compartment" was +0.0010 for each of compartments 1 to 4 to the northeastward of the station Pikes Peak in zone J.

---

* These 68 stations are Nos. 6, 9–16, 19–23, 32–53, 56–65, 67–79, 81–89.

† This is station No. 6, Rayville, La. It is an apparent exception only in that the negative sign does not appear until zone 18, the corrections being zero for zones J to O inclusive.

If the station lies much below the surrounding country, the corrections in the tables for zones II to L for "Station below compartment" are large negative values and, therefore, tend to make the change to a minus sign occur nearer the station than it otherwise would occur. For example, in the extreme case at station No. 69, Grand Canyon, Ariz., the correction is −0.0012 for zone H, this being the only case among the 89 in which there is a negative correction for that zone. This station lies near the bottom of the Grand Canyon, far below the surrounding country and 1300 meters lower than station No. 68, Yavapai, which is less than 3 kilometers distant. The correction for "Station below compartment" was −0.0015 dynes for compartment No. 9 to the south of the station in zone H.

Let the reason for this change of sign of the combined effect of topography and compensation at distances from 4 to 20 kilometers from the station be examined from the theoretical point of view. Illustration No. 14 represents a case involving topography and compensation near a station and illustration No. 15 represents two cases for distant topography and compensation. In each figure S is the gravity station, B is a vertical cross section of the mass above sea level in a compartment, b is a vertical cross section of the corresponding compensating defect of mass, β_1 and β_2 are the angles of depression from the horizon of the station SH, to the effective centers of the two masses, respectively, and C is the center of the earth.

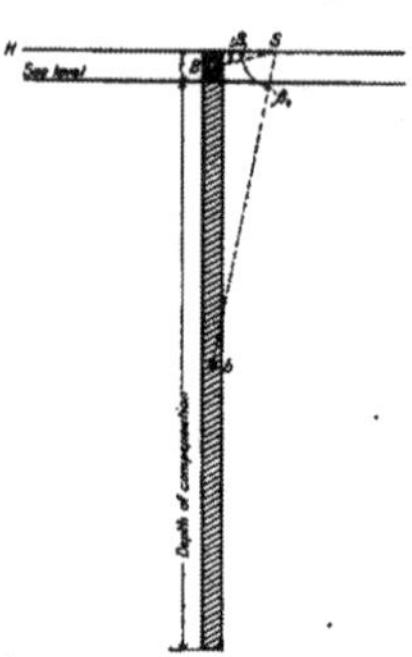

ILLUSTRATION No. 14.—Showing topography and compensation near station.

Consider the fundamental formula (9), page 14, expressing the vertical component of the attraction at the station and apply it to illustration No. 14. For this purpose the formula may be written

$$\text{Vertical component of the attraction} = km\,\frac{\sin\beta}{D^2}.$$

The negative mass, b, is numerically equal to the positive mass, B. In illustration 14 as drawn $\sin\beta_1 = 0.3$, $\sin\beta_2 = 1.0$, and the distance Sb is about 8 times SB. Hence in this case the quantity $\frac{\sin\beta}{D^2}$ is about 21 times as large for the topography as for the compensation. In other words, although the topography lies at a much smaller angle of depression from the station than the compensation it lies so much nearer that the vertical component of its effect (positive) is 21 times that of the compensation (negative). The combined effect of the topography and compensation is, therefore, an increase in the vertical component of the attraction at the station. Illustration No. 14 is drawn to scale to represent topography at an elevation of about 5000 meters above sea level in zone I, the station being at the same elevation as the compartment and the compensation extending to a depth of 113.7 kilometers. In practice the compensation is assumed to extend 113.7 kilometers below the actual surface of the ground. (See p. 10.)

This illustrative statement is approximate and has been made in this form merely for the sake of simplicity and clearness. The exact computation must be made by an integration of many such quantities as are indicated in formula (9), page 14, and in more detail in formulæ (10), (15), and (16), pages 15 and 16. The results of the exact integration will be considerably greater than that indicated in the preceding paragraph for the compensation. The results of the exact computation in a case similar to that shown in illustration No. 14 are given in the reduction tables for zone I (distance from station 5.2 to 8.4 kilometers) (p. 37). In the second and third columns of this table it is shown that if the station and topography have each an elevation of 15 000 feet (nearly 5000 meters) the effect of the topography in one compartment of the zone is +0.0031 dyne and of the compensation −0.0007, the positive effect of the topography being therefore more than 4 times the negative effect of the compensation.

Now consider such a case as that indicated on the left-hand side of illustration No. 15, in which the topography and compensation are at a considerable distance, say 40° of a great circle, from the station. The distances to the topography and compensation, SB and Sb, are nearly the same, but $\sin\beta_2$ is approximately 4/3 $\sin\beta_1$. Hence the quantity $\frac{\sin\beta}{D^2}$ is nearly 4/3 as large for the compensation as for the topography. In other words, the positive mass (topography) and the negative mass (compensation) are in this case so nearly at the same distance that the excess in the angle of depression of the compensation over that of the topography makes the vertical component of its effect greater than that of the topography. The combined effect is therefore a decrease in the vertical component of the attraction at the station.

In this figure the depth of compensation has been greatly exaggerated, as otherwise it would be difficult to make the illustration clear. The illustration, if considered as being drawn to scale, represents the compensation as extending to a depth of more than 1000 kilometers. If there be substituted for this by imagination an illustration drawn to scale in which the depth of compensation is only 113.7 kilometers it will be found that $\sin \beta_2$ is approximately 24/23 $\sin \beta_1$, and the resultant effect will therefore be a decrease in the vertical attraction at the station about 1/23 as great as the increase which would be produced by the topography alone.

This also is an approximate statement made in this form for the sake of clearness and simplicity. Again the results of the complicated, exact computation are available. In the table on page 25 are shown values of E_r and E_c corresponding to the distance $\theta = 40°$ from the station and their algebraic sum E_z, these values being, respectively, $+180.138(10^{-20})$, $-187.877(10^{-20})$, and $-7.739(10^{-20})$. The effects of the topography, of the compensation, and the resultant effect are proportional to these quantities. Note that E_c is the negative of E_r and is about 24/23 E_r, and that E_z is therefore negative and about 1/23 E_r. In other words, the exact computation shows that in this case the resultant effect of topography and compensation is a decrease in vertical attraction about 1/23 as great as the increase which would be produced by the topography alone.

Next consider such a case as that shown on the right-hand side of illustration No. 15, in which topography and compensation are at B_1 and b_1 near the antipodes of the station. In this case the two angles of depression are very nearly the same, but $\sin \beta_2$ is slightly greater than $\sin \beta_1$ and Sb_1 is slightly less than SB_1. For both these reasons the vertical component of the effect of the compensation is slightly greater than that of the topography.

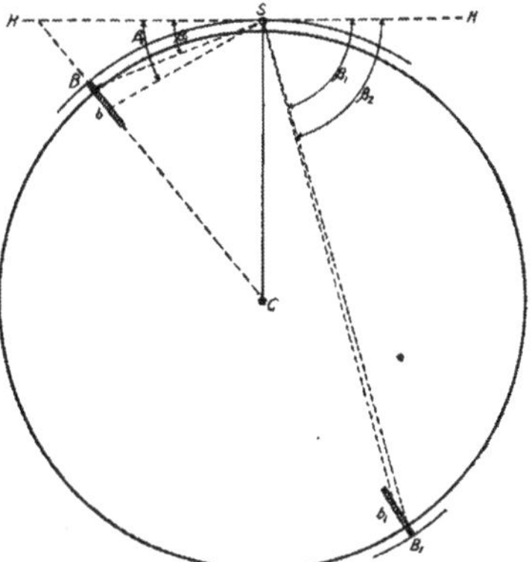

ILLUSTRATION No. 15.—Showing distant topography and compensation.

The combined effect is therefore a slight decrease of the vertical component of the attraction at the station. Again it should be kept in mind that in illustration No. 15 the depth of compensation is shown greatly exaggerated, and that therefore the actual resultant effect is even less than the illustration indicates. The results of the exact computation are available, page 25, where it is shown that for $\theta = 150°$, $E_r = +63.7846(10^{-20})$, $E_c = -64.3793(10^{-20})$ and their algebraic sum E_z is $-0.5947(10^{-20})$, indicating that the resultant effect is opposite to that of the topography alone and about 1/107 as great.

The second, third, and fourth columns of the reduction tables for the lettered zones, pages 30–43, and a table showing certain values of E_r, E_c, and E_z, page 25, show the relative values of the effects of topography and of compensation and of their resultant effect at various distances from the stations, as fixed by the exact computations.

For example, in zones A to D, at distances from the station not greater than 590 meters, the effect of the compensation is less than 1/20 as great as that of the topography. The ratio gradually increases to about 1/10 in zone G at 2 to 4 kilometers from the station, and to approximately unity at 12 to 19 kilometers from the station in zone K. In zone K the resultant is therefore nearly zero. In each of these cases the value of the ratio varies with the elevation of the station and topography as shown in the tables. At still greater distances from the station the effect of the topography is smaller than that of the compensation and the resultant is negative. The effect of the topography in zone N at 59 to 99 kilometers from the station is in general less than 1/10 that of the compensation.

Let the tables of E_T, E_c, and E_s, shown on page 25, be now examined. It will be noted that both E_T and E_c, and therefore the effects of topography and compensation, decrease rapidly as the distance from the station increases and that they also approach equality. Hence their algebraic sum E_s and also the resultant of both topography and compensation decrease still more rapidly. E_s retains the negative sign even to the antipodes. The ratio $\frac{E_T}{E_c}$ is $\frac{1}{22}$ at $\theta = 1° 25'$. This value of θ falls in zone O. Compare this ratio 1/22 with columns 2 and 3 of the reduction table for zone O (p. —). The ratio $\frac{E_T}{E_c}$ is about 1/10 at $\theta = 2° 20'$, approximately 1/2 at $\theta = 7° 45'$, approximately 9/10 at $\theta = 24°$; and approximately 111/112 at the antipodes, where $\theta = 180°$.

The relation of the effect of topography to the effect of its compensation is indicated in another way in the following table:

Effect of 1 square meter of topography having an elevation of 5000 feet and of its compensation at a station also having an elevation of 5000 feet.[*]

Distance from station to center of topography	Effect of topography	Effect of compensation	Ratio of effects, topography divided by compensation	Resultant effect
Meters	*Dynes*	*Dynes*		*Dynes*
0	$+200000(10^{-10})$	Very small	Large	$+200000(10^{-10})$
35	$+5000(10^{-10})$	Very small	Large	$+5000(10^{-10})$
150	$+1100(10^{-10})$	$-18(10^{-10})$	60	$+1100(10^{-10})$
940	$+90(10^{-10})$	$-2(10^{-10})$	46	$+90(10^{-10})$
2900	$+7(10^{-10})$	$-1(10^{-10})$	7	$+6(10^{-10})$
Kilometers				
10	$+.2(10^{-10})$	$-.2(10^{-10})$	1	$0(10^{-10})$
16	$+.06(10^{-10})$	$-.12(10^{-10})$	.5	$-.06(10^{-10})$
24	$+.02(10^{-10})$	$-.08(10^{-10})$	.2	$-.06(10^{-10})$
44	$+.003(10^{-10})$	$-.036(10^{-10})$	.1	$-.033(10^{-10})$
79	$+.001(10^{-10})$	$-.014(10^{-10})$	.07	$-.013(10^{-10})$
139(=1° 25')	$+.0001(10^{-10})$	$-.0030(10^{-10})$	.04	$-.0029(10^{-10})$
° ′				
2 20	$+.0001(10^{-10})$	$-.0009(10^{-10})$	.1	$-.0008(10^{-10})$
7 45	$+.000025(^{-10})$	$-.000049(10^{-10})$	.5	$-.000024(10^{-10})$
13	$+.000015(10^{-10})$	$-.000020(10^{-10})$	.7	$-.000005(10^{-10})$
29	$+.0000067(10^{-10})$	$-.0000072(10^{-10})$	.93	$-.0000005(10^{-10})$
70	$+.00000292(10^{-10})$	$-.00000297(10^{-10})$	.98	$-.00000005(10^{-10})$
180	$+.00000167(10^{-10})$	$-.00000169(10^{-10})$	.99	$-.00000002(10^{-10})$

[*] The quantities in this table have been computed approximately from the values given in the reduction tables and from other values available in the computations. The table is not of a high degree of accuracy, but is sufficient for the purposes of illustration, for which it is intended.

The effect of the topography decreases continuously without change of sign as the distance from the station is increased. This is also true of the effect of the compensation. These two effects decrease according to different laws. At a near station the effect of the topography is very large in comparison with that of compensation. The ratio of the two effects is unity at a distance of about 10 kilometers from the station. The ratio continues to decrease until it reaches a minimum of about 0.04 at about 139 kilometers (1° 25') from the station. It then increases continuously again to a value (0.99) which is nearly unity at the antipodes. The positive resultant effect shown in the last column decreases very rapidly from 200 000(10⁻¹⁰) at the station to zero at a distance of about 10 kilometers where the effects of topography and compensation just counterbalance each other. For all greater distances the resultant effect is negative, the effect of the compensation being greater than that of the topography. As the distance from the station is increased beyond 10 kilometers the negative resultant effect increases to a negative maximum at about 20 kilometers from the station and then decreases continuously to a very small value, $-0.00000002(10^{-10})$, at the antipodes.

The above table is computed and the comments are written for topography having an elevation of 5000 feet, and the elevation of the station is assumed to be 5000 feet. If a different elevation were assumed either for the topography or for the station the characteristic points of the curve which might be drawn representing the resultant effect would be somewhat changed in position—that is, the change of sign might occur at a less or greater distance than 10 kilometers and the negative maximum might be found to occur at a less or a greater distance than that indicated in the table—but the general form of the curve would not be changed.

It must be clear from the preceding that as successive zones of topography and compensation are considered the resultant effect changes sign comparatively near the station even if there is no change from land to ocean. This change of sign due to distance occurs between 8 and 20 kilometers from the station, and usually at about 10 kilometers. It is important to keep this prominently before one when considering the relation between the value of gravity at a station and the surrounding topography, for with this in mind it is evident that a proper consideration of near topography and compensation not only fails to give a good approximation to the effect of all topography and compensation but that it may even give an estimate which is opposite in sign to the actual effect.

Station No. 49, Salt Lake City, Utah (p. 56), furnishes an extreme illustration. All of the topography and compensation within 8.4 kilometers of the station, out to zone I inclusive, has the effect of increasing the vertical component of the attraction upon a unit mass at the station by $+0.1230$ dyne, this being the sum of the corrections for the separate zones as shown in the table. Moreover, since for zones E to I the effects are in order $+0.0325$, $+0.0216$, $+0.0109$, $+0.0059$, and $+0.0019$, it is easy to conclude, as these values are evidently approaching zero, that it is safe to neglect the values for more distant zones. But if one knows of the change of sign due to distance and, therefore, carries the computation out to zone 17, it is found that the sum of the corrections for zones J to 17 is -0.1292, and the total effect of all topography and compensation from the station out to zone 17 inclusive—that is, to a distance $1°\ 54'\ 52''$ (212 kilometers) from the station—is -0.0062, of the sign contrary to that of the effect of the topography and compensation within 8.4 kilometers of the station. The largest positive correction for a near zone is $+0.0325$ for zone E. This is exceeded by the negative correction of -0.0336 for the much more distant zone M. In considering the preceding statements it is important to note that no oceanic areas are encountered at this station until one reaches zone 10 at a distance from the station more than four times as great as for the most distant parts of zone 17. At this station, if one carries the computation to the antipodes, the total correction found is -0.0414, in extreme contrast to the correction $+0.1230$ found for the first nine zones. At this station a hasty decision, made in ignorance of the fundamental change of sign due to distance, to stop the computation at 8.4 kilometers from the station would have given a computed effect of $+0.1230$ dyne; a decision to extend the computation to the distance of 213 kilometers would have given a computed effect of -0.0062 dyne; and the safe decision to carry the computation to the antipodes gave the true correction of -0.0414 dyne. In considering the preceding sentence it is well to keep in mind that the vertical component of the attraction upon a unit mass at the station is determined by the pendulum observations with an error which is usually less than 0.004 dyne and very rarely exceeds 0.010 dyne. (See p. 87.)

Aside from the unfamiliar change of sign thus far commented upon, due entirely to increase of distance from the station, there is another which occurs at nearly every station due to an entirely different and ordinarily well-recognized cause, namely, the change from land to oceanic zones. Since about three-fourths of the world's surface is covered with deep oceans, sooner or later, as successively more zones are taken, a zone is reached in which the water in the zone predominates largely over the land. This produces a change in the sign of the resultant effect upon the vertical component of the attraction at the station. (See pp. 20 and 27, and also consult the reduction tables, pp. 30–47.)

In general, therefore, at every station situated on land, as successively larger zones are considered, two changes of sign are found—one due simply to increase of distance from the station. and one due to a change from land zones to water zones.

Station No. 49, Salt Lake City, Utah, is a typical inland station at a large elevation. The change of sign, from plus to minus, due to distance, occurs at this station (see p. 56) between zones I and J. The second change of sign, from minus to plus, occurs between zones 10 and 9. In zone 9, of which the inner and outer radii are 1190 and 1570 kilometers, the effect of the deep water of the Pacific in the western part of the zone predominates over the effect of the topography (mainly of small elevation) in the remainder of the zone. For all larger zones out to the antipodes the water effect predominates.

At stations Nos. 58, 59, and 60, which are still farther from the ocean, being in Minnesota and South Dakota, the first change of sign, from plus to minus, due to distance, occurs between zones I and J. The second change, from minus to plus, due to change from land to water, does not occur until zone 7 is reached. The radii of zone 7 are 2300 and 2960 kilometers.

On the other hand, at station No. 54, San Francisco, the change of sign due to distance occurs between zones I and J, and that due to change from land to water occurs between zones M and N. The predominating influence of water effects is first seen in this case in compartments 11 and 12 of zone N (consult the computation shown on p. 49), which lie slightly south of west from San Francisco and in which the mean depths of water are about 900 fathoms, giving for each of these compartments a correction of +0.0010. (See reduction table, p. 42.) The computation shows that in zone O seven compartments to the westward of the station have positive corrections greater than 0.0010, but that those to the eastward of the station, mainly on land, have negative corrections with a single exception. The negative corrections persist in one or more compartments of each zone from 13 to 8. Commencing with zone 7 all compartments have either zero corrections or positive corrections, showing the predominance of water in all compartments. Zone 7 has radii of 2300 and 2960 kilometers and, therefore, the eastern compartment of this zone includes portions of the Gulf of Mexico as well as portions of the Pacific Ocean to the southeastward of San Francisco.

San Francisco is a shore station, with mountains near it on the land side. In contrast to San Francisco, stations Nos. 2 to 5 and 18 are shore stations, with low topography near them on the land side. Hence at each of them the change of sign due to change from land to water comes at so small a zone as to be confused with the change of sign due to distance. At these stations there is apparently no change of sign. A long series of zeros occurs in each case, which extends from zone B to zone K for station No. 2 and from B to O for station No. 5, and the plus signs then reappear.

At station No. 1, Key West, Fla., where the topography is very low and the station very near the shore, the change of sign due to change from land to water occurs between zones B and C and the change due to distance occurs much farther away, between zones L and M.

At station No. 17, Charleston, S. C., the change due to predominance of water occurs before zone N and that due to distance comes slightly farther away, between zones N and O.

At stations Nos. 6, 8, and 55 besides the change of sign due to distance there are in each case three changes of sign due to alternating predominance of land and water effects.

The foreign gravity stations Nos. 2, 3, 4, and 5, for which the corrections for separate zones are shown on page 84, were located on a vessel out on the Pacific Ocean. For these stations the water effects predominate in every zone. Hence in zones near the station the signs are minus, and the change of sign due to distance (in this case from minus to plus) occurs somewhere between zones J and M for each station.

DISTANT TOPOGRAPHY NECESSARILY CONSIDERED.

It should be evident from the preceding discussion of the change of sign due to distance that any treatment of the problem of computing the effect of topography and compensation upon gravity is liable to lead to errors so large as to make the conclusions reached unreliable if it is based upon the theory that because the computed effects for certain zones at moderate distances from the station are very small, the effect of zones at great distances is negligible. The effects of topography and compensation at 8 to 12 kilometers from the station (zone J) are usually small simply because a change of sign due to distance takes place about there.

For each of the 89 stations in the United States the water effects expressed by positive corrections predominate in all zones from 7 to 1, the antipodes of each station (in the middle of zone 1) being in the deep water of the Indian Ocean south of Asia. Hence if all the topography and compensation in zone 7 and beyond were neglected—that is, all topography and compensation more than 2300 kilometers from the station were neglected—the error made would, for every station in the United States, be either 0.004 or 0.005 dyne, a quantity larger in many cases than the error of observation. It is important to note that this error would be of one sign for all stations in the United States, the neglected quantity being in each case an increase in the computed value of gravity at the station. Even in the 16 foreign stations shown on pages 84, widely scattered over the world, the error would be 0.004, 0.005, or 0.006 dyne for each of the stations 1 to 10 and 12, and 0.002 or 0.003 dyne for stations 11 and 13 to 16. The sign would be in each case the same as for stations in the United States.

An instance has already been given (p. 69), in which if all topography and compensation beyond zone 17—that is, beyond 213 kilometers from the station—were ignored, the error introduced would be $+0.035$ dyne or at least nine times as great as the average error of the determination of the intensity of gravity at a station.

At each of stations 41 to 52 (see p. 56) the neglect of the single zone M (inner radius 28.8, outer radius 58.8 kilometers) would introduce an error greater than 0.020 dyne or at least five times as great as the average error of the observed value of the intensity of gravity at the station. Also there are many still more distant zones at these stations for each of which the computed effect of topography and compensation is more than 0.020 dyne.

If one wishes to secure reliable conclusions it is certainly necessary to extend to great distances the computations of the effects of topography and compensation. The only safe rule is to extend the computations to cover the whole earth.

CURVATURE MUST BE CONSIDERED.

As soon as it is conceded that the computation of the effects of topography and compensation must be extended to cover the whole earth it is evident that the curvature of the sea-level surface must be considered. Any formulæ based upon the supposition that the sea-level surface is a plane must be grossly in error when applied to very distant toporgaphy and compensation.

A proper consideration of the curvature places topography at a distance of 20 000 kilometers from the station directly below the station at the antipodes, whereas if the sea-level surface were a plane it would be in the horizon of the station. In the actual case the whole of the attraction due to this topography is in the vertical of the station and is a direct correction to the vertical component of the attraction at the station, whereas a formula ignoring curvature would make it a horizontal force at the station.

Similarly, if curvature is neglected topography at 10 000 kilometers (one-fourth the circumference of the earth) from the station is treated as being in the horizon of the station, whereas in fact it lies 45° below the horizon of the station.

In connection with the two preceding paragraphs consult illustration No. 15 (p. 67).

Even for topography within 50 kilometers of the station the computations connected with the present investigation have shown that curvature must be considered if results are to be secured which are in error by less than 1 part in 200. (See p. 22.)

In the exact formulæ (10), (15), and (16) (pp. 15 and 16), which were used to make the computations of this investigation, θ becomes zero in every case if the curvature of the sea-level surface is neglected. If θ is made zero E becomes zero in all cases in formula (10), and the computed effect of any material lying at the same elevation as the station becomes zero. As a matter of fact, by the exact formula E is found to be much too large to be negligible. In formula (15) it is evident that the effects of curvature predominate over the effects of difference of elevation (between the station and topography and represented by h) if in the numerator of the fraction E_1, $\frac{\theta}{2}$ becomes larger than

$$\sin^{-1}\left(\frac{h \cos \frac{\theta}{2}}{\sqrt{D_1^2 + h^2 + 2D_1 h \sin \frac{\theta}{2}}}\right)$$

The latter quantity tends to decrease as the distance from the station increases, becoming very small at great distances on account of the very large value of D_1. On the other hand, $\frac{\theta}{2}$ increases in proportion to the distance from the station. Hence at great distances $\frac{\theta}{2}$ becomes much greater than the quantity referred to above with which it is combined by subtraction.

This is shown in another form by the reduction tables (pp. 30–46), in which it is evident that a change of elevation of the station makes a large change in the computed corrections in a near zone, such as zone E at 0.6 to 1.3 kilometers from the station, and makes very little change, always less than 10 per cent, in zone O at 99 to 167 kilometers from the station. Moreover (see p. 45) in zone 13 and beyond—that is, at distances greater than 340 kilometers—the relative elevation of the station and the topography may be entirely ignored without introducing appreciable error into the computation.

It would be difficult to show satisfactorily by pure theory without numerical values why and to what extent the curvature and distant topography and compensation must be considered. In the present investigation no such attempt has been made. Instead the computations have been made to cover the whole earth by formulæ which are practically exact, curvature being adequately taken into account. This having been done the numerical results, as shown on pages 54–58, demonstrate conclusively and clearly that both distant topography and curvature must be considered if one is to secure even a fair approximation to the truth.

PRINCIPAL FACTS FOR EIGHTY-NINE STATIONS IN THE UNITED STATES.

Complete computations, taking into account all of the topography of the world and its compensation, have been made for 89 stations in the United States with the results shown in the two tables which follow.

The theoretical value of gravity at sea level was computed by Helmert's formula of 1901 (see p. 12), namely:

$$\gamma_0 = 978.046(1 + .005302 \sin^2\phi - 0.000007 \sin^2 2\phi)$$

The correction for elevation of station was computed by the formula $-0.0003086H$, in which H is the elevation in meters. (See p. 13.) Note that this is the reduction from sea level, to the station, a correction to the theoretical value not to the observed value. It takes account of the increased distance of the station from the attracting mass, the earth, as if the station were in the air at the stated elevation and there were no topography on the earth.

The correction for topography and compensation was computed with the new reduction tables. This is also a correction to be applied to the theoretical value at sea level. The corrections referred to in the preceding two paragraphs are applied in the reverse of the customary way. Usually corrections are applied to the observed values of the intensity of gravity to reduce them to sea level and to correct for the supposed influence of topography. In this publication the corrections are applied to the theoretical value of the intensity of gravity at sea level to obtain the theoretical value at the station, a value which is directly comparable with the observed value. This seems to the authors to be a more logical method and more conducive to clear thinking than the usual method.

The computed value of gravity at the station g_c is the theoretical value of gravity at sea level, γ_0, corrected for elevation and for topography and compensation. It is therefore directly comparable with the observed value of gravity at the station g. The column $g-g_c$ therefore represents the departures of the observed values from computed values based upon the Helmert formula of 1901, upon the usual reduction for elevation, and upon the new reductions that take account of topography and compensation.

All observed values, g, in the following table depend upon relative determinations with the half-second pendulums and are based on 980.111 dynes (in centimeter-gram-second units) as the absolute value of gravity at the Coast and Geodetic Survey Office at Washington. This value depends upon the absolute determination of the value of gravity at Potsdam,* Germany, and upon the relative values of gravity at Potsdam and Washington, as determined by Mr. G. R. Putnam in 1900.†

The gravity observations for stations Nos. 22, 26, 54, 55, and 56 were made by Dr. T. C. Mendenhall, formerly Superintendent of the Coast and Geodetic Survey. The details of the observations at these stations are published in Appendix 15, Report of the Coast and Geodetic Survey for 1891.

The observations at stations Nos. 27, 28, 37 were made by Assistant E. Smith, of the Coast and Geodetic Survey. The details of the observations for stations Nos. 27 and 28 are published in Appendix 4 of the Report for 1899, while those for station No. 37 are not yet in print.

The observations at station No. 23 were made by Mr. E. D. Preston, of the Coast and Geodetic Survey, and the details of the observations are published in Appendix 2 of the Report for 1894.

The observations at the following stations were made by Mr. G. R. Putnam, assistant, Coast and Geodetic Survey, and the details are published in Appendix 1, Report for 1894, and Appendix 6, Report for 1897, except station No. 53, the details of which are not in print: Nos. 1, 5, 7, 9, 10, 11, 13, 15, 17, 19, 20, 24, 25, 29–36, 38–52, and 53.

The observations at stations Nos. 2–4, 6, 8, 12, 14, 16, 18, 57–73, 84–89 were made in 1909–10 by Mr. William H. Burger, and the observations at stations Nos. 74–83 were made in 1910 by Mr. Harold D. King, both assistants in the Coast and Geodetic Survey. Mr. King also reoccupied, in 1910, stations Nos. 57 and 85. (See p. 87.) None of the details for the stations established by Messrs. Burger and King have been published.

The gravity observations at each of the stations used in this investigation were made with the half-second pendulum apparatus.‡ The methods used by Mr. Putnam are described by him in Appendix 1, Report for 1894. These same methods were employed by Messrs. Burger and King with very few exceptions. They were instructed to obtain a probable error for the adopted mean value at a station of not more than ± 0.004 dyne. The flexure of the pendulum case and pier was determined by them, in terms of the wave length of light, with an interferometer, as described in Appendix 6, Report for 1910.

---

* Bestimmung der Absoluten Grösse der Schwerkraft zu Potsdam mit Reversionspendeln von Prof. Dr. F. Kühnen und Prof. Dr. Ph. Furtwängler, Seite 380.

† Determination of Relative Value of Gravity in Europe and the United States in 1900, G. R. Putnam, Appendix 5, Coast and Geodetic Survey Report, 1901, pp. 354–355.

‡ Described in Appendix 15, Report for 1891.

Table of principal facts for 89 gravity stations in the United States.

Number and name of station	ϕ	λ	H (Meters)	γ_0	Correction for elevation	Correction for topography and compensation	Computed gravity at station (g_c)	Observed gravity at station (g)	($g-g_c$)
1. Key West, Fla.	24 33.6	81 48.4	1	978.938	0.000	+0.032	978.970	978.969	−0.001
2. West Palm Beach, Fla.	26 42.8	80 02.8	2	979.089	− .001	+ .031	979.119	979.128	+ .009
3. Punta Gorda, Fla.	26 56.2	82 03	1	979.105	.000	+ .020	979.125	979.126	+ .001
4. Apalachicola, Fla.	29 43.5	84 58.8	4	979.316	− .001	+ .015	979.330	979.321	− .009
5. New Orleans, La.	29 57.0	90 04.2	2	979.333	− .001	+ .013	979.345	979.323	− .022
6. Rayville, La.	32 28	91 45	26	979.535	− .008	+ .008	979.535	979.542	+ .007
7. Galveston, Tex.	29 18.2	94 47.5	3	979.283	− .001	+ .007	979.289	979.271	− .018
8. Point Isabel, Tex.	26 04.7	97 12.4	8	979.044	− .002	+ .015	979.057	979.075	+ .018
9. Laredo, Tex.	27 30.5	99 31.2	129	979.147	− .040	+ .003	979.110	979.081	− .029
10. Austin, Tex. (capitol)	30 16.5	97 44.3	170	979.359	− .052	− .003	979.304	979.287	− .017
11. Austin, Tex. (university)	30 17.2	97 44.2	189	979.360	− .058	− .001	979.301	979.282	− .019
12. McAlester, Okla.	34 56.2	95 46.2	240	979.741	− .074	+ .001	979.668	979.632	− .036
13. Little Rock, Ark.	34 45.0	92 16.4	89	979.725	− .027	+ .001	979.699	979.720	+ .021
14. Columbia, Tenn.	35 36.7	87 02.5	207	979.799	− .064	+ .006	979.741	979.758	+ .017
15. Atlanta, Ga.	33 45 0	84 23.3	324	979.641	− .100	+ .014	979.555	979.523	− .032
16. McCormick, S. C.	33 54.8	82 18.0	163	979.655	− .050	+ .012	979.617	979.623	+ .006
17. Charleston, S. C.	32 47.2	79 56.0	6	979.561	− .002	+ .016	979.575	979.545	− .030
18. Beaufort, N. C.	34 43.1	76 30.8	1	979.722	.000	+ .036	979.758	979.728	− .030
19. Charlottesville, Va.	38 02.0	78 30.3	166	980.008	− .051	+ .002	979.959	979.937	− .022
20. Deer Park, Md.	39 25.0	79 19.8	770	980.130	− .238	+ .041	979.933	979.934	+ .001
21. Washington, D. C. (Coast and Geodetic Survey Office)	38 53.2	77 00.5	14	980.083	− .004	+ .004	980.083	980.111	+ .028
22. Washington, D. C. (Smithsonian Institution)	38 53.8	77 01.5	10	980.083	− .008	+ .008	980.083	980.113	+ .030
23. Baltimore, Md.	39 17.8	76 37.3	30	980.119	− .009	+ .006	980.116	980.096	− .020
24. Philadelphia, Pa.	39 57.1	75 11.7	18	980.178	− .005	+ .009	980.182	980.195	+ .013
25. Princeton, N. J.	40 21.0	74 39.5	64	980.212	− .020	+ .013	980.205	980.177	− .028
26. Hoboken, N. J.	40 44	74 02	11	980.248	− .003	+ .008	980.253	980.268	+ .015
27. New York, N. Y.	40 48.5	73 57.7	38	980.254	− .012	+ .011	980.253	980.266	+ .013
28. Worcester, Mass.	42 16.5	71 48.5	170	980.386	− .052	+ .018	980.352	980.323	− .029
29. Boston, Mass.	42 21.6	71 03.8	22	980.393	− .007	+ .013	980.399	980.395	− .004
30. Cambridge, Mass.	42 22.8	71 07.8	14	980.395	− .004	+ .010	980.401	980.397	− .004
31. Calais, Me.	45 11.2	67 16.9	38	980.649	− .012	+ .010	980.647	980.630	− .017
32. Ithaca, N. Y.	42 27.1	76 29.0	247	980.402	− .076	+ .005	980.331	980.299	− .032
33. Cleveland, Ohio	41 30.4	81 36.6	210	980.317	− .065	.000	980.252	980.240	− .012
34. Cincinnati, Ohio	39 08.3	84 25.3	245	980.105	− .076	+ .002	980.031	980.003	− .028
35. Terre Haute, Ind.	39 28.7	87 23.8	151	980.135	− .047	+ .001	980.089	980.071	− .018
36. Chicago, Ill.	41 47.4	87 36.1	182	980.342	− .056	+ .007	980.293	980.277	− .016
37. Madison, Wis.	43 04.6	89 24.0	270	980.458	− .083	+ .003	980.378	980.364	− .014
38. St. Louis, Mo.	38 38.0	90 12.2	154	980.061	− .048	+ .001	980.014	980.000	− .014
39. Kansas City, Mo.	39 05.8	94 35.4	278	980.101	− .086	− .001	980.014	979.989	− .025
40. Ellsworth, Kans.	38 43.7	98 13.5	469	980.069	− .145	− .004	979.920	979.925	+ .005
41. Wallace, Kans.	38 54.7	101 35.4	1,005	980.085	− .310	.000	979.775	979.754	− .021
42. Colorado Springs, Colo.	38 50.7	104 49.0	1,841	980.080	− .568	− .007	979.505	979.489	− .016
43. Pikes Peak, Colo.	38 50.3	105 02.0	4,293	980.079	−1.325	+ .187	978.941	978.953	+ .012
44. Denver, Colo.	39 40.6	104 56.9	1,638	980.153	− .505	− .015	979.633	979.608	− .025
45. Gunnison, Colo.	38 32.6	106 56.0	2,340	980.053	− .722	− .001	979.330	979.341	+ .011
46. Grand Junction, Colo.	39 04.2	108 33.9	1,398	980.099	− .431	− .051	979.617	979.632	+ .015
47. Green River, Utah	38 59.4	110 09.9	1,243	980.092	− .384	− .043	979.665	979.635	− .030
48. Pleasant Valley Junction, Utah	39 50.8	111 00.8	2,191	980.168	− .676	+ .024	979.516	979.511	− .005
49. Salt Lake City, Utah	40 46.1	111 53.8	1,322	980.250	− .408	− .041	979.801	979.802	+ .001
50. Grand Canyon, Wyo.	44 43.3	110 29.7	2,386	980.607	− .736	+ .038	979.909	979.898	− .011
51. Norris Geyser Basin, Wyo.	44 44.2	110 42.0	2,276	980.608	− .702	+ .031	979.937	979.949	+ .012
52. Lower Geyser Basin, Wyo.	44 33.4	110 48.1	2,200	980.592	− .679	+ .028	979.941	979.931	− .010
53. Seattle, Wash. (university)	47 39.6	122 18.3	58	980.872	− .018	− .020	980.834	980.732	− .102
54. San Francisco, Cal.	37 47.5	122 25.7	114	979.986	− .035	+ .045	979.996	979.964	− .032
55. Mount Hamilton, Cal.	37 20.4	121 38.6	1,282	979.947	− .396	+ .120	979.671	979.659	− .012
56. Seattle, Wash. (high school)	47 36.5	122 19.8	74	980.867	− .023	− .018	980.826	980.724	− .102
57. Iron River, Mich.	46 05.4	88 38.4	458	980.730	− .141	+ .014	980.603	980.632	+ .029
58. Ely, Minn.	47 48.6	92 01.0	448	980.886	− .138	+ .008	980.756	980.770	+ .014
59. Pembina, N. Dak.	48 58.1	97 14.9	243	980.990	− .075	− .009	980.906	980.916	+ .010
60. Mitchell, S. Dak.	43 41.8	98 01.8	408	980.514	− .126	− .006	980.382	980.374	− .006
61. Sweetwater, Tex.	32 28.4	100 24.1	655	979.535	− .202	+ .009	979.342	979.304	− .038
62. Kerrville, Tex.	30 01.3	99 07.6	498	979.339	− .154	+ .013	979.198	979.220	+ .022
63. El Paso, Tex.	31 46.3	106 29.0	1,146	979.478	− .354	+ .001	979.125	979.123	− .002
64. Nogales, Ariz.	31 21.3	110 56.6	1,181	979.445	− .364	+ .038	979.119	979.060	− .059
65. Yuma, Ariz.	32 43.3	114 37.0	54	979.555	− .017	− .010	979.528	979.528	.000
66. Compton, Cal.	33 53.4	118 13.2	20	979.652	− .006	.000	979.646	979.587	− .059
67. Goldfield, Nev.	37 42.2	117 14.5	1,716	979.979	− .529	+ .027	979.477	979.455	− .022
68. Yavapai, Ariz.	36 03.9	112 07.1	2,179	979.837	− .672	+ .034	979.199	979.191	− .008
69. Grand Canyon, Ariz.	36 05.3	112 06.8	849	979.839	− .252	− .096	979.491	979.462	− .019
70. Gallup, N. Mex.	35 31.8	108 44.2	1,990	979.791	− .614	+ .014	979.191	979.169	− .022
71. Las Vegas, N. Mex.	35 35.8	105 12.1	1,960	979.797	− .605	+ .017	979.209	979.203	− .006
72. Shamrock, Tex.	35 12.8	100 11.4	708	979.764	− .218	+ .007	979.553	979.578	+ .025
73. Denison, Tex.	33 45.3	96 32.8	230	979.841	− .071	− .001	979.569	979.565	− .004
74. Minneapolis, Minn.	44 58.7	93 13.9	256	980.630	− .079	− .005	980.546	980.596	+ .050
75. Lead, S. Dak.	44 21.1	103 45.6	1,590	980.573	− .491	+ .044	980.126	980.169	+ .043
76. Bismarck, N. Dak.	46 48.5	100 47.0	516	980.795	− .159	− .008	980.628	980.635	+ .007
77. Hinsdale, Mont.	48 23.8	107 05.3	661	980.939	− .204	− .017	980.718	980.738	+ .020
78. Sandpoint, Idaho	48 16.4	116 33.3	637	980.927	− .197	− .044	980.686	980.679	− .007
79. Boise, Idaho	43 37.2	116 12.3	821	980.507	− .253	− .042	980.212	980.211	− .001
80. Astoria, Oreg	46 11.3	123 50.2	1	980.740	.000	+ .008	980.748	980.726	− .022
81. Sisson, Cal.	41 18.3	122 19.6	1,048	980.296	− .323	+ .015	979.990	979.971	− .019
82. Rock Springs, Wyo.	41 35.1	109 13.2	1,910	980.324	− .589	− .001	979.734	979.738	+ .004
83. Paxton, Nebr.	41 07.4	101 21.3	932	980.282	− .288	+ .002	979.996	979.994	− .002
84. Washington, D.C. (Bureau of Standards)	38 56.3	77 04.0	103	980.086	− .032	+ .012	980.066	980.094	+ .028
85. North Hero, Vt.	44 49.1	73 17.5	35	980.615	− .011	− .009	980.595	980.587	− .008
86. Lake Placid, N. Y.	44 17.5	73 59.1	571	980.567	− .176	+ .032	980.423	980.430	+ .007
87. Potsdam, N. Y.	44 40.1	74 58.8	130	980.602	− .040	− .004	980.558	980.570	+ .012
88. Wilson, N. Y.	43 18.4	78 49.6	87	980.478	− .027	− .002	980.449	980.430	− .019
89. Alpena, Mich.	45 03.8	83 27.0	178	980.638	− .055	.000	980.583	980.554	− .029

CORRECTION TO HELMERT'S FORMULA OF 1901.

The mean of the above 89 values of $g - g_c$ is -0.009 dyne and the probable error of a single value is ± 0.017 dyne. The two residuals from this mean for stations No. 53 and No. 56 at Seattle are each -0.093 dyne, which is more than five times the probable error of a single value. Hence, it is believed that these two values should be rejected, as being due to some very unusual disturbance.

After rejecting the two Seattle stations the mean value of '$g - g_c$ is -0.007 ± 0.0015 dyne and the probable error of a single value is ± 0.014 dyne. As this mean is five times its own probable error it is believed that it represents a real correction to the Helmert formula of 1901 for the theoretical value of gravity at sea level, and that this correction should be applied in connection with the new method of reduction for topography and compensation. Accordingly, in the following tables the quantities called "Anomaly, new method," are $(g - g_c) + 0.007$ dyne. These are, therefore, the anomalies in gravity as given by the new reduction and referred to the following formula for the theoretical value of gravity at sea level:

$$\gamma_0 = 978.039\ (1 + 0.005\ 302\ \sin^2\phi - 0.000\ 007\ \sin^2 2\phi),$$

this being Helmert's formula of 1901 with a constant correction of -0.007.* A plus sign on the anomaly means that at the station in question the intensity of gravity is in excess of that which would occur there if the isostatic compensation were complete and uniformly distributed to the depth of 113.7 kilometers, while if the anomaly is minus the intensity of gravity is less than it would be if the compensation were complete and uniformly distributed to the depth of 113.7 kilometers.

COMPARISON OF APPARENT ANOMALIES BY THE NEW AND OLD METHODS.

The values $g_0'' - \gamma_0$ and of $g_0 - \gamma_0$ in the following tables have the same meaning as in the 1906 report of the International Geodetic Association.

The quantity $g_0'' - \gamma_0$ is the apparent anomaly when the Helmert formula of 1901 and the Bouguer reduction are used. The Bouguer reduction "has been very generally applied in reducing pendulum observations to the level of the sea. This formula is $dg = +\dfrac{2gH}{r}\left(1 - \dfrac{3\delta}{4\varDelta}\right)$, where dg is the correction to observed gravity, g is gravity at sea level, H is elevation above sea level, r is radius of the earth, δ is density of matter lying above sea level, and $\varDelta$ is mean density of the earth. The first term takes account of the distance from the earth's center, and the second term of the vertical attraction of the matter lying between the sea level and station, on the supposition that the latter is located on an indefinitely extended horizontal plain. Wherever the topography about a station departs materially from this condition of a horizontal plain a third term must be added to the above formula, being a correction to the second term or to observed gravity on account of such irregularities." † The Bouguer reduction thus takes no account of isostatic compensation and neglects all curvature of the sea-level surface, the topography being treated as if it were standing on a plane of indefinite extent.

The quantity $g_0 - \gamma_0$ is the apparent anomaly when the Helmert formula of 1901 is used in connection with the so-called reduction to sea level in free air only, $(0.000\ 308\ 6\ H)$. This reduction ignores both the topography and the isostatic compensation. It takes account simply of the increased distance of the station from the earth's center when the station is above sea level.

A comparison of the anomalies by the new method, on the one hand, with those by the two older methods, as shown in the colums headed $g_0'' - \gamma_0$ and $g_0 - \gamma_0$ on the other hand, will

---

* The correction to his own formula of 1901, communicated by Dr. Helmert in the letter printed in the footnote on p. 12, changes the first term only of the formula, making it 978.030 instead of 978.046. The first term, as derived from the gravity determinations in the United States, namely, 978.039, therefore differs from the Helmert formula of 1901, as referred to Potsdam, by only 0.009 and lies almost midway between the values on the Vienna and Potsdam systems.

† This excellent statement of the nature of the Bouguer reduction is quoted from Mr. G. R. Putnam. (See Appendix 1 of the Coast and Geodetic Survey Report for 1894, pp. 21–22.)

therefore show the merits of the new method of reduction in comparison with the Bouguer and the free-air methods.

The comparison of the new method is made with the Bouguer and free-air reductions, for the Bouguer postulates a total lack of compensation and a consequent high rigidity of the earth's crust while the free-air method assumes that each piece of topography is completely compensated for at zero depth. In his investigation, published in Appendix 1, Report for 1894, Mr. Putnam used what he called Faye's reduction, which is a modification of the free-air reduction, in that a correction is applied for the lack of compensation. This correction is added to or subtracted from the observed value and is equal to the vertical effect at the station of the attraction of an indefinitely extended horizontal plane of a thickness equal to the difference in elevation between the station and the surrounding country and of a density equal to the mean density of the surface of the earth. By this reduction, Mr. Putnam obtained anomalies which were, in general, much smaller than those obtained by either the Bouguer or free-air reduction. (See pp. 25–27, Appendix 1, Report for 1894.)

Number and name of station	Anomaly		
	New method $(g - g_0 + 0.007)$	Bouguer $(g_0'' - \gamma_0)$	In free air $(g_0 - \gamma_0)$
1. Key West, Fla.	+0.006	+0.031	+0.031
2. West Palm Beach, Fla.	+.016	+.040	+.040
3. Punta Gorda, Fla.	+.008	+.021	+.021
4. Apalachicola, Fla.	—.002	+.006	+.006
5. New Orleans, La.	—.015	—.009	—.009
6. Rayville, La.	+.014	+.012	+.015
7. Galveston, Tex.	—.011	—.011	—.011
8. Point Isabel, Tex.	+.025	+.032	+.033
9. Laredo, Tex.	—.022	—.039	—.026
10. Austin, Tex. (capitol)	—.010	—.038	—.020
11. Austin, Tex. (university)	—.012	—.040	—.020
12. McAlester, Okla.	—.029	—.062	—.035
13. Little Rock, Ark.	+.028	+.013	+.022
14. Columbia, Tenn.	+.024	.000	+.023
15. Atlanta, Ga.	—.025	—.053	—.018
16. McCormick, S. C.	+.013	.000	+.018
17. Charleston, S. C.	—.023	—.014	—.014
18. Beaufort, N. C.	—.023	+.006	+.006
19. Charlottesville, Va.	—.015	—.038	—.020
20. Deer Park, Md.	+.008	—.036	+.042
21. Washington, D. C. (Coast and Geodetic Survey Office)	+.035	+.031	+.032
22. Washington, D. C. (Smithsonian Institution)	+.037	+.032	+.033
23. Baltimore, Md.	—.013	—.017	—.014
24. Philadelphia, Pa.	+.020	+.020	+.022
25. Princeton, N. J.	—.021	—.021	—.015
26. Hoboken, N. J.	+.022	+.022	+.023
27. New York, N. Y.	+.020	+.020	+.024
28. Worcester, Mass.	—.022	—.031	—.011
29. Boston, Mass.	+.003	+.007	+.008
30. Cambridge, Mass.	+.003	+.005	+.006
31. Calais, Me.	—.010	—.011	—.007
32. Ithaca, N. Y.	—.025	—.050	—.027
33. Cleveland, Ohio	—.006	—.033	—.012
34. Cincinnati, Ohio	—.021	—.051	—.026
35. Terre Haute, Ind.	—.011	—.033	—.017
36. Chicago, Ill.	—.009	—.029	—.000
37. Madison, Wis.	—.007	—.041	—.011
38. St. Louis, Mo.	—.007	—.031	—.013
39. Kansas City, Mo.	—.018	—.055	—.026
40. Ellsworth, Kans.	+.012	—.046	—.001
41. Wallace, Kans.	—.014	—.122	—.021
42. Colorado Springs, Colo.	—.009	—.205	—.023
43. Pikes Peak, Colo.	+.019	—.221	+.199
44. Denver, Colo.	—.018	—.199	—.040
45. Gunnison, Colo.	+.018	—.246	+.010

Number and name of station	Anomaly		
	New method $(g - g_0 + 0.007)$	Bouguer $(g_0'' - \gamma_0)$	In free air $(g_0 - \gamma_0)$
46. Grand Junction, Colo.	+0.022	—0.175	—0.036
47. Green River, Utah	—.023	—.197	—.073
48. Pleasant Valley Junction, Utah	+.002	—.204	+.019
49. Salt Lake City, Utah	+.008	—.163	—.040
50. Grand Canyon, Wyo.	—.004	—.225	+.027
51. Norris Geyser Basin, Wyo.	+.019	—.194	+.043
52. Lower Geyser Basin, Wyo.	—.003	—.210	+.018
53. Seattle, Wash. (university)	—.095	—.128	—.122
54. San Francisco, Cal.	—.025	+.002	—.013
55. Mount Hamilton, Cal.	—.005	—.014	+.108
56. Seattle, Wash. (high school)	—.095	—.128	—.120
57. Iron River, Mich.	+.026	—.006	+.043
58. Ely, Minn.	+.021	—.027	+.022
59. Pembina, N. Dak.	+.017	—.025	+.001
60. Mitchell, S. Dak.	—.031	—.057	—.014
61. Sweetwater, Tex.	—.031	—.101	—.029
62. Kerrville, Tex.	+.029	—.020	+.035
63. El Paso, Tex.	+.005	—.128	—.001
64. Nogales, Ariz.	—.052	—.149	—.021
65. Yuma, Ariz.	+.007	—.016	—.010
66. Compton, Cal.	—.052	—.058	—.059
67. Goldfield, Nev.	—.015	—.183	+.005
68. Yavapai, Ariz.	—.001	—.179	+.026
69. Grand Canyon, Ariz.	—.012	—.190	—.115
70. Gallup, N. Mex.	—.015	—.228	—.006
71. Las Vegas, N. Mex.	+.001	—.206	+.011
72. Shamrock, Tex.	+.030	—.048	+.030
73. Denison, Tex.	+.003	—.029	—.005
74. Minneapolis, Minn.	+.057	+.017	+.045
75. Lead, S. Dak.	+.050	—.089	+.087
76. Bismarck, N. Dak.	.000	—.069	—.012
77. Hinsdale, Mont.	+.027	—.070	+.003
78. Sandpoint, Idaho	.000	—.122	—.051
79. Boise, Idaho	+.006	—.134	—.043
80. Astoria, Oreg.	—.015	—.014	—.014
81. Sisson, Cal.	—.012	—.120	—.004
82. Rock Springs, Wyo.	+.011	—.206	+.003
83. Paxton, Nebr.	—.006	—.116	—.013
84. Washington, D. C. (Bureau of Standards)	+.035	+.029	+.040
85. North Hero, Vt.	—.001	—.021	—.017
86. Lake Placid, N. Y.	+.004	—.034	+.029
87. Potsdam, N. Y.	+.019	—.006	+.008
88. Wilson, N. Y.	—.012	—.031	—.021
89. Alpena, Mich.	—.022	—.048	—.029

For all of the 89 stations considered as a single group the means are as follows:

	Anomaly		
	New method	Bouguer	In free air
Mean with regard to sign	—0.002	—0.065	—0.001
Mean without regard to sign	.018	.073	.028
Mean with regard to sign *	.000	—.064	+.002
Mean without regard to sign *	.017	.072	.026

* The last two lines of table show the means with the two Seattle stations omitted.

For the 89 stations the mean anomaly without regard to sign for the new method of reduction is about six-tenths as large as for the free-air method of reduction, and is about one-fourth as large as for the Bouguer method.

At 60 stations out of 89 the new-method anomaly is less than the free-air anomaly, and at 3 other stations the two are equal. At 68 stations out of 89 the new-method anomaly is less than the Bouguer anomaly, and at 5 other stations the anomalies of the two methods are equal.

The maximum anomaly by the new method is −0.095 (stations 53 and 56, both at Seattle, Wash.), by the free-air method is +0.199 (station 43, Pikes Peak), and by the Bouguer method −0.246 (station 45, Gunnison, Colo.).

The comparisons and the table on which they are based show clearly that the new method of reduction is a much closer approximation to the truth than either of the older methods.

POSSIBLE RELATIONS OF ANOMALIES TO TOPOGRAPHY.

It is important to know whether the anomalies as determined by the new method of reduction show any relation to the topography. Therefore, in the following tables the 89 stations have been arranged in groups with reference to their relation to the topography.

Sixteen coast stations, in the order of their distance from the 1000-fathom line.

Name and number of station	Distance from 1000-fathom line	Anomaly			Name and number of stations	Distance from 1000-fathom line	Anomaly		
		New method $(g-g_0 +0.007)$	Bouguer $(g_0''-\gamma_0)$	In free air $(g_0-\gamma_0)$			New method $(g-g_0 +0.007)$	Bouguer $(g_0''-\gamma_0)$	In free air $(g_0-\gamma_0)$
	Kilometers					*Kilometers*			
54. San Francisco, Cal.	85	−0.025	+0.002	−0.013	3. Punta Gorda Fla.	280	+0.006	+0.021	+0.021
18. Beaufort, N. C.	95	− .023	+ .006	+ .006	7. Galveston, Tex.	330	− .011	− .011	− .011
80. Astoria, Oreg.	120	− .015	− .014	− .014	29. Boston, Mass	300	+ .003	+ .007	+ .009
1. Key West, Fla.	150	+ .006	+ .031	+ .031	80. Cambridge, Mass.	300	+ .003	+ .005	+ .005
8. Point Isabel, Tex.	160	+ .025	+ .032	+ .033	17. Charleston, S. C.	305	− .023	− .014	− .014
5. New Orleans, La.	210	− .015	− .009	− .009					
4. Apalachicola, Fla	225	− .002	+ .006	+ .006	Mean with regard to sign		− .004	+ .005	+ .005
27. New York, N. Y.	225	+ .020	+ .020	+ .024	Mean without regard to sign		.017	.019	.020
56. Compton, Cal.	230	− .052	− .058	− .059					
26. Hoboken, N. J.	230	+ .022	+ .023	+ .023					
2. West Palm Beach, Fla.	243	+ .016	+ .040	+ .040					

Eighteen stations near the coast, in the order of their distances from the open coast.

Number and name of station	Distance from open coast	Anomaly			Number and name of station	Distance from open coast	Anomaly		
		New method $(g-g_0 +0.007)$	Bouguer $(g_0''-\gamma_0)$	In free air $(g_0-\gamma_0)$			New method $(g-g_0 +0.007)$	Bouguer $(g_0''-\gamma_0)$	In free air $(g_0-\gamma_0)$
	Kilometers					*Kilometers*			
31. Calais, Me.	50	−0.010	−0.011	−0.007	9. Laredo, Tex.	215	−0.022	−0.039	−0.026
25. Princeton, N. J.	60	− .021	− .021	− .015	65. Yuma, Ariz.	220	+ .007	− .016	− .010
23. Baltimore, Md	75	− .013	− .017	− .014	16. McCormick, S. C.	235	+ .013	.000	+ .018
28. Worcester, Mass.	85	− .022	− .031	− .011	10. Austin, Tex. (capitol)	245	− .010	− .038	− .020
24. Philadelphia, Pa.	90	+ .020	+ .020	+ .022	11. Austin, Tex. (university)	245	− .012	− .040	− .020
81. Sisson, Cal.	142	− .012	− .120	− .004	19. Charlottesville, Va.	250	− .015	− .038	− .020
21. Washington, D. C. (Coast and Geodetic Survey Office)	170	+ .035	+ .031	+ .032	32. Ithaca, N. Y.	305	− .025	− .050	− .027
22. Washington, D. C. (Smithsonian Institution)	170	+ .037	+ .032	+ .033	62. Kerrville, Tex.	310	+ .029	− .020	+ .035
84. Washington, D. C. (Bureau of Standards)	175	+ .035	+ .029	+ .040	6. Rayville, La.	325	+ .014	+ .012	+ .015
					Mean with regard to sign		+ .002	− .018	+ .001
					Mean without regard to sign		.020	.031	.020

Twenty-seven stations in the interior of the continent and not in mountainous regions, arranged in the order of elevation.

Number and name of station	Elevation	Anomaly: New method $(g-g_0+0.007)$	Anomaly: Bouguer $(g_0''-\gamma_0)$	Anomaly: In free air $(g_0-\gamma_0)$
	Meters			
88. Wilson, N. Y.	87	−0.012	−0.031	−0.021
13. Little Rock, Ark.	89	+ .028	+ .013	+ .022
87. Potsdam, N. Y.	130	+ .019	− .006	+ .008
35. Terre Haute, Ind.	151	− .011	− .033	− .017
38. St. Louis, Mo.	154	− .007	− .031	− .013
89. Alpena, Mich.	178	− .022	− .049	− .029
36. Chicago, Ill.	182	− .009	− .029	− .009
14. Columbia, Tenn.	207	+ .024	.000	+ .023
33. Cleveland, Ohio	210	− .005	− .033	− .012
73. Denison, Tex.	230	+ .003	− .029	− .006
12. McAlester, Okla.	240	− .029	− .062	− .035
59. Pembina, N. Dak.	243	+ .017	− .025	+ .001
34. Cincinnati, Ohio	245	− .021	− .051	− .026
74. Minneapolis, Minn.	256	+ .057	+ .017	+ .045
37. Madison, Wis.	270	− .007	− .041	− .011
39. Kansas City, Mo.	278	− .018	− .055	− .026
15. Atlanta, Ga.	324	−0.025	−0.053	−0.018
60. Mitchell, S. Dak.	408	− .001	− .057	− .014
58. Ely, Minn.	448	+ .021	− .027	+ .022
57. Iron River, Minn.	458	+ .036	− .008	+ .043
40. Ellsworth, Kans.	469	+ .012	− .046	− .001
76. Bismarck, N. Dak.	516	.000	− .069	− .012
61. Sweetwater, Tex.	655	− .031	− .101	− .029
77. Hinsdale, Mont.	661	+ .027	− .070	+ .003
72. Shamrock, Tex.	708	+ .030	− .048	+ .030
83. Paxton, Nebr.	932	− .008	− .116	− .013
41. Wallace, Kans.	1005	− .014	− .122	− .021
Mean with regard to sign		+ .002	− .043	− .004
Mean without regard to sign		.018	.045	.019

Sixteen stations in mountainous regions and below the general level, arranged in the order of their distances below the general level.

Number and name of station	Average elevation within 100 miles of station minus elevation of station	Elevation of station	Anomaly: New method $(g-g_0+0.007)$	Anomaly: Bouguer $(g_0''-\gamma_0)$	Anomaly: In free air $(g_0-\gamma_0)$
	Meters	*Meters*			
70. Gallup, N. Mex.	30	1900	−0.015	−0.228	−0.008
67. Goldfield, Nev.	112	1716	− .015	− .183	+ .006
85. North Hero, Vt.	167	35	− .001	− .021	− .017
63. El Paso, Tex.	205	1146	+ .005	− .128	− .001
45. Gunnison, Colo.	390	2340	+ .018	− .246	+ .010
82. Rock Springs, Wyo.	379	1910	+ .011	− .208	+ .003
42. Colorado Springs, Colo.	420	1841	− .009	− .205	− .023
49. Salt Lake City, Utah	570	1322	+ .008	− .163	− .040
44. Denver, Colo.	574	1638	− .018	− .199	− .040
79. Boise, Idaho	575	821	+ .006	− .134	− .043
78. Sandpoint, Idaho	588	637	.000	− .122	− .051
69. Grand Canyon, Ariz.	824	849	− .012	− .190	− .115
46. Grand Junction, Colo.	850	1398	+ .022	− .175	− .036
47. Green River, Utah	870	1243	−0.023	−0.197	−0.073
56. Seattle, Wash. (high school)	456	74	− .095	− .128	− .120
53. Seattle, Wash. (university)	472	58	− .095	− .128	− .122
Mean with regard to sign			− .013	− .166	− .042
Mean without regard to sign			.022	.166	.044
After rejecting the two Seattle stations, No. 56 and No. 53: Mean with regard to sign			− .002	− .171	− .031
Mean without regard to sign			.012	.171	.033

Twelve stations in mountainous regions and above the general level, arranged in the order of their distance above the general level.

Number and name of station	Elevation of station minus average elevation within 100 miles	Elevation of station	Anomaly: New method $(g-g_0+0.007)$	Anomaly: Bouguer $(g_0''-\gamma_0)$	Anomaly: In free air $(g_0-\gamma_0)$
	Meters	*Meters*			
71. Las Vegas, N. Mex.	18	1960	+0.001	−0.206	+0.011
52. Lower Geyser Basin, Wyo.	63	2200	− .003	− .210	+ .018
51. Norris Geyser Basin, Wyo.	139	2276	+ .019	− .194	+ .043
48. Pleasant Valley Junction, Utah	147	2191	+ .002	− .204	+ .019
50. Grand Canyon, Wyo.	249	2386	− .004	− .225	+ .027
64. Nogales, Ariz.	288	1181	− .052	− .149	− .021
20. Deer Park, Md.	291	770	+ .008	− .036	+ .042
86. Lake Placid, N. Y.	306	571	+ .004	− .034	+ .029
75. Lead, S. Dak.	468	1590	+0.050	−0.089	+0.087
68. Yavapai, Ariz.	512	2179	− .001	− .179	+ .028
55. Mount Hamilton, Cal.	1202	1282	− .005	− .014	+ .108
43. Pikes Peak, Colo.	2035	4293	+ .019	− .221	+ .199
Mean with regard to sign			+ .003	− .147	+ .049
Mean without regard to sign			.014	.147	.052

This particular method of separating the stations into five groups has been chosen in order to show clearly whether for these stations there is any perceptible relation between the anomalies by the new method and the topography, and because it was desired especially to ascertain whether the particular relations known to exist between the anomalies by the two older methods of reduction and the topography still persist when the new method is employed.

In all that follows the comments are made, unless otherwise stated, upon the figures as they stand after the two Seattle stations (Nos. 53 and 56) have been omitted. No conclusions would be changed, however, by including these stations.

As shown on page 76, the mean without regard to sign of the new-method anomalies is 0.017 for the 87 stations. For the five separate groups, as shown in the preceding tables, the corresponding means are 0.017, 0.020, 0.018, 0.012, and 0.014, of which no one is much above the general mean for all.

The means with regard to sign for the five groups are: -0.004, $+0.002$, $+0.002$, -0.002, $+0.003$. The probable error of a single value being ±0.014, as shown on page 75, the probable error of the mean of each of the first three groups is ±0.003 and of each of the last two groups is ±0.004. In every group except the first, therefore, the mean is smaller than its own probable error, a strong proof that there are no systematic errors peculiar to each group.

Within each group the writers find no tendency to a progressive change in passing down the column of new anomalies. In other words, in the first group the anomalies show no relation to the distance from the 1000-fathom line, in the second group no relation to the distance from the open coast, in the third group no relation to the elevation, and in the fourth and fifth groups no relation to the distance below or above the general level of the surrounding country. In the fourth and fifth groups a rearrangement in order of elevations, not here shown, indicated no apparent relation between anomalies by the new method and elevations.

The general conclusion from the examination is that the anomalies by the new method, of which the mean without regard to sign is only 0.017, show no relation to the topography either in sign or average magnitude. This shows that in general the effects of the topography and its compensation have been fully and correctly taken into account in the new method of computation and that the remaining anomalies are due to some cause or causes having no fixed relation to topography.

In considering small anomalies by the new method it should be remembered that the errors of observation and computation may frequently exceed 0.004 dyne and may be as great as 0.010 dyne in rare cases.

For these same 89 stations it is shown on the following pages that the Bouguer and free-air anomalies show the definite relations to the topography which have frequently been noted in connection with them.

COMPARISON OF BOUGUER ANOMALIES WITH NEW-METHOD ANOMALIES.

The mean of the Bouguer anomalies without regard to sign is 0.072. (See p. 76.) For the separate groups in the preceding tables the corresponding means are 0.019, 0.031, 0.045, 0.171, and 0.147. The last two means, for stations in mountainous country, are excessively large. Although the mean for all stations by the Bouguer method, 0.072, is four and one-fourth times the corresponding mean for the new method, 0.017, yet for the first two groups, stations on the coast and stations near the coast, the Bouguer means, 0.019 and 0.031, are but little larger than by the new method. It is important to note that the stations in these two groups have small elevations.

The mean of the Bouguer anomalies with regard to sign is -0.064 for all stations (see p. 76) and for the separate groups is $+0.005$, -0.018, -0.043, -0.171, and -0.147, showing a wide divergence between groups. This divergence shows the general tendency for the anomalies computed by this method to be negative, and larger the greater the elevation of the station, the groups being arranged in the order of the mean elevations. Even within some of the separate groups this relation of Bouguer anomalies to elevations is evident. For example, in the third group the mean anomaly for the first seven stations, all of which are at elevations less than 200 meters, is − 0.024, for the next 14, at each of which the elevation is between 200 and 500 meters, the mean anomaly is − 0.033, and for the last 6 stations, at each of which the elevation is more than 500 meters, the mean anomaly is − 0.088. In the fourth group the mean anomaly for the 8 stations at elevations less than 1400 meters is − 0.141 and for the remaining 6 at greater elevations the mean is − 0.212. In the fifth group the mean anomaly for the 6 stations at elevations less than 2000 meters is − 0.076, and for the 6 stations of greater elevation is − 0.205.

In short, the Bouguer anomalies show a definite relation to the topography, being in general negative and larger the greater the elevation of the station, whereas the new-method anomalies show no relation to the topography; the Bouguer anomalies are four and one-fourth times as large on an average as the new-method anomalies; and if the comparison be limited to stations in mountainous regions, the fourth and fifth groups, the Bouguer anomalies are twelve times as large as the new-method anomalies (without regard to sign). This is clear and positive proof that the new method of computation is a much closer approximation to the truth than the Bouguer method.

COMPARISON OF FREE-AIR ANOMALIES WITH NEW-METHOD ANOMALIES.

· The means without regard to sign of the free-air anomalies are 0.020, 0.020, and 0.019 for the first, second, and third groups, respectively (pp. 77 and 78), being in each case but little greater than the corresponding mean of the new-method anomaly, 0.017, 0.020, or 0.018. On the other hand, in the fourth group the mean without regard to sign is 0.033 for the free-air method in contrast with 0.012 for the new method, and in the fifth group it is 0.052 in sharp contrast with 0.014 for the new method. In other words, although there is little difference in the average magnitude of these two kinds of anomalies at the coast and plains stations of the first three groups, the new-method anomalies are less than one-third as large on an average as the free-air method anomalies for the stations in mountainous regions comprised in the last two groups.

Even in the first three groups a clear advantage of the new method over the free-air method is shown; for in the first group the new-method anomaly is smaller than the free-air anomaly at 10 stations out of 16, in the second group at 12 stations out of 18, and in the third group·at 16 stations out of 27.

The mean of the free-air anomalies with regard to sign is + 0.002 for all stations, and for the separate groups is + 0.005 for the coast stations, + 0.001 for the stations near the coast, − 0.004 for the interior stations not in mountainous regions, − 0.031 for the stations in mountainous regions and below the general level, and + 0.049 for stations in mountainous regions and above the general level. These means show faintly the well-known contrast by this method between coast stations and low inland stations. They also show very strongly the well-known contrast by this method between stations below and stations above the general level in mountainous regions.* The farther the station is below the general level the larger the negative anomaly tends to be by this method, and the farther the station is above the general level the larger the positive anomaly tends to be, as may be seen by examining the fourth and fifth groups in detail. In the fourth group the mean is − 0.004 for the first 7 stations, all less than 500 meters below the general level, and − 0.057 for the remaining 7 stations, all more than 500 meters below the general level. Similarly, in the fifth group the mean is + 0.024 for the first 5 stations, all less than 250 meters above the general level, and + 0.067 for the remaining 7 stations all more than 250 meters above. Neither this relation nor the tendency for coast stations to have positive anomalies appears in the new-method anomalies.

---

* See p. 25 of Appendix 1 of the Coast and Geodetic Survey Report for 1894, "Relative determinations of gravity with half-second pendulums," by G. R. Putnam.

TEST BY STATIONS NOT IN THE UNITED STATES.

The evidence from 89 stations in the United States has been supplemented by applying the new method of reduction to a few selected determinations of gravity at other stations. For this additional test the stations selected have been, as a rule, those for which the older methods of reduction gave unusually large apparent anomalies.

In the following tables the quantities have the same meanings as in the preceding tables for stations in the United States.

The observed value of gravity at the Japanese station was taken from a printed leaflet received from Prof. H. Nagaoka in 1909. The remaining observed values of gravity have been taken unchanged from the reports of the International Geodetic Association and from the report in 1910 by Dr. O. Hecker on determinations of gravity at sea.[*]

For Hecker's observations at sea the Bouguer reduction has been computed by the formula $+\dfrac{2gD}{r}\dfrac{3(\delta-1.03)}{4\Delta}$ in which D is the depth of water at the station. For those stations the reduction in free air has been assumed to be zero.

The computations of the corrections for topography and compensation given in the following table may be improved in some cases by the use of better and more complete maps than were available to the writers when the computations were made:

General summary for gravity stations not in the United States.

Number and name of station	Elevation H	ϕ	λ	Correction for topography and compensation	Anomaly		
					New method $(g-g_0 +0.007)$	Bouguer $(g_0''-r_0)$	In free air (g_0-r_0)
1. Between Honolulu and San Francisco, Hecker, at sea, depth 5100 meters	*Meters* 0	28 10	146 35	+0.004	−0.007	+0.336	−0.010
2. Tonga Plateau, Hecker, at sea, depth 2700 meters	0	−28 20	178 27	+ .016	+ .255	+ .447	+ .264
3. Tonga Plateau, Hecker, at sea, depth 2700 meters	0	−27 15	177 40	+ .019	+ .149	+ .344	+ .161
4. Tonga Deep, Hecker, at sea, depth 6500 meters	0	−22 07	174 13	− .082	− .184	+ .167	− .273
5. Tonga Deep, Hecker, at sea, depth 8500 meters	0	−17 09	171 42	− .078	− .160	+ .331	− .245
6. Near Hawaiian Islands, Hecker, at sea, depth 4000 meters	0	22 50	160 23	+ .019	+ .060	+ .333	+ .062
7. Near Oahu, Hecker, at sea, depth 1700 meters	0	21 17	156 17	+ .078	+ .233	+ .419	+ .304
8. Honolulu	6	21 18.1	157 51.8	+ .162	+ .062	+ .206	+ .207
9. Mauna Kea, Hawaiian Islands	3981	19 49.2	155 28.8	+ .469	+ .183	+ .253	+ .645
10. Hachinohe, Japan	21	40 31	141 30	+ .049	+ .110	+ .150	+ .152
11. St. Georges, Bermuda Islands	2	32 21	64 40	+ .218	+ .018	+ .229	+ .229
12. Jamestown, St. Helena	10	−15 55	5 43.7	+ .177	+ .058	+ .227	+ .228
13. Sörvaagen, Norway	19	67 53.6	13 02	+ .016	+ .146	+ .153	+ .155
14. Kala-i-Chumb, Turkestan	1345	38 27.3	70 46.5	− .086	− .053	− .295	− .146
15. Gornergrat, Switzerland	3016	45 59.0	−7 46.8	+ .165	+ .049	− .110	+ .207
16. St. Maurice, Switzerland	419	46 13.0	−7 00.2	− .091	+ .003	− .116	− .094
Mean with regard to sign, all stations					+ .056	+ .192	+ .115
Mean without regard to sign, all stations					.107	.257	.211
Mean with regard to sign for the seven stations at sea					+ .048	+ .340	+ .038
Mean without regard to sign for the seven stations at sea					.148	.340	.188
Mean with regard to sign for the nine stations on land					+ .063	+ .077	+ .176
Mean without regard to sign for the nine stations on land					.075	.193	.229

For these 16 stations the mean anomaly without regard to sign for the new method of reduction is about one-half as large as for the free-air method of reduction, and four-tenths as large as for the Bouguer method. There is no station at which the anomaly by the new method is larger than by the free-air method. There is only one station, No. 4, the first of the Tonga Deep stations, at which the anomaly by the new method is larger than by the Bouguer method.

The mean anomaly without regard to sign for the new method of reduction is much larger at these 16 stations (0.107) than for the 89 United States stations (0.018). This indicates that in selecting foreign stations at which the apparent anomalies by the older methods of reduction are unusually large there has been a decided tendency to secure abnormal stations.

In the preceding table the mean anomaly without regard to sign for the new method of reduction is much larger for the seven stations at sea (0.148) than for the nine stations on land (0.075).

* Bestimmung der Schwerkraft auf dem Schwarzen Meere und an dessen Küste sowie neue Ausgleichung der Schwerkraftsmessungen auf dem Atlantischen Indischen und Grossen Ozean mit vier Tafeln von Prof. Dr. O. Hecker, pp. 150-158.

15593°—12——6

Possibly this is due to the greater difficulties encountered at sea than on land in making the gravity observations.

The first station of the table, between Honolulu and San Francisco, is typical of stations far from land and over a part of the ocean bottom which is nearly level. The correction for topography and compensation is very small, +0.004 dyne. The anomaly is also small, −0.007 dyne.

At the two stations over the Tonga Plateau and two over the Tonga Deep (Nos. 2–5) though the anomalies by the new method are clearly much smaller upon an average than by the two older methods, yet they are so large as to indicate a considerable departure from perfect isostatic compensation within the depth, 113.7 kilometers.

At the two stations near the Hawaiian Islands and at the two stations on these islands (Nos. 6–9) the anomalies by the new method all have the plus sign, indicating an excess of gravity, but in each case they are clearly smaller than the apparent anomalies by the older methods.

At Hachinohe, Japan (No. 10), the anomaly by the new method is seven-tenths as large as by the older methods and indicates an excess of gravity.

In marked contrast to the two stations on the Hawaiian Islands and the Japanese station (Nos. 8–10), in regions in which vulcanism has been active in recent geologic times, and at which there is a comparatively large excess of gravity in each case, note the small anomalies by the new method at the Bermuda Islands (+0.018) and at St. Helena Island (+0.058) (Nos. 11 and 12). These are small excesses only, though the stations are on small oceanic islands. At these two stations the apparent anomalies by the older methods of reduction are nearly +0.230 dyne, large apparent excesses, which correspond to the general experience with these methods of reduction when applied to stations on small oceanic islands.

At the Norway station (No. 13) the new reduction shows but a slight advantage over the older reductions.

At the selected station in Turkestan (No. 14) the anomaly by the new method is only −0.053, 0.093 less than by the free-air method of reduction. This station, at an elevation of 1345 meters, is in the midst of a group of 28 stations in this region, at a mean elevation of 1320 meters, recently mentioned by Dr. Helmert* as having an average apparent negative anomaly by the free-air method of reduction of 0.106 dyne. If the new method of reduction were applied to all of these 28 stations, it is reasonably certain that all of the anomalies would be reduced, and if the apparent anomalies were reduced on an average by 0.093 dyne (the reduction of anomaly at station No. 14), then the mean anomaly for the group would be −0.013 dyne instead of −0.106 dyne, as given by Dr. Helmert.

At Gornergrat and St. Maurice in Switzerland (Nos. 15 and 16) the new method of reduction shows anomalies much smaller than either of the older methods.†

At Gornergrat (No. 15), the anomaly by the new method +0.049 corresponds to an excess of mass beneath the station. Since the computations were made it has come to the attention of the writers that the density of the mountain upon which this station stands has been estimated from geological evidence to be 2.73,‡ 0.06, or nearly one-fortieth part greater than that assumed in making the computations, namely, 2.67. The geologic evidence thus corroborates that given by the gravity observations reduced by the new method.

In connection with this test by 16 stations outside the United States it is important to note the general relation of each of the stations to the surrounding topography.

---

* Unvollkommenheiten im Gleichgewichtszustande der Erdkruste von F. R. Helmert, Sitzungsberichte der Königlich Preussischen Akademie der Wissenschaften, 1908, XLIV, Sitzung der Physikalisch-Mathematischen Classe vom 5, November, p. 1066.

† In the Proces-Verbal de la 56me Seance de la Commission Géodésique Suisse tenue au Palais Fédéral a Berne le 30 Avril 1910, p. 47, there is printed a table which shows that for 13 stations in Switzerland, including St. Maurice and Gornergrat, the new-method anomaly is in every case less than the Bouguer anomaly, being upon an average less than one-fifth as large as the Bouguer anomaly. Pages 48–49 of the Proces-Verbal should be consulted in connection with the table on p. 47, as the conclusions drawn are not those which one might expect from a study of the table alone.

‡ Astronomisch-geodätische Arbeiten in der Schweiz herausgegeben von der Schweizerischen geodätischen Kommission, Zwölfter Band Schwerebestimmungen in den Jahren 1900–1907. p. 43.

Station No. 1, between San Francisco and Honolulu, is far from the land, over a deep part of the ocean, where the bottom is nearly level to a great distance from the station.

Stations Nos. 2 and 3 are over moderate depths in the ocean and not far from the Tonga Deep, one of the most remarkable of the deep areas found in the oceans. Stations Nos. 4 and 5 are over the Tonga Deep, the sounding at the latter station being 8500 meters, a depth exceeded in but few places on the earth.

Station No. 6, near the Hawaiian Islands, is over deep water, 4000 meters, but near to shallow water, and No. 7 is over shallow water of moderate depth, 1700 meters, with great depths not far away in one direction and with land near in another direction.

The observations at these seven stations were all made upon a ship at sea.

Station No. 8, Honolulu, is at the coast of an oceanic island on which there are high, steep mountains and which is surrounded on all sides to a great distance by a deep ocean. Station No. 9, Mauna Kea, is on a similar island at the top of a very high mountain, at an elevation of 3981 meters.

Station No. 10, Hachinohe, Japan, is near the coast of a large island near which there is a steep submarine slope from the coast to great depths.

Stations Nos. 11 and 12 are both on small oceanic islands surrounded by water of great depth, a type of location in which one is reasonably certain to find a large excess of gravity by the older methods of computation.

Station No. 13 is on one of the Lofoden Islands about 80 kilometers from a steep part of the coast of Norway. The 1000-fathom curve lies about 130 kilometers to the northwestward of this station.

Station No. 14 is on one of the extensive, high plateaus of the world.

Stations Nos. 15 and 16 are both in the Alps, in the midst of some of the most rugged topography in the world. From among the many gravity stations available in the Alps these two were chosen as extremes. Gornergrat, No. 15, is one of the highest available stations, standing on a prominent summit. St. Maurice, No. 16, on the other hand, is near the bottom of a very deep valley and is, therefore, far below the general level of the surrounding country.

The 16 stations bear widely differing relations to the topography surrounding them.

At these 16 widely scattered stations, located in various relations to the topography, the anomalies by the new method of computation are much smaller on an average than by either of the older methods of reduction, just as was found to be the case for the 89 stations in the United States. In consequence of this it seems to the writers that it is safe to extend the conclusions drawn for the United States to the whole world. The writers are, therefore, confident that if the new method of reduction is applied to a considerable number of stations in any part of the world, it will show apparent anomalies which are smaller than those computed by either of the two older methods and thereby show that as a rule, the world over, it is a close approximation to the truth to state that the isostatic compensation is complete and uniformly distributed to a depth of about 114 kilometers.

The following table shows some of the details of the computations at the 16 stations outside the United States. The table is directly comparable with the one printed on pages 54–58, and the explanation given for that table applies to this one as well. The values in the tables are all expressed in units of the fourth decimal place in dynes.

Correction for topography and isostatic compensation, separate zones.

[Stations not in the United States.]

Zone	Between Honolulu and San Francisco, No. 1	Tonga Plateau, No. 2	Tonga Plateau, No. 3	Tonga Deep, No. 4	Tonga Deep, No. 5	Near Hawaiian Islands, No. 6	Near Oahu, No. 7	Honolulu, No. 8	Mauna Kea, No. 9	Hachinohe, Japan No. 10	St. Georges, Bermuda, No. 11	Jamestown, St. Helena Island, No. 12	Sörvaagen, Norway, No. 13	Kala-i-Chumb, Turkestan, No. 14	Gornergrat, Switzerland, No. 15	St. Maurice, Switzerland, No. 16
A	− 1	− 1	− 1	− 1	− 1	− 1	− 1	+ 2	+ 2	+ 2	+ 2	+ 2	+ 1	+ 2	+ 2	+ 2
B	− 44	− 40	− 40	− 44	− 44	− 44	− 40	0	+ 72	+ 16	− 2	+ 8	+ 16	+ 68	+ 64	+ 64
C	−104	−100	−100	−108	−108	−104	−100	0	+ 168	+ 4	0	− 5	+ 4	+156	+ 160	+120
D	−222	−204	−204	−228	−234	−210	−180	0	+ 342	0	0	− 17	0	+282	+ 311	+114
E	−376	−312	−312	−408	−424	−344	−232	0	+ 568	0	0	− 8	0	+328	+ 487	+ 58
F	−440	−300	−300	−500	−540	−390	−180	0	+ 625	0	0	− 7	0	+220	+ 508	+ 16
G	−408	−204	−204	−492	−552	−324	−113	0	+ 523	0	0	0	0	+120	+ 371	− 21
H	−368	−144	−144	−464	−592	−272	− 50	+ 1	+ 429	0	0	0	0	+ 64	+ 289	− 50
I	−360	−120	−120	−505	−720	−240	− 72	0	+ 376	0	0	0	0	+ 40	+ 212	− 88
J	−176	− 32	− 32	−296	−464	− 96	− 6	+ 3	+ 160	− 1	+ 5	− 2	0	0	+ 73	− 72
K	− 60	+ 20	+ 20	−152	−300	− 20	+ 16	+ 5	+ 73	− 5	+ 8	+ 5	0	−105	− 9	−105
L	+ 96	+ 96	+ 96	+ 45	− 24	+ 96	+ 50	+ 6	− 21	− 8	+ 55	+ 37	0	−183	− 97	−139
M	+448	+266	+266	+490	+560	+384	+167	+ 101	− 59	− 3	+ 277	+ 260	+ 1	−484	− 246	−327
N	+478	+215	+242	+526	+668	+379	+270	+ 253	+ 153	+ 22	+ 397	+ 328	+ 3	−382	− 217	−236
O	+504	+254	+246	+463	+584	+370	+327	+ 344	+ 340	+ 35	+ 451	+ 362	+ 14	−391	− 160	−151
18	+105	+ 51	+ 55	+ 91	+106	+ 53	+ 79	+ 77	+ 72	+ 20	+ 97	+ 74	+ 6	− 75	− 32	− 23
17	+105	+ 51	+ 58	+ 89	+101	+ 86	+ 81	+ 83	+ 75	+ 25	+ 97	+ 77	+ 6	− 75	− 31	− 25
16	+106	+ 58	+ 65	+ 85	+100	+ 89	+ 86	+ 80	+ 82	+ 32	+ 101	+ 79	+ 7	− 70	− 23	− 28
15	+106	+ 69	+ 70	+ 80	+ 90	+ 88	+ 82	+ 74	+ 82	+ 39	+ 101	+ 81	+ 8	− 75	− 17	− 27
14	+107	+ 75	+ 75	+ 78	+ 83	+ 90	+ 77	+ 73	+ 84	+ 42	+ 101	+ 85	+ 8	− 77	− 11	− 15
13	+166	+123	+132	+123	+113	+174	+138	+ 138	+ 156	+ 73	+ 168	+ 126	+ 18	−107	− 11	− 9
12	+105	+ 85	+ 82	+ 76	+ 83	+108	+ 97	+ 96	+ 102	+ 50	+ 108	+ 78	+ 14	− 51	− 6	− 7
11	+ 84	+ 69	+ 68	+ 66	+ 65	+ 83	+ 81	+ 81	+ 82	+ 46	+ 86	+ 65	+ 13	− 35	+ 3	− 2
10	+ 59	+ 51	+ 51	+ 50	+ 49	+ 60	+ 60	+ 64	+ 62	+ 29	+ 56	+ 46	+ 9	− 28	− 1	− 1
9	+ 38	+ 32	+ 32	+ 33	+ 34	+ 40	+ 41	+ 36	+ 38	+ 16	+ 27	+ 32	+ 2	− 14	+ 3	+ 3
8	+ 37	+ 30	+ 30	+ 29	+ 28	+ 42	+ 40	+ 38	+ 40	+ 17	+ 18	+ 26	+ 4	− 11	+ 8	+ 8
7	+ 19	+ 15	+ 15	+ 13	+ 15	+ 21	+ 20	+ 19	+ 20	+ 8	+ 8	+ 7	+ 1	− 2	+ 5	+ 5
6	+ 18	+ 18	+ 18	+ 17	+ 16	+ 18	+ 18	+ 18	+ 18	+ 9	+ 7	+ 8	+ 4	+ 3	+ 4	+ 4
5	+ 10	+ 11	+ 11	+ 11	+ 11	+ 10	+ 10	+ 10	+ 10	+ 3	+ 3	+ 7	+ 4	+ 3	+ 1	+ 1
4	+ 6	+ 8	+ 8	+ 8	+ 8	+ 5	+ 5	+ 5	+ 5	+ 5	+ 5	+ 6	+ 3	+ 5	+ 3	+ 3
3	+ 4	+ 3	+ 3	+ 3	+ 3	+ 4	+ 4	+ 4	+ 4	+ 6	+ 3	+ 4	+ 4	+ 7	+ 4	+ 4
2	+ 4	+ 2	+ 2	+ 2	+ 2	+ 4	+ 4	+ 4	+ 4	+ 5	+ 4	+ 3	+ 4	+ 4	+ 5	+ 5
1	0	0	0	0	0	0	0	0	0	+ 1	+ 1	+ 1	+ 1	+ 1	+ 1	+ 1
Total	+ 43	+155	+188	−818	−784	+189	+779	+1615	+4687	+488	+2183	+1786	+156	−862	+1653	−914

Note that for the ocean stations, Nos. 1 to 7, there is in each case but one change of sign as successive zones are considered, namely, the change of sign due to distance. The water compartments predominate in their effects in every zone.

At station No. 1, over a deep part of the ocean where the bottom is nearly level to a great distance from the station, the positive corrections beyond the change of sign due to distance have nearly the same aggregate as the negative corrections before the change of sign, and, therefore, the total correction for topography and compensation is small. At stations Nos. 2 and 3, near the Tonga Deep, this balance of positive and negative corrections is slightly disturbed in one sense—the positive correction predominates; and at stations Nos. 4 and 5, over the Tonga Deep, the balance is greatly disturbed in the opposite sense, the negative corrections being largely in excess. These are probably typical cases.

Note that stations Nos. 6 to 9 constitute a progressive series of four in relation to topography. No. 6 is over deep water near an oceanic island, No. 7 over water of moderate depth nearer to the oceanic island, No. 8 near sea level on the coast of a high oceanic island, and No. 9 on a high summit of such an island. Note that the corrections for topography and compensation stand in order, namely, $+0.019$, $+0.078$, $+0.162$, and $+0.469$. A comparison of values for corresponding zones in the preceding table for these four stations will indicate the manner in which the positive corrections gradually gain predominance as the station is made to approach from deep water to the summit of an oceanic island. While making this comparison it will be well to consult pages 65–71 in regard to the change of sign due to distance. .

Stations Nos. 11 and 12 are like station No. 8 in being near sea level on the shore of an oceanic island surrounded by deep water. Note the resemblance between these three stations as to the correction for separate zones. In each case the sum of the corrections out to zone L is small, but beyond that large positive corrections appear and the total correction for each station is positive and large, corresponding to the known fact that large values of gravity are ordinarily observed in such a location.

Station No. 13 is remarkable for having unusually small corrections in every zone—all positive.

Station No. 14 shows a succession of values characteristic of stations on a high plateau far from any ocean. The large positive corrections for near zones are more than offset by still larger and more numerous negative corrections beyond the change of sign due to distance, which occurs at zone J, and the total correction is, therefore, large and negative. The very large negative values in zones K to O are due to the fact that the high plateau extends far enough from the station to fill these zones. The negative corrections are numerous because, the station being far from the nearest ocean, the water effects do not predominate and positive corrections do not appear again until a very large zone is reached, namely, No. 6, of which the inner radius is 2900 kilometers.

A comparison in detail of the corrections for separate zones at stations Nos. 15 and 16 will show why the corrections for topography and compensation tend to be large and positive for a station above the general level in a mountainous country and negative for a station far below the general level in the same region. Note that the positive corrections for small zones are much smaller at station No. 16 at the bottom of one of the deep valleys than at station No. 15 on a high summit of the Alps, and that the change of sign due to distance occurs before zone G at No. 16 and after zone J at No. 15. These two differences between the two stations are due largely to the effect of corrections due to the differences of elevation of the station and the zone ("station below compartment" and "station above compartment") shown in the reduction tables on pages 30–43. Consult especially the reduction table for zone G on page 35 in connection with the correction for zone G at these two stations. It will also be noted that for the same reason the negative corrections, beyond the change of sign due to distance and before the water effects begin to predominate, are larger for corresponding zones at station No. 16 as a rule. This is especially noticeable for zones K, L, M, and N.

DISCUSSION OF ERRORS.

As the methods of computation used in this investigation are novel in many respects, it is important to consider the accuracy of each part of the process. As it has been stated that the desirability of selecting such methods as would give the required results with the minimum expenditure of time has been continually kept in mind, it may seem probable that this close attention to the economics of the problem has diverted attention from the requirements of the problem as to accuracy.

Throughout the investigation very close attention has been paid at every step to insuring the maintenance of the required degree of accuracy. It is not feasible within the allowed limit of length of this publication, and without printing all the details of the computation, to put before the reader all the evidence which has been considered by the writers in estimating the magnitude of errors from various sources. The discussion of errors which follows serves, however, to show in a general way the methods by which the estimates of error were made and to put the estimates on record for future reference and for reexamination by others.

Let it be assumed for the moment that the purpose of the present investigation is to compute the value of gravity at each observation station by taking adequately into account the effect of every portion of the earth's mass in producing an attraction at the station. In order to accomplish this the computation must take into account adequately all the facts as to the shape of the earth's surface (its topography) and all the facts as to density at all points within the earth. These two sets of facts serve to locate with reference to the station every portion of the attracting mass.

If this be considered the true purpose of the investigation, the real measures of the total errors made in the attempt are the residuals of the attempt, namely, the apparent anomalies by the new method shown in the table on page 74. Each anomaly is the difference between the computed value of the attraction upon a unit mass (1 gram) at the station and the directly observed value of that attraction. The degree of accuracy attained may be expressed by saying that the largest anomaly is −0.095 dyne (at stations Nos. 53 and 56, Seattle, Wash.), that the mean anomaly without regard to sign is 0.017 (p. 76), and that as computed from these anomalies considered as errors the probable error of the result at a single station is ±0.014 (p. 75).*

The total error, as defined above, the apparent anomaly at each station, is the aggregate of errors of three different classes. The first class comprises the errors in the observed value of the attraction at the station. The second class includes all errors in the computed values of the attraction at the station. Among these are errors due to numerical inaccuracy in the computations, due to errors of approximation in the formulæ used, and errors due to the faults and incompleteness of the maps which were used. The third class includes such errors as are due to the difference between the actual arrangement of density in the earth and the arrangement which has been assumed. The assumed distribution of densities is that fixed by the statement that under every part of the earth's surface the isostatic compensation is complete and uniformly distributed with respect to depth down to a limiting depth of 113.7 kilometers (p. 10).

The purpose of this discussion is to give the reader an estimate of the probable average magnitude of the errors of the first and second classes and to compare this with the total error as expressed by the anomalies, thereby securing an estimate of the magnitude of the errors of the third class. From this point of view the errors of the third class are the portions of the apparent anomalies which may not be accounted for as due to errors of the first or second class. The smaller the errors of this third class are found to be the more nearly the assumed distribution of densities agrees with the actual. The errors of this class furnish a good basis for further investigation as to the actual distribution of densities in the earth.

---

* This mean and probable error are based upon the anomalies at 87 stations in the United States, the two stations Nos. 53 and 56, at Seattle, Wash., being rejected.

ERRORS OF OBSERVATION.

The half-second pendulums, described in Appendix 15, Coast and Geodetic Survey Report for 1891, were used in the relative determination of gravity at each of the 89 stations in the United States used in this investigation.   The observations were made during seasons of less than 6 months each, and the pendulums were standardized at the base station (in the basement of the office of the Coast and Geodetic Survey at Washington) both before and after each season. Three pendulums constituted a set, each pendulum being swung through at least two periods of approximately eight hours each in determining the intensity of gravity at a station or while obtaining the periods of the pendulums at the base stations.   The necessary time observations were made with a portable astronomical transit set up in the vicinity of the gravity station. The apparatus was used during standardizations in the same manner as in the field.

The following table shows the magnitude of the probable errors of the relative intensity of gravity at 85 of the stations in the United States used in this investigation.   The stations for which no probable errors were computed are the base stations, the Smithsonian Institution, Washington, D. C., Baltimore, and Seattle University.

Stations	Probable error, in dynes
8	±0. 003
14	± . 002
58	± . 001
5	. 000
Average	± . 0013

The probable errors shown above are those due to the accidental errors made at the stations in the field.   Let it be assumed that the accidental errors in obtaining the mean periods at Washington from the standardizations of the pendulums are approximately equal to the probable errors in the field means.   Then the total probable error for a station may be considered as a combination of the probable error of the standardization and the probable error of the field station.   On this assumption the maximum probable error is ±0.004, and the average probable error is ±0.0018 for the mean result at any station.   The actual error is probably at no station more than four times the average probable error, or 0.0072 dyne, and the average actual error is much lower than that.   It is believed that the assumption stated above tends to give estimates which are too large rather than too small.

The following special statement is necessary for the seven stations, Ely, Pembina, Mitchell Lake Placid, Potsdam, Wilson, and Alpena.   Upon the return of the gravity party to the base station, in November, 1909, after having observed at these stations, it was found that the period of each of the three pendulums used during the season had considerably shortened.   After having made two complete determinations of the periods a very thin film of foreign substance was discovered on the supporting plane of each of the three pendulums.   Upon the removal of this substance the pendulums resumed their former periods.   In addition to the stations mentioned above, North Hero and Iron River were occupied while the pendulums were probably affected by the foreign substance on the planes.   These two stations were reoccupied during a subsequent season, and the values obtained for the intensity of gravity agreed closely with those obtained during the first occupation of those stations, provided it was assumed that the foreign substance affected the periods of the pendulums to the same extent at those stations as during the first determination of the periods at Washington in November.   North Hero and Iron River were considered as base stations in determining the value of the intensity of gravity at Lake Placid, Potsdam, Wilson, and Alpena, which stations had been occupied after North Hero and before Iron River.   Iron River and Washington were considered as base stations for Ely, Pembina, and Mitchell, these three stations having been occupied after Iron River and just before the return to Washington after the close of the season.   The intensity of gravity used for North Hero and Iron

River was that determined during the reoccupation of those stations in 1910, and the value of the period at the base station was that determined by the first standardization after the close of the season in 1909.

The periods for the first and second occupation of North Hero differed by 0.0000057 second, while at Iron River they differed by 0.0000042 second, and at the base station the difference between the period given by the first standardization in November, 1909, and the mean period of the two standardizations in May and October, 1910, was 0.0000033 second. This seems to indicate that the effect of the foreign substance on the periods at the stations between North Hero and the base station gradually decreased during the season between July and November, 1909. If the error in the adopted mean period at any of these stations is as much as 0.000 002 5 second, then the error in the value of the intensity of gravity at the stations from this cause is 0.010 dyne. If a similar error was made at one of the base stations (North Hero, Iron River, or Washington), the error due to this cause is 0.005 dyne. Hence, it is possible that there may be errors as great as 0.015 dyne in the adopted values of the intensity of gravity at the stations Lake Placid, Potsdam, Wilson, Alpena, Ely, Pembina, and Mitchell. It is believed, however, that the actual error for each of those stations from all causes is less than 0.010 dyne.

In general the pendulums show approximately the same period at the base station in Washington during successive standardizations. There is given below a table showing the mean period of the three pendulums forming the "A" set for the base station:

Date of standardization	Period in seconds
Jan., 1909	0. 500 707 5
June, 1909	. 500 707 7
Dec., 1909	. 500 706 4
May, 1910	. 500 705 7
Oct., 1910	. 500 707 0
Mean	. 500 706 9

It was assumed in each case that the pendulums were in normal condition. The values obtained at the base stations in November, 1909, were not included in this table, on account of the presence of foreign substance on the planes in the heads of the pendulums during those standardizations. For the gravity work done during the years 1909 and 1910, the period adopted for the base station in reducing a season's work (except the season between July and November, 1909) was the mean of the periods obtained at the beginning and at the end of the season.

ERRORS OF COMPUTATION.

The first step in computing the attraction at a' station was to compute by the Helmert formula of 1901 the attraction γ_0, at a point on an ideal earth at sea level in the same latitude as the actual station. The ideal earth referred to is one having the same size and shape as the ellipsoid of revolution which most nearly coincides with the sea-level surface of the real earth, and having no topography and no variations in density at any given depth below the surface. (See p. 12.)

The Helmert formula of 1901 is based upon many gravity determinations widely distributed over the earth's surface, and in consequence probably gives a close approximation to the desired values. The available indirect evidence gives strong support to the belief that this formula, in which the constants are computed from gravity observations, is of a very high degree of accuracy. For example, the values of the flattening of the earth, as computed by this formula and as computed from geodetic observations in the United States, are of about the same degree of accuracy and agree closely. The value of the reciprocal of the flattening derived from the Helmert formula of 1901 is 298.3 ± 0.7, and from geodetic observations in the United States is 297.0 ± 0.5.[*]

---

[*] Supplementary Investigation in 1909 of the Figure of the Earth and Isostasy, p. 60.

This is a confirmation, by independent observations of a different kind from those on which the formula is based, of the accuracy of the second constant in the Helmert formula.

But, on the other hand, the Helmert formula of 1901 is based upon selected coast and inland stations. The present investigation indicates that even at these carefully selected stations there is probably small systematic error due to the failure, by the methods of reduction used in connection with the derivation of the Helmert formula, to take account properly of the effects of the topography and its isostatic compensation. A correction (0.007) serving to eliminate this systematic error as completely as is possible at present, has been derived from the observations in the United States and applied to the first constant in the Helmert formula of 1901. (See p. 75.) It is believed that the Helmert formula of 1901 so corrected is a true representation within less than 0.003 dyne on an average of the attraction at sea level on the ideal earth, if the formula is limited in application to the range of latitudes occurring in the United States.

The correction for elevation (p. 13), the next step in the computation, is of such a nature that it is reasonably certain that the errors made in computing it are very small, usually not more than 0.001 dyne. An error of 3 meters in the elevation makes but 0.001 dyne error in the computed correction. For the gravity stations in the United States the elevations are known as a rule within 3 meters and at very few if any of the stations is the error in elevation more than 15 meters.

The value of the gravitation constant (k) adopted in this investigation is 6673 (10^{-11}), and it is estimated that the probable error of this adopted value is one part in 1330. (See p. 14.) This constant enters directly as a factor into each formula for computing the correction for topography and isostatic compensation. (See formulæ (10), (15), (16), (17), and (18), pp. 15–17.) Hence, the probable error of one part in 1330 in the gravitation constant produces an error of the same proportional part in each computed correction for topography and compensation. The largest of these corrections (see p. 74) is only 0.187 for station No. 43, Pikes Peak. Even for this case the probable error in the correction due to error in the gravitation constant is only 0.0001 dyne (0.187/1330), and is therefore negligible in connection with the present investigation.

Similarly, any error in the assumed mean surface density of the earth will produce an error of the same proportional part in the computed correction for topography and compensation corresponding to each land compartment. The mean surface density has been assumed to be 2.67 in this investigation. It is reasonably certain that the mean density of the whole of that portion of the earth which lies above sea level does not differ from this by as much as one-twentieth part.* At Pikes Peak, station No. 43, the sum of the corrections for all land compartments is probably greater than for any other one of the 89 stations in the United States used in this investigation. At this station this sum is about +0.180 dyne.† An error of one-twentieth part in this would be only 0.009 dyne. An inspection of the tables on pages 54–58 indicates that as a rule the sum of the corrections for land compartments for stations in the United States is less than 0.020 and an error of one-twentieth part would, therefore, ordinarily be less than 0.001 dyne.

In general the density of sedimentary rocks tends to be less than 2.67, not unfrequently as much as one-tenth part less.‡ On the other hand, igneous rocks and rocks which have been buried to a great depth tend to be of density greater than 2.67. These local departures of the densities from the assumed mean, 2.67, produce errors of the third class, which have been defined as errors due to the difference between the actual arrangement of densities in the earth and the assumed arrangement. These effects of local departures of density from the mean are a part of the anomaly at the station rather than errors in determining the anomaly. Hence, the discussion of them will be taken up later as a part of the discussion of the meaning of the anomalies.

---

* The adopted value of the mean surface density of the earth, 2.67, and this estimate of its uncertainty are based largely upon the information given in The Solar Parallax and Its Related Constants, by William Harkness, Washington, Government Printing Office, 1891, pp. 91–92.

† The sum is 0.182 for zones A to 10 at this station. (See p. 56.) Zone 9 is the nearest zone containing any oceanic compartments.

‡ For example, consult the estimates of density of rocks in the vicinity of 10 of the gravity stations here treated as given on p. 53 of Appendix I of the Coast and Geodetic Survey Report for 1894, "Relative determinations of gravity with half-second pendulums and other pendulum observations," by G. R. Putnam and G. K. Gilbert.

On page 15 attention is called to the fact that in deriving the formulæ by which all computations for distant zones have been made the earth is treated as a sphere with a radius of 637 000 000 centimeters, although it is actually a spheroid.

In zones M, N, and O errors due to this approximation are evidently negligible for, as shown on page 22 and in the reduction tables for those zones, pages 41–43 (consult the column headed "Station at same elevation as compartment"), if all of the curvature were neglected and the earth's surface treated as a plane, the error introduced would be only 0.0001 dyne in any one compartment of these zones. The curvature of the actual spheroid in any azimuth within the limits of the United States differs by less than one five-hundredth part from that of the assumed sphere and, therefore, the error for any compartment due to the cause under discussion must necessarily be much less than 1/500 of 0.0001 dyne in zones M, N, and O. The errors must be still smaller for near zones.

For more distant zones a general consideration of the geometric relations, shown in illustration No. 15, page 67, indicates that the error is probably considerably greater. Without a detailed investigation the three following considerations seem to the writers sufficient to assure one that the total error due to this cause is probably less than 0.001 dyne at every station. First, the total correction for topography and isostatic compensation beyond zone O is less than −0.060 dyne at every one of the 89 stations. Second, the actual radius of the earth varies from 6357 kilometers at the pole to 6378 kilometers at the equator; that is, from 13 kilometers less (1/490 part) to 8 kilometers greater (1/800 part) than the assumed radius. These differences may be considered as maximum vertical displacements of material in very distant zones from its assumed position. The displacements are small in comparison with the distance to the zone in these cases. Third, on the actual spheroid the radii in various azimuths from the station are different. For example, for a station in the central portion of the United States in latitude 39° the radius of curvature in the meridian is 6361 kilometers, 9 kilometers less (one part in 710) than the assumed value, 6370 kilometers, and in the prime vertical at this same station the radius of curvature is 6387 kilometers, 17 kilometers greater (one part in 370) than the assumed value. Hence, in each zone the errors of the kind under consideration tend to be compensating to a considerable extent, some parts of the zone lying farther from the center of the earth than the assumed curvature places them and other parts of the same zone, lying in different azimuths, being nearer to the center than the assumed curvature would place them.

Assuming for the moment that the elevations and depths shown on the maps and charts used are correct, the errors made by the computer in estimating the mean elevation or mean depth within each compartment did not, as a rule, produce any error even in the fourth decimal place in dynes. In zone A an error of at least 5 feet in estimated elevation is necessary in order to make an error of 0.0001 dyne in the computed correction even if the elevation of the station is less than 10 feet. In this zone if the station has an elevation greater than 10 feet, the correction is 0.0002 dyne in every case. In zone F it takes an error of 200 feet or more in the estimated elevation to produce an error of 0.0001 dyne in the computed correction; in zone M 500 feet or more; in zones 18 to 14, 100 feet; and in zones beyond 14, 1000 feet or more. (Consult the reduction tables, pp. 30–47.) In many cases the total range of elevation within a compartment, as shown by the map, is less than that necessary to produce a change of 0.0001 dyne in the correction taken from the reduction table. In these cases no error in the correction arose from the estimation of the mean elevation. Still more frequently the range of elevation within the compartment is not more than three or four times that necessary to produce a change of 0.0001 dyne. It is probable that in such cases the estimate of mean elevation was rarely in error by more than the quantity corresponding to 0.0001 dyne. For perhaps one-tenth of all the compartments the computer found so large a range of elevations shown on the map that his estimate of mean elevations was necessarily made with considerable care and attention to the details of the contour lines, and even then the correction taken from the reduction table may be in error by two or more units in the fourth decimal place. It is believed that the aggregate of such errors for a station is seldom greater than 0.001 dyne. For, as indicated above, difficulties were encountered in making the estimate of the mean elevation with sufficient accuracy at only a small percentage of the compartments; the errors so made tend to be in the accidental class; the difficulties were obvious to the computer and he, therefore, exercised unusual care in the extraordinary cases, even to the extent of subdividing the compartments and making a separate estimate for each subcompartment; and finally for each station a second computer inspected the computation made by the first and made a second estimate covering some of the compartments in which there were obvious difficulties in making a sufficiently accurate estimate. For compartments for which two estimates were made the mean of the two was used, unless they differed so much as to lead to detection of an error in one or the other.

In making the computations for topography and isostatic compensation, the elevations of compartments were read from the maps without making any allowance for the fact that glaciers have a much lower density than the land. A computation was made to show the effect upon the intensity of gravity at station Gornergrat of the defect of density of the glacial ice in its vicinity in comparison with solid earth of the assumed density, 2.67. An inspection of the maps of this region showed that 37 of the 102 compartments in the zones E to K were over ice, and the shapes of the clear portions of the valleys indicated that the average thickness of this ice in the several compartments varies from a few feet to more than 600 feet. The presence of ice in the zones closer to the station than zone E and farther from the station than zone K was believed not to affect the intensity of gravity at the station.

An average density of unity was assumed for the glacial material in making this computation. This is believed to be near the truth, for the heavy material carried by the glacier (sand and gravel) is probably approximately balanced by cavities and the lightness of the clear ice in comparison with water. This makes a defect of density of approximately 1.67 in portions of the topography of certain compartments. This should make a minus correction to the computed effect of the topography and a plus correction to the effect of the isostatic compensation. The largest correction found for any one compartment due to this lack of density was 0.0004 dyne, while the average correction for a compartment was less than 0.0001 dyne. In the near zones the effect of ignoring the lack of density in the glacier made the computed value of gravity too great, while, owing to the change of sign with distance from the station (see pp. 65–70), the effect of such neglect in the more distant zones was to decrease the computed value of gravity. The total result for station Gornergrat was to make the computed value of gravity too great by 0.0006 dyne, a negligible quantity. It is probable that the effect on the intensity of gravity of assuming glacial ice to have a density of 2.67 in the computations of the effect of topography and isostatic compensation upon the intensity of gravity has not caused an error of more than 0.0010 dyne at any one of the stations treated in this investigation.

In using the mean elevation within a compartment as the argument in entering the reduction tables on pages 30–47, it is tacitly assumed that the influence of a unit of area of a given elevation is the same wherever it is located in the compartment. This is only approximately true. For example, in zone 13 (limiting radii 3° 03′ 05″ and 4° 19′ 13″) E_R is 5000 at the outer edge of the zone and 13 600 at the inner edge. (See p. 25.) The influence of a unit of area of a given elevation on the outer edge of the zone is, therefore, $5000/13600 = 0.37$ as great as on the inner edge. If, therefore, in this zone the elevations nearer the outer edge in one compartment happen to be much greater than elevations nearer the inner edge, the correction taken from the table by using the mean elevation as an argument will be too large. Similarly, if the slope in the compartment happens to be downward from the inner edge toward the outer edge the correction taken from the table will be too small.

When the arbitrary selection of radii of zones and of number of compartments in each zone was being made the danger of errors from this source was kept constantly in mind (see p. 18), and each compartment was made so small that the estimated errors due to this cause in any compartment would ordinarily be less than 0.0002 dyne. The details of the manner in which this estimate was made can not be conveniently shown here. Evidently the narrower the zone is made the smaller the error from this cause, both because E_R will be more nearly the same on the two edges of the zone and because the difference between the average elevation of the near topography and of the distant topography in each of the compartments of a zone tends to be small. Similarly, after the width of the zone is fixed, the smaller the compartments are made within the zone the smaller will be the error, for the less will be the range of elevations included within the compartment and the larger will be the change of elevation corresponding to an effect of 0.0001 dyne. The values of E_R were before the investigator for all outer zones at the time each decision was made. For inner zones for which formula 18, page 17, was used, an indirect method of obtaining the equivalent of the change in E_R was utilized. The investigator also had before him the experience and data obtained in connection with the previous investigation of the figure of the earth * which enabled him to estimate the maximum difference of elevation between the inner and outer edges of any given compartment which would probably be found at any station.

Errors due to this cause will evidently be of the accidental class, since in some zones a downward slope toward the station will produce an error of one sign and in others the reverse slope will produce an error of the opposite sign. In the 317 compartments concerned in the computation at a given station there will be but few compartments, sometimes none, in which this error is as great as 0.0001 dyne, and errors of both signs will probably occur among these few. It is believed that the aggregate error due to this cause at a station seldom exceeds 0.0005 dyne.

The errors due to the faults and incompleteness of the maps and charts used are believed to be very small as a rule. The aggregate error for all numbered zones is probably seldom, if ever, greater than 0.002 dyne. For the lettered zones, zones which lie near the station, the aggregate error in some cases may be two or three times this limit. The reduction tables (pp. 30-47) show that for the nearer lettered zones the elevations must be known with greater accuracy in general than for the more distant numbered zones, and since the compartments are small in the lettered zones it is necessary to know the details of the topography. The magnitude of the aggregate error at a given station, due to faults and incompleteness of maps and charts, therefore, depends principally upon the accuracy of the maps and charts covering the region close to the station rather than that of those covering distant regions.†

Some errors are made in locating the compartment boundaries on the maps, due to unavoidable inaccuracy in constructing the templates, to inaccuracy in placing the templates on the maps, to special difficulties encountered in connection with the distortion of scale on Mercator charts, and to shrinkage and, therefore, error of scale of the maps and charts. With the templates and maps before one it is evident that the aggregate effect of these errors at a station is ordinarily negligible. In general the effect of an error in locating a compartment boundary is simply to throw a small part of the area which belongs in one compartment into an adjoining compartment, where its influence on the computed correction is nearly the same as if it had been placed in its proper compartment.

The methods followed in computing the reduction tables have been stated on pages 19-28. The precautions taken were such as to insure that no tabular value is in error by more than 0.0002 dyne, and that in general the tabular values are correct to within 0.0001 dyne. The intervals between tabulated values have been so selected, with due regard to second differences, as to insure that the errors made in interpolating between them, using first differences only, shall ordinarily be less than 0.0001 dyne.

How large are the errors introduced into the computed topographic effect on the intensity of gravity by the interpolation of values corresponding to outer zones? The complete computation was made for only six stations. Each new station to be computed was so chosen, if possible, as to lie within the triangle defined by the nearest three stations for which the computation had already been made, and near the center of said triangle. From these three surrounding stations the interpolation, if any, was made.

The computation was commenced with the inner smaller zones and proceeded outward. The two rules used by the computers in deciding at what zone it was allowable to begin to accept the interpolated values and to accept them for all larger zones were, as stated on page 63, as follows:

---

* The Figure of the Earth and Isostasy, etc., pp. 125-127.

† For a more detailed statement of the considerations upon which the judgment expressed in this paragraph is founded, see The Figure of the Earth and Isostasy, etc., p. 124.

Rule 1.—Commence to accept the interpolated values as final with the first zone for which such interpolation is allowable under rule 2, provided that it is beyond the zone containing the nearest of the three stations from which the interpolation is made.

Rule 2.—Let 0.0005 dyne be the interpolation limit for any zone. Subject to rule 1, acceptance of the interpolation may begin with a given zone if each of the three zones next within it shows an agreement between the interpolated and computed values which is within the interpolation limit.

Under rule 2, at any station the maximum error made by accepting interpolated values would be, in dynes, 0.0005 times the number of zones interpolated, if the error of interpolation $I-C$ (interpolated minus computed) always had the same sign. It was believed, however, that the agreement between the interpolated and computed values (commencing with zones not smaller than those contemplated under rule 1) would tend strongly to be closer and closer for successive zones proceeding outward. It was also believed that there would be a strong tendency for the various differences between interpolated and computed values for several zones such as are interpolated under the rules to include values having both the plus and minus signs, and, therefore, for the errors in the accepted interpolation to tend to be eliminated from the final result for the station.

The correctness of these beliefs is established by the results secured during the progress of the computations. From the results of the computations of 48 stations a comparison between the computed and interpolated values was secured at each station on from 2 to 10 zones. In 81 per cent of the cases the average value, without regard to the sign of $I-C$ (interpolated minus computed) was less for the outer one-half of the zones on which both interpolation and computation was made at that station than for the inner half of such zones. Also in 56 per cent of the cases there were found to be both plus and minus signs of the values of $I-C$ at the station.

These tests confirm the theory to such an extent that it is believed that the total error introduced into the computed effect of topography and compensation at a station by the acceptance of interpolated values is seldom greater than 0.0022 dyne and is, as a rule, not more than one-half that amount. In addition to the evidence stated in the paragraph above, this estimate of 0.0022 dyne is based upon the fact that the average difference between the computed and the interpolated values for the three zones (see rule 2) next within the one for which the interpolation is accepted, at any station, is in general 0.0002 dyne or less. The average number of zones per station for which interpolated values were accepted is 11. If the error for each interpolated zone were 0.0002 and all were of the same sign, the error would be 0.0022 on an average. However, as the outer zones have more overlapping of areas, the interpolated and computed values for those zones should agree on an average more closely than these values for the three zones next preceding the zone at which interpolation begins, and as these errors are of the accidental class and not all of the same sign, there is a tendency for the errors of interpolation to be eliminated from the final result for the station. One may, therefore, conclude that the total error caused by accepting the interpolated values is so small as to be negligible.

The depth to which the isostatic compensation extends has been assumed to be fixed by a surface which lies 113.7 kilometers below sea level, but, as noted on page 10, in order to simplify and to facilitate the computations the depth of compensation has in the computations really been reckoned from the solid surface of the earth, not from sea level. This computing device has, therefore, virtually displaced the isostatic compensation upward on land areas by a distance equal to the elevation of the surface of the area above sea level, and downward for ocean areas by a distance equal to the depth of the particular part of the ocean considered. For near zones this displacement of the compensation produces negligible effects because the total effect of the compensation is small (consult the reduction tables for zones A to I, pp. 30–37). For the very distant zones, 13 to 1, this displacement of the compensation produces effects which are certainly negligible, since the reduction tables, pages 45 and 46, show that there is no appreciable correction for elevation in these zones. For intermediate zones J to 14 small appreciable effects are probably produced in some cases by the virtual displacement of the isostatic compensation introduced as a computing device. Though no special investigation of the aggregate of effects has been made it is believed to be small. In other words, the actual computation made on the supposition that the depth of compensation is 113.7 kilometers measured from the solid surface, is believed to be practically in agreement as to numerical results with the computation which theoretically should have been made on the supposition that the depth of compensation is 113.7 kilometers measured from sea level.

Within the great depth, 113.7 kilometers, to which isostatic compensation extends there is probably a slight increase of density with increase of depth, due to increased pressure. No account has been taken of this in the process of computation, as already noted on page 7. It may appear at first sight that this neglect introduces some error into the computed results, but it does not. The isostatic compensation as used in the computation is essentially an excess or defect of density referred to the normal density for each level concerned within the depth of compensation. It matters not in the computation of the effects of topography and isostatic compensation whether the normal relation of density to depth is such that there is no appreciable increase of density within the depth of compensation or whether there is considerable increase within that depth, for the excesses and defects of density constituting the isostatic compensation are referred to this normal law, not to a constant density for all depths. The point at which the relation of density to depth enters this investigation, though not explicitly, is in the derivation of the Helmert formula of 1901. Any actual change in the distribution of density with respect to depth would in general change the observed value of the intensity of gravity and would cause one or more of the constants of this formula to change. Therefore, the constants in this formula as derived from observations correspond to the actual relation between depth and density, though that relation is not known.

NATURE OF APPARENT ANOMALIES.

There have been discussed on the preceding pages the principal possible sources of error of the first and second classes, defined on page 86. Among these sources are the errors in the instrumental determinations of gravity at each station, errors in the corrected Helmert formula of 1901, errors in the corrections for elevation, errors in the adopted values of the gravitation constant and the mean surface density, the erroneous assumption in certain parts of the computation that the sea-level surface is a sphere rather than a spheroid, errors in the estimated mean elevations in the different compartments, errors due to variations of elevation within each compartment, errors in the maps and charts used, errors in locating compartment boundaries, errors of interpolation for outer zones, and errors in computing the reduction tables. The errors of each of these kinds are nearly or quite independent of the others, and follow different laws of distribution. In estimating the effects of all these errors at a station one must therefore consider them as accidental errors and that their combined effect is the square root of the sum of their squares rather than merely their sum. On this basis the writers estimate that the probable error of the computed anomaly at a station by the new method is about ± 0.003 dyne on an average. In other words, the chances are even for and against the proposition that the actual error in the computed anomaly at a station is greater than 0.003.

The basis for this estimate is in part indicated in the following table:

Estimate of errors of the first and second classes.

Source of error	Maximum probable error of any station	Average probable error of any station
Observations of gravity	±0.004	±0.002
Helmert formula of 1901, corrected	±0.003	±0.002
Correction for elevation	±0.003	±0.001
Gravitation constant	±0.000	±0.000
Mean surface density	±0.005	±0.001
Defects and incompleteness of maps	±0.004	±0.001
Acceptance of interpolation	±0.001	±0.000
From all other causes	±0.001	±0.001
The square root of the sum of the squares, or the probable error of the the final result subject to all the separate errors enumerated	±0.009	±0.003

If the whole anomaly be considered as an error, then the probable error for all stations due to all causes is ±0.014 (see p. 75), this probable error being computed from the 87 apparent anomalies available in the United States after rejecting the two Seattle stations. It should be noted that this computation includes the third class of errors defined on page 86, those due to the departures of the actual arrangement of densities beneath the surface from the arrangement which has been assumed. The magnitude of the errors of this third class, the real anomalies sought, may be estimated as that part of the total error computed, as indicated above, from the apparent anomalies, which is not accounted for by errors of the first and second classes, namely,

$$\sqrt{(0.014)^2 - (0.003)^2} = \pm 0.0137.$$

These two values, ±0.003 and ±0.0137, may be interpreted as follows: The second being about five times the first, the apparent anomalies shown on page 76 under the designation "Anomalies, new method," are upon an average composed of one part errors of observation and computation to five parts actual anomaly at the station, due to the departure of the actual arrangement of densities from the assumed arrangement. The quantities labeled "Anomalies, new method," are therefore a close approximation to the real anomalies sought. They are a possible basis for further investigation as to the actual distribution of density within the earth.

THE METHOD NOT SUBJECT TO HIDDEN ERRORS.

This discussion of errors would be seriously incomplete if it were closed without calling attention to certain characteristics of the computations on which this investigation is based which insure safety against certain classes of obscure but serious errors.

The process of integration by the method of computing a large number of separate values of the function (see pp. 23–27), which has been used in this investigation, is very clumsy and inelegant, as seen from the mathematical point of view, but from the practical point of view of one who desires to solve the problem of computing the effect of all the topography of the world and of its isostatic compensation upon the intensity of gravity at a given station, it has a very different aspect. From the latter point of view it appears that the method is sufficiently rapid to make its use permissible and that it is clearly safe against errors, whereas the alternative mathematically elegant method is unsafe.

As to the rapidity of the method, it was found in practice that the necessary reduction tables for zones covering the whole earth were computed in the equivalent of about 800 hours of time for one computer. This seems to be a reasonable time when one considers the importance and difficulty of the problem solved. Moreover, these tables made it possible to make the remaining portions of the computation very rapidly. They enabled the computer in 17 hours to compute the effect of all the topography of the world and its isostatic compensation upon the intensity of gravity at any given station on the earth's surface, and to be certain that the errors of the computed result are confined within the very narrow limits indicated by the preceding discussion of errors. This in turn furnishes a safe basis, and in the opinion of the writers the only safe basis yet available, for an accurate determination of the flattening of the earth from gravity observations; for any effective investigation of the theory of isostasy by means of gravity observations; for any investigation of the real meaning of the apparent anomalies of gravity, such, for example, as those on small oceanic islands; and in fact for any safe general conclusions from observations of the intensity of gravity on the earth's surface.

The method used in this investigation of obtaining the integrals of the expressions (9), (15), and (16), pages 14–16, by computing many numerical values, is safe against excessive or unseen errors because of the fact that the computer has before him in these many numerical values a clear and definite means of knowing how large are his errors of approximation. For example, when facing the actual problem of determining the mean value E_c (see p. 23) with various computed values of E before him, there is little difficulty in deciding safely how many values of E to compute in order to be certain of a given degree of accuracy in the mean value. Various similar examples from this investigation might be cited.

On the other hand, if the computer resorts to the more elegant method, from the mathematical point of view, and first transforms formulæ (9), (15), and (16) by simplification into forms which can be integrated by calculus, he is, while making the simplification, in grave danger of introducing errors of approximation which he believes to be small, but which are in reality large. The writers believe that in this particular problem this danger has not been escaped in the past. For example, the conclusion that it is not necessary to take distant topography into account, a conclusion which has been acted upon in many previous investigations, and which this investigation shows to be erroneous, has apparently been reached in the past by dealing with unsafe approximations in the literal or symbolic form. So, too, it seems to the writers that one can not overlook the necessity of taking curvature very fully into account if one has the numerical values before him, but may easily overlook it if he is dealing with symbols and formulæ only.

Another characteristic of the method of computation used in this investigation, which is very important as a means of securing safety against unseen errors, is the fact that it deals with the actual irregular surface of the earth rather than with a geometrical surface which is assumed to fit the earth's surface in the vicinity of the station. It is true that the irregular surface actually used in the computation is made up of 317 level surfaces, one for each compartment of each zone, the mean elevation in each compartment being the argument with which the reduction tables are entered. But the compartments near the station are so small that the surface upon which the computation is based is, in these zones, a very close approximation to the actual irregular surface. The one compartment of zone A is a circle with a 2-meter radius. Each of the four compartments of zone B has an area of less than 4000 square meters. The agreement between the assumed surface and the actual irregular surface of the earth is less close for the more distant topography, but there is still, even for the most distant zones, an approximation to the actual irregular surface. The precautions taken in fixing the size and shape of the separate compartments insure, in fact, that even for these distant zones the approximation to the actual irregular surface is sufficiently exact to keep the errors in the computed effects of topography and compensation well within the allowable limits.

In any computation of the effects of topography and compensation in which any part of the earth's surface is assumed to conform to the geometrical surface, in which, for example, a mountain or an oceanic island is assumed to have a conical shape, or the distant topography is assumed to be a plain of indefinite extent, it is desirable to consider with extreme care how much error may be introduced into the computations by such assumptions, to consider carefully what evidence the computer has that these errors are small in each separate case. Such errors once introduced into an investigation remain there regardless of the degree of mathematical elegance and precision which may be maintained thereafter. The writers believe that the more carefully this point is examined the more fully the advantages of the methods of computation used in the present investigation will be appreciated.

EFFECTS OF TOPOGRAPHY AND COMPENSATION—WHY COMBINED.

In the investigation of the figure of the earth and isostasy by means of observed deflections of the vertical, the whole effect of the topography was first computed and later the effect of the isostatic compensation was combined with it.* In the present investigation, based on gravity determinations, the effects of topography and of compensation have been combined as early as was feasible in the processes of deriving formulæ and of computing. Thus, as indicated on pages 23 and 24, instead of computing the two effects separately for distant zones they were combined in formula (20) and the resultant effect computed at once and tabulated in the reduction tables on pages 44–47. So, too, for near zones the principal part of the reduction tables (pp. 30–43) refers to resultant effects, not to separate effects. The only columns in these tables showing separate effects are columns 2 and 3, and these were not used in the regular computations.

Why was this departure made from the methods of the earlier investigation?

This departure was decided upon immediately after a preliminary reconnoissance of the problem. It then appeared probable that, for all zones except for those very near the station, the two opposing effects of topography and compensation would be nearly equal, and their difference, therefore, much smaller than either one. Under these circumstances it appeared that to compute each of the opposing effects with sufficient accuracy to secure the required degree of accuracy in their difference it would be necessary to secure several significant figures in the computation. If this supposition were true, it would be necessary in making the separate computations, either to make the compartments of the separate zones very small and numerous, and hence the computation very slow, or, otherwise, if large compartments were used, it would be necessary to make the estimate of mean elevation in each compartment with such a high degree of accuracy as to be both slow and difficult. On the other hand, it appeared that in the direct computation of the resultant difference of effects, it would be necessary to use but two or three significant figures in the computation, that the compartments could be made large and therefore not very numerous, and that only an approximate estimate of the mean elevation in each compartment would be required and could, therefore, be made quickly and easily. It seemed, therefore, that so much would be gained in rapidity and ease of computation by the proposed departure from the earlier practice that these gains should outweigh all other considerations.

Now, this investigation being complete, the writers have an opportunity to review the decision in the light of accumulated facts and greater experience. In that light it appears that the decision was wise for zones which are more than 26° from the station—zones 6 to 1 of the present investigation. For these zones the difference of the effect of the topography and the effect of the compensation is less than one-tenth of either; that is, E_R is less than one-tenth of either E_T or E_C (p. 25). For nearer zones the difference, as a rule, is a much greater proportional part. Hence, for these nearer zones the gain in rapidity and ease made by dealing directly with the difference of effects rather than with the separate effects was not great, and therefore the decision was not wise. Moreover, it appears now that if the separate effects had been computed for these nearer zones it would have given the investigator a clearer and more precise insight into the problems involved. It would also have facilitated studies of the relation of the computed results to the assumption as to the depth of compensation and possibly to some other assumptions.

If, therefore, an entire new investigation were being made the writers believe it would be wise to compute the two effects separately for zones A to O and 18 to 7, but the gain to be secured does not seem to be sufficiently great to warrant the revision of the present investigation and the remodeling of the reduction tables here printed.

---

* The Figure of the Earth and Isostasy from Measurements in the United States pp. 68–73.

REGIONAL VERSUS LOCAL DISTRIBUTION OF COMPENSATION.[*]

The question whether each topographic feature is completely compensated for by a defect or excess of mass exactly equal in amount directly under it, or whether the topographic feature is compensated for by a defect or excess of mass distributed through a more extensive portion of the earth's crust than that which lies directly beneath it, is a very important one. The theory of local compensation postulates that the defect or excess of mass under any topographic feature is uniformly distributed in a column extending from the topographic feature to a depth of 113.7 kilometers below sea level. The theory of regional compensation postulates, on the other hand, that the individual topographic features are not compensated for locally, but that compensation does exist for regions of considerable area considered as a whole.

In order to have local compensation there must be a lower effective rigidity in the earth's crust than under the theory of regional compensation only. In the latter case there must be sufficient rigidity in the earth's crust to support individual features, such as Pikes Peak, for instance, but not rigidity enough to support the topography covering large areas.

Certain computations have been made to ascertain which is more nearly correct, the assumption of local compensation or the assumption of regional compensation only. In making such computations it is necessary to adopt limits for the areas within which compensation is to be considered complete. A reconnoissance showed that the distant topography and compensation need not be considered, for their effect would be practically the same for both kinds of distribution. As a result of this reconnoissance it was decided to make the test for three areas, the first extending from the station to the outer limit of zone K (18.8 kilometers), the second from the station to the outer limit of zone M (58.8 kilometers), and the third, to the outer limit of zone O (166.7 kilometers).

The computed effect of the topography in each compartment and zone is the same under the two methods. The effect of compensation is assumed to be the same for each compartment and zone which is beyond the limit of the area adopted for the test. The effect of compensation within that limit is computed for each compartment in the case of the theory of complete local compensation, while in the case of regional compensation only, it is obtained from one operation after the average elevation within the area considered is known.

The regular computations of the effect of topography and compensation had been completed at 56 stations in the United States, Nos. 1 to 56, inclusive, and at all of the stations not in the United States, used in this investigation, before it was planned to make computations based on the theory of regional compensation within limited areas. In the regular computations for these stations the effect of topography and compensation for zones A to O was taken from the fourth column of the reduction tables (see pp. 30–43), and no record was made of the elevations of the several compartments as read from the maps. In making the supplemental computations these tables were entered with the previously computed values of the combined effect of the topography and compensation as arguments, and the approximate values of the elevations of the several compartments of zones A to O were taken from column 1 of the reduction tables, and the values of the effect of compensation taken from column 3. The supplementary computations were not made for all of the stations between Nos. 1 and 56 on account of the large amount of work involved.

While making the computations of the effect of topography and compensation for stations Nos. 57 to 89 (except station No. 84), a table was made for each station, giving the elevation of each compartment out to zone O as read from the map. With these elevations the reduction tables were entered and the effect of compensation was taken out separately from column 3. The total effect of compensation under the theory of local distribution was obtained for each of the areas considered by adding the values of the effect of compensation for the several compartments of each of the zones. The mean value of the elevation of each zone was obtained by taking the mean of the elevations of its several compartments, and the mean elevation of

---

[*] The investigation under this heading was made at the suggestion of Mr. G. R. Putnam, of the Coast and Geodetic Survey.

each of the three areas considered (limited by zones K, M, and O) was obtained by combining the elevations of the various zones, the elevation of each zone being given a weight equal to its percentage of the total area under consideration.

The regional compensation for the total amount of topography in the area considered was assumed to be uniformly distributed both vertically and horizontally throughout a column of depth 113.7 kilometers and of a cross section equal to the area of the topography—that is, successively from the station to the outer limits of zones K, M, and O. The effect of the compensation upon the intensity of gravity at the station was computed by formula (17), in which the several terms have the same significance as stated on page 17.

The table following shows the comparison of the effects of local compensation and regional compensation for 41 stations in the United States and 4 stations not in the United States. It also shows the anomalies by the first method and for 3 cases at each station by the second method. The first column gives the number and name of the station. The second column gives the total correction for topography and compensation by the method of local compensation. In the third column are shown the values of the compensation for the topography included in the area extending from the station out to zone K, the compensation being assumed to be complete and local. In the fourth column are given the values of the compensation for the topography within the same area, but with regional compensation only, which is assumed to be uniformly distributed and complete, within the area limited by the outer circumference of zone K.

Columns 5 and 6 are similar to 3 and 4, except that the area considered extends from the station to the outer limit of zone M. The same statement applies to columns 7 and 8, except that the area considered extends from the station to the outer limits of zone O. The ninth column contains the new-method anomalies, based upon complete local compensation, and the last three columns show the anomalies for the three cases under the theory of regional compensation only.

Number and name of station	Effect of topography and compensation	Effect of compensation within outer limit of— Zone K Local	Zone K Regional	Zone M Local	Zone M Regional	Zone O Local	Zone O Regional	Anomaly, new method [1] $(g-g_0+0.007)$ (local compensation)	Anomaly with regional compensation within outer limit of— Zone K	Zone M	Zone O
Stations in United States											
42. Colorado Springs, Colo.	−0.007	−0.036	−0.036	−0.094	−0.093	−0.165	−0.164	−0.009	−0.009	−0.010	−0.010
43. Pikes Peak, Colo.	+ .187	− .052	− .044	− .113	− .100	− .189	− .172	+ .019	+ .011	+ .006	+ .002
44. Denver, Colo.	− .015	− .026	− .028	− .076	− .085	− .152	− .169	− .018	− .016	− .009	− .001
45. Gunnison, Colo.	− .001	− .041	− .044	− .120	− .128	− .212	− .210	+ .018	+ .021	+ .025	+ .016
46. Grand Junction, Colo.	− .051	− .026	− .028	− .082	− .089	− .156	− .170	+ .022	+ .024	+ .029	+ .036
48. Pleasant Valley Junction, Utah	+ .024	− .040	− .041	− .103	− .100	− .171	− .159	+ .002	+ .003	− .001	− .010
49. Salt Lake City, Utah	− .041	− .026	− .028	− .075	− .078	− .137	− .143	+ .008	+ .010	+ .011	+ .014
54. San Francisco, Cal.	+ .045	.000	.000	− .002	− .008	+ .009	+ .033	− .025	− .025	− .024	− .049
55. Mt. Hamilton, Cal.	+ .120	− .012	− .012	− .017	− .009	− .018	− .003	− .005	− .005	− .013	− .020
57. Iron River, Mich.	+ .014	− .007	− .008	− .020	− .020	− .031	− .024	+ .036	+ .037	+ .036	+ .029
58. Ely, Minn.	+ .008	− .006	− .008	− .018	− .021	− .031	− .029	+ .021	+ .023	+ .024	+ .019
59. Pembina, N. Dak.	− .009	− .004	− .004	− .011	− .012	− .023	− .025	+ .017	+ .017	+ .018	+ .019
60. Mitchell, S. Dak.	− .006	− .006	− .007	− .016	− .019	− .033	− .037	− .001	.000	+ .002	+ .003
61. Sweetwater, Tex.	+ .009	− .011	− .012	− .028	− .029	− .049	− .049	− .031	− .030	− .030	− .031
62. Kerrville, Tex.	+ .013	− .009	− .010	− .024	− .025	− .038	− .032	+ .029	+ .030	+ .030	+ .023
63. El Paso, Tex.	+ .001	− .020	− .021	− .054	− .055	− .098	− .104	+ .005	+ .006	+ .006	+ .011
64. Nogales, Ariz.	+ .038	− .020	− .020	− .046	− .041	− .076	− .069	− .052	− .052	− .057	− .059
65. Yuma, Ariz.	− .010	− .001	− .001	− .004	− .006	− .012	− .018	+ .007	+ .007	+ .009	+ .013
66. Compton, Cal.	.000	.000	− .001	− .002	− .004	− .011	− .024	− .052	− .051	− .050	− .039
67. Goldfield, Nev.	+ .027	− .030	− .030	− .077	− .078	− .137	− .141	− .015	− .015	− .014	− .011
68. Yavapai, Ariz.	+ .034	− .030	− .030	− .080	− .080	− .137	− .129	− .001	− .001	− .001	− .009
69. Grand Canyon, Ariz.	− .098	− .028	− .029	− .079	− .080	− .136	− .127	− .012	− .011	− .011	− .021
70. Gallup, N. Mex.	+ .014	− .036	− .036	− .095	− .095	− .163	− .156	− .015	− .015	− .015	− .022
71. Las Vegas, N. Mex.	+ .017	− .036	− .035	− .094	− .094	− .160	− .150	+ .001	.000	+ .001	− .009
72. Shamrock, Tex.	+ .007	− .013	− .012	− .031	− .031	− .055	− .056	+ .030	+ .029	+ .030	+ .031
73. Denison, Tex.	− .001	− .004	− .004	− .010	− .009	− .018	− .017	+ .003	+ .003	+ .002	+ .002
74. Minneapolis, Minn.	− .005	− .004	− .005	− .012	− .013	− .022	− .024	+ .057	+ .058	+ .058	+ .069
75. Lead, S. Dak.	+ .044	− .026	− .027	− .064	− .061	− .102	− .089	+ .050	+ .051	+ .047	+ .037
76. Bismarck, N. Dak.	− .005	− .008	− .009	− .024	− .026	− .044	− .047	.000	+ .001	+ .002	+ .003
77. Hinsdale, Mont.	− .017	− .010	− .012	− .030	− .034	− .058	− .067	+ .027	+ .029	+ .031	+ .036
78. Sandpoint, Idaho	− .044	− .014	− .014	− .045	− .049	− .086	− .095	.000	.000	+ .004	+ .009
79. Boise, Idaho	− .042	− .016	− .018	− .047	− .051	− .094	− .108	+ .006	+ .008	+ .010	+ .020
80. Astoria, Oreg.	+ .008	.000	.000	− .002	− .005	.000	+ .008	− .015	− .015	− .012	− .023
81. Sisson, Cal.	+ .015	− .022	− .026	− .058	− .059	− .096	− .088	− .012	− .008	− .011	− .020
82. Rock Springs, Wyo.	− .001	− .036	− .034	− .093	− .093	− .169	− .177	+ .011	+ .009	+ .011	+ .019
83. Paxton, Nebr.	+ .002	− .014	− .016	− .041	− .043	− .073	− .077	− .008	− .006	− .006	− .004
85. North Hero, Vt.	− .009	.000	− .001	− .003	− .007	− .012	− .018	− .001	.000	+ .003	+ .003
86. Lake Placid, N. Y.	+ .032	− .011	− .012	− .024	− .021	− .033	− .020	+ .004	+ .005	+ .001	− .009
87. Potsdam, N. Y.	− .004	− .002	− .003	− .008	− .010	− .017	− .017	+ .019	+ .020	+ .021	+ .019
88. Wilson, N. Y	− .002	.000	− .002	− .003	− .004	− .011	− .017	− .012	− .010	− .011	− .006
89. Alpena, Mich.	.000	− .004	− .003	− .010	− .008	− .016	− .016	− .022	− .023	− .024	− .022
Mean with regard to sign								+ .002	+ .003	+ .003	+ .001
Mean without regard to sign								.017	.017	.017	.019
Stations not in United States											
15. Gornergrat, Switzerland	+ .165	− .049	− .047	− .099	− 081	− 140	− .093	[2]+ .049	+ .047	+ .031	+ .002
16. St. Maurice, Switzerland	− .091	− .021	− .024	− .064	− .069	− 103	− .086	+ .003	+ .006	+ .008	− .014
8. Honolulu, Hawaiian Islands	+ .162	− .001	− .001	+ .011	+ 019	+ 072	+ .137	+ .052	+ .052	+ .044	− .018
9. Mauna Kea, Hawaiian Islands	+ .489	− .049	− .036	− .070	− 036	− 020	+ .108	+ .183	+ .170	+ .149	+ .055
Mean with regard to sign								+ .072	+ .069	+ .058	+ .007
Mean without regard to sign								.072	.069	.058	.021

[1] See p. 74.   [2] See p. 81.

The mean, without regard to sign, of the anomalies by the new method for the 41 stations in the United States shown in the above table is 0.017 dyne. For the regional compensation the means, without regard to sign, for the anomalies of the same stations are 0.017 dyne, 0.017 dyne, and 0.019 dyne, respectively, for the three cases of areas limited by zones K, M, and O.

The mean anomaly, without regard to sign, for these 41 stations in the United States is practically the same for the two methods of distribution of compensation. The mean, without regard to sign, for the regional compensation only, with zones K and M limiting the area, is the same as for the local compensation—that is, 0.017 dyne—while the mean, without regard to sign, for the regional compensation is 0.019 dyne for zone O.

The means, without regard to sign, of the anomalies for the six stations, Nos. 54, 62, 65, 66, 80, 81, on or near the coast, are as follows: Local compensation, 0.023 dyne; regional compensation to zones K, M, and O, 0.023, 0.023, and 0.028 dyne, respectively.

The means, without regard to sign, of the anomalies for the 14 stations, Nos. 57, 58, 59, 60, 61, 72, 73, 74, 76, 77, 83, 87, 88, 89, which are in the interior of the United States and not in mountainous regions, are: Local compensation, 0.020 dyne; regional compensation to zones K, M, and O, 0.020, 0.021, and 0.020 dyne, respectively.

The means, without regard to sign, of the anomalies for the 21 stations, Nos. 42, 43, 44, 45, 46, 48, 49, 55, 63, 64, 67, 68, 69, 70, 71, 75, 78, 79, 82, 85, 86, in the above table, which are in the mountainous regions, are: Local compensation, 0.013 dyne; regional compensation to zones K, M, and O, 0.013, 0.014, and 0.017 dyne, respectively.

The means for the stations in the interior not in mountainous regions show that there are no differences of importance in the four mean anomalies. This is what one would expect with no prominent topographic features near a station, the effect of the compensation being practically the same whether the compensation is local or distributed uniformly over an area of greater extent.

The results for the stations at or near the coast and those in mountainous regions show that the mean, without regard to sign, is practically the same for the method of local distribution and for regional distribution with zones K and M limiting the area considered. The mean anomaly for the method of regional distribution, with zone O limiting the area in the case of stations on or near the coast, is 22 per cent larger than the anomaly of the method of local compensation. The mean anomaly for the mountain stations in the case of regional distribution to zone O is 31 per cent greater than the anomaly for the local compensation.

If the separate anomalies in the United States be compared, it is found that in 16 cases out of 41 the anomaly with local compensation assumed is smaller than with regional compensation assumed uniformly distributed to zone K (18.8 kilometers), and only 13 cases in which it is larger. Similarly, there are 20 cases out of 41 in which the anomaly with local compensation is smaller than with regional compensation extending to zone M (58.8 kilometers), and only 15 cases in which it is larger. There are 26 cases out of 41 in which the anomaly with local compensation assumed is smaller than with regional compensation assumed to extend to zone O (166.7 kilometers), and only 12 cases in which it is larger. In all other cases the two anomalies compared are identical to the last decimal place used, the third.

The evidence either for or against local compensation in comparison with such regional compensation distributed uniformly over these moderate distances is necessarily slight and possibly inconclusive. For, as shown in the table, the difference between computed effects of compensation in the two cases compared is very small upon an average. The whole evidence is furnished by these very small differences, which are frequently less than the errors of observation and computation. As shown by the table, there is but one station among the 41—namely, No. 43, Pikes Peak—at which the difference between the computed effect of local compensation and the computed effect of regional compensation uniformly distributed to zone K exceeds 0.004. Such a difference tends to become greater as the distance over which the regional compensation is supposed to be uniformly distributed is increased, but columns 7 and 8 of the table show that even when the regional compensation is assumed to extend to zone O, a distance of 166.7 kilometers from the station, there is only one station among the 41—namely, station No. 54, San Francisco—at which the difference between the computed effect of local compensation and the computed effect of regional compensation exceeds 0.017 dyne.

Nevertheless the evidence, slight as it necessarily is, indicates that the assumption of local compensation is nearer the truth than the assumption of regional compensation uniformly distributed to zone K (18.8 kilometers). The evidence is still stronger in the same direction when the comparison is made between local compensation and regional compensation extending uniformly to the greater distances, 58.8 and 166.7 kilometers, represented by zones M and O.

It is possible that the assumption of regional compensation only, extending uniformly to some distance from the station less than 18.8 kilometers, may be nearer the truth than the assumption of local compensation. But it is evident that it would be exceedingly difficult to test this supposition effectively by gravity observations, for the evidence available would necessarily consist in general of still smaller differences than the very small differences dealt with above in connection with the comparison of local compensation and regional compensation extending to zone K. It appears to the writers, therefore, that the large amount of labor necessary to extend this investigation to the remaining 48 stations in the United States, or to smaller assumed distances as limits for the assumed regional compensation, would not be justified at this time by the results, as the evidence secured would probably be inconclusive. At some future time, when more evidence is available from additional gravity stations, an extension of the investigation may be advisable.

The evidence shown at the bottom of the table from four stations not in the United States is conflicting and inconclusive. In this connection one should consider the peculiar conditions at the two stations on the Hawaiian Islands. These are islands which are evidently of volcanic origin and where the processes of vulcanism are still apparently active.

It is stated above, in substance, to be the belief of the writers that the evidence indicates, though it does not prove, that the assumption of local compensation is nearer the truth than the assumption of regional compensation only, distributed uniformly to a distance of 166.7 kilometers, or 58.8 kilometers, or even to the small distance 18.8 kilometers from the station. It is also admitted as a possibility that an assumption of regional compensation only, distributed to some still smaller distance from the station, may be nearer the truth than the assumption of local compensation. If the writers stopped their statement of the case here their real views might be misunderstood. It is hoped, therefore, that the following quotations from page 11 of this publication will prevent misunderstanding:

"The authors do not believe that any one of these assumptions upon which the computations are based is absolutely accurate."

"It is especially improbable that the compensation is complete under each separate small area, under each hill, each narrow valley, and each little depression in the sea bottom. It is exceedingly improbable, for example, that as each ton of material is eroded from a land area, carried out of a river mouth, and deposited on the ocean bottom, the corresponding changes of isostatic compensation occur at the same time under the eroded area and under the area of deposition at just such a rate as to keep the compensation complete under each. The authors believe that the assumptions upon which the computations are based are a close approximation to the truth.".

The following paragraph,* written before the investigation of this particular question by means of gravity observations was commenced, expresses the belief of the writers of the present publication:

"In the above statement that the separate topographic features of the continent are compensated, it is not intended to assert that every minute topographic feature, such, for example, as a hill covering a single square mile, is separately compensated. It is believed that the larger topographic features are compensated. It is an interesting and important problem for future study to determine the maximum size, in the horizontal sense, which a topographic feature may have and still not have beneath it an approximation to complete isostatic compensation. It is certain from the results of this investigation that the continent as a whole is closely compensated and that areas as large as States are also closely compensated. It is the writer's belief that each area as large as one degree square is generally largely compensated. The writer predicts that future investigations will show that the maximum horizontal extent which a topographic feature may have and still escape compensation is between one square mile and one square degree. This prediction is based, in part, upon a consideration of the mechanics of the problem."

It seems clear to the writers that if the area taken be sufficiently small immediately surrounding a station, the assumption of regional compensation only, uniformly distributed over this area will be nearer the truth than local compensation distributed strictly in accordance with the elevations within an area. It appears, however, from the inconclusive evidence furnished by the gravity observations that the radius of this area is probably less than 18.8 kilometers, which radius is within the outer limit indicated in the preceding paragraph. It also appears that the gravity observations will probably not yield conclusive evidence as to which hypothesis is nearer the truth for still smaller areas since the differences between the effects according to the two hypotheses applied to these very small areas are so minute as to be very difficult to observe.

---

* From p. 169 of The Figure of the Earth and Isostasy from Measurements in the United States.

TEST OF DEPTH OF COMPENSATION.

In this investigation, as stated on page 10, the isostatic compensation has been assumed to be complete and uniformly distributed to the depth of 113.7 kilometers. This was the most probable value of the depth of compensation available at the time the investigation was commenced. This depth had been obtained from investigations based entirely upon observed deflections of the vertical in the United States. Later portions of those investigations have shown that the most probable value now available for the depth of compensation is 122 kilometers.[*]

It is evidently desirable, before concluding the present investigation, to ascertain whether it is possible to determine the depth of compensation from the gravity observations with as great accuracy as it has already been determined from the observed deflections of the vertical, and whether numerical corrections of importance would result from changing the assumed depth from 113.7 to 122 kilometers. Accordingly, the approximate test here reported upon was made to settle these two questions.

For the assumed depth of compensation, 85.3 kilometers, the values of E_R were computed for a few values of θ (θ being the distance from the station expressed in angular measure) by the methods and formulæ set forth on pages 23 and 24. Each of these values was compared with the corresponding values, as shown on page 25, computed for the assumed depth of compensation, 113.7 kilometers. The comparisons indicated that the reduction in E_R caused by changing the assumed depth from 113.7 to 85.3 kilometers, if expressed as a percentage, varied but little from zone to zone among the numbered zones. Accordingly, a few computations only, made it possible to construct the part of the table shown below which refers to numbered zones.

Similarly, the effect of compensation alone was computed for some of the lettered zones on the assumption that the depth of compensation is 85.3. It appeared that the change of the assumed depth from 113.7 to 85.3 reduced the computed effect of compensation by amounts which, expressed as a percentage, were practically constant (at 33 per cent) from zones A to zone F, and beyond that point changed in a regular manner, as shown in the first part of the table printed below.

Percentage of change in compensation and in E_R when the assumed depth of compensation is changed from 113.7 to 85.3 kilometers.

Zone	Compensation	Zone	E_R
A	+33	18	−17
B	+33	17	−18
C	+33	16	−19
D	+33	15	−21
E	+33	14	−22
F	+33	13	−23
G	+32	12	−24
H	+32	11	−24
I	+31	10	−24
J	+29	9	−24
K	+27	8	−25
L	+23	7	−25
M	+14	6	−25
N	+03	5	−25
O	−11	4	−25
		3	−25
		2	−25
		1	−25

By use of this table the changes shown in the following table for 10 stations in the United States and 1 in the Hawaiian Islands were computed. In making the special investigations stated under the heading, "Regional versus local distribution of compensation," the effect of compensation alone for each lettered zone had already been computed for certain stations, including the 11 used in the present test. Hence, for these zones the required change, as shown below, was obtained at once by multiplying the effect of compensation for a given zone by the percentage shown in the preceding table for that zone. For each numbered zone at a station the total correction for that zone, as shown in the tables on pages 54–58 and 84, was multiplied by the percentage of reduction in E_R for the zone, as shown in the above table, the total correction for the zone being sensibly proportional to E_R.

Changes in computed correction for topography and compensation produced by changing the assumed depth of compensation from 113.7 to 85.3 kilometers.

[All tabular values are in units of the fourth decimal place in dynes.]

Zone	Pembina, No. 59	Grand Canyon, No. 69	Pikes Peak, No. 43	San Francisco, No. 54	Mauna Kea, Hawaiian Islands	Gallup, No. 70	Grand Junction, No. 46	Mount Hamilton, No. 55	Salt Lake City, No. 49	Lake Placid, No. 86	Iron River, No. 57
A	0	0	0	0	0	0	0	0	0	0	0
B	0	0	− 2	0	− 1	0	0	0	0	0	0
C	0	0	− 2	0	− 3	− 1	− 1	0	− 1	0	0
D	0	− 2	− 5	0	− 6	− 2	− 2	−2	− 2	0	0
E	0	− 3	− 8	0	− 8	− 5	− 3	−3	− 3	− 1	0
F	0	− 3	−12	0	−13	− 7	− 3	−3	− 3	− 2	0
G	0	− 5	−13	0	−16	− 8	− 5	−4	− 5	− 4	0
H	0	− 8	−18	0	−18	−10	− 7	−5	− 7	− 2	0
I	0	−15	−28	0	−30	−19	−13	−6	−13	− 6	− 6
J	−5	−18	−28	0	−23	−23	−15	−6	−17	− 7	− 5
K	−5	−29	−38	0	−30	−32	−26	−8	−25	−11	−10
L	−5	−34	−42	− 2	−26	−39	−36	−4	−32	−12	−10
M	−7	−50	−60	− 3	−15	−58	−56	−3	−49	−10	−12
N	0	0	− 1	0	0	− 1	− 1	0	− 1	0	0
O	+7	+29	+40	−11	−37	+35	+38	0	+33	+ 5	+ 6
18	+2	+10	+12	− 4	−12	+11	+13	0	+11	+ 2	+ 1
17	+2	+10	+12	− 4	−14	+11	+14	0	+12	+ 2	+ 1
16	+2	+ 9	+13	− 4	−16	+12	+14	0	+12	+ 2	+ 1
15	+3	+10	+13	− 4	−17	+14	+14	0	+14	+ 2	+ 1
14	+3	+11	+13	− 4	−18	+14	+14	−2	+14	+ 2	+ 2
13	+6	+19	+19	− 6	−36	+21	+23	−5	+25	+ 3	+ 4
12	+3	+13	+12	− 6	−24	+11	+13	−5	+15	+ 1	+ 3
11	+3	+ 6	+ 7	− 5	−20	+ 8	+ 8	−5	+ 9	− 1	+ 2
10	+3	+ 1	+ 4	− 3	−15	+ 2	+ 4	−4	+ 3	− 3	+ 2
9	+2	− 1	0	− 2	− 9	− 1	− 1	−2	− 1	− 2	0
8	+1	− 3	− 2	− 4	−10	− 3	− 3	−4	− 3	− 3	0
7	−1	− 2	− 2	− 2	− 5	− 2	− 2	−2	− 2	− 2	− 1
6	−2	− 2	− 2	− 2	− 5	− 2	− 2	−2	− 2	− 2	− 2
5	−3	− 2	− 2	− 2	− 2	− 2	− 2	−2	− 2	− 2	− 2
4	−2	− 2	− 2	− 2	− 1	− 2	− 2	−2	− 2	− 2	− 1
3	−1	− 2	− 1	− 1	− 1	− 1	− 1	−1	− 1	− 1	− 1
2	−1	− 1	− 1	− 1	− 1	− 1	− 1	−1	− 1	− 1	− 1
1	0	0	0	0	0	0	0	0	0	0	0
Total.	+5	−64	−124	−72	−432	−80	−27	−81	−24	−55	−28

The total change shown for each station at the bottom of the above table is repeated to three decimal places in the third column of the following table. The values in the second column were obtained from the table on page 74. The values in the fourth column were obtained by combining those in the second and third columns. The values in the fifth column were obtained from the table on page 76. The values in the last column were obtained by combining those in the third and fifth columns.

Number and name of station	Correction for topography and compensation, depth 113.7 km.	Effect of change of depth from 113.7 to 85.3 km.	Correction for topography and compensation, depth 85 3 km.	Anomaly g-γ +0.007, depth 113.7 km.	Anomaly g-γ +0.007, depth 85.3 km.
	Dynes	*Dynes*	*Dynes*	*Dynes*	*Dynes*
59. Pembina	−0. 009	+0. 001	−0. 008	+0. 017	+0. 016
69. Grand Canyon	− . 096	− . 006	− . 102	− . 012	− . 006
43. Pikes Peak	+ . 187	− . 012	+ . 175	+ . 019	+ . 031
54. San Francisco	+ . 045	− . 007	+ . 038	− . 025	− . 018
70. Gallup	+ . 014	− . 008	+ . 006	− . 015	− . 007
46. Grand Junction	− . 051	− . 003	− . 054	+ . 022	+ . 025
55. Mount Hamilton	+ . 120	− . 008	+ . 112	− . 005	+ . 003
49. Salt Lake City	− . 041	− . 002	− . 044	+ . 008	+ . 010
86. Lake Placid	+ . 032	− . 006	− . 026	+ . 004	+ . 010
57. Iron River	+ . 014	− . 003	+ . 011	+ . 036	+ . 039
Means without regard to sign		.006		.016	.016

The maximum change at any one station is only 0.012 dyne and the mean of the changes without regard to sign is only 0.006. These changes, though due to a large change in assumed depth of compensation, namely, from 113.7 to 85.3. are all smaller than the average anomaly without regard to sign, 0.017. (See p. 76.)

A comparison of the anomalies in the last two columns shows very little advantage of either column over the other. The mean without regard to sign is 0.016 in each case. Five values in the last column are larger and five smaller than the corresponding values in the preceding column. The sum of the squares of the quantities in the last column is, however, 0.003 981, which is larger than the corresponding sum 0.003 529 of the preceding column. This last test furnishes a slight indication that the assumed depth 113.7 is nearer the truth than 85.3. *

On the whole, the figures indicate that the depth of compensation can not be determined from these 10 stations, and probably could not be determined from all of the 89 gravity stations available in the United States, with an accuracy nearly as great as that with which it has already been determined from the 765 deflections of the vertical observed in the United States. Hence, it does not seem desirable to make the attempt.

As the average effect of changing the assumed depth by 28.4 kilometers from 113.7 to 85.3 was a change of only 0.006 dyne, it appears that a change of 8 kilometers in the assumed depth from 113.7, that used in this publication, to 122, the best value now available, would produce a change of less than 0.002 dyne in the computed anomalies on an average. Such changes are too small to be of importance in the present investigation. They would not affect any of the conclusions drawn.

It should be noted that the values in the third column in the above table are all negative save one; that is, a decrease in the assumed depth of compensation produces a negative change as a rule in the computed effect of topography and compensation and a positive change in the computed anomaly. Hence, if the assumed depth were changed from 113.7 to the more probable value, 122 kilometers, the general tendency would be to produce a negative change in the computed anomalies probably little more than 0.001 dyne on an average.

As it appears from this approximate test that the depth of compensation may be determined from the gravity observations with a low degree of accuracy only, so also it seems evident that there is little hope of determining from the gravity observations the distribution of the compensation with respect to depth. Such an investigation was attempted by the use of observed deflections of the vertical with but little success. †

---

*For Mauna Kea, in the Hawaiian Islands, it was found that the change of assumed depth of compensation from 113.7 to 85.3 decreased the correction for topography and compensation by 0.043 dyne. The computed anomaly corresponding to depth 113.7 was found to be +0.183 dyne and for depth 85.3 was found to be +0.226 dyne.

† The Figure of the Earth and Isostasy, etc., p. 149–163, 175.

GRAPHICAL COMPARISON OF THREE KINDS OF ANOMALIES.

A comparison of illustrations Nos. 16, 17, and 18, contained in the pocket at the end of this volume, will supplement the comparisons of the three kinds of anomalies made on pages 79 and 80.

On each of these illustrations the location of each station is shown by a black circle and near it the number of the station (see table on p. 76) is shown in black. The anomaly at the station is shown in black. In order to bring out more clearly the information contained in the anomalies as printed on these maps, lines of equal anomaly at intervals of 0.010 dyne have been drawn through points fixed by interpolating between adjacent stations. In constructing these contour lines of the surface representing anomalies, each station was connected by straight lines with the stations nearest it in each direction. Interpolations were then made along each of these lines to fix points through which the contours were drawn. This method is arbitrary in part, and it leads in some rare cases to apparent absurdities. In a few cases only have contours been changed and the apparent absurdities thereby eliminated. These few cases will be noted later. The contours are to be considered as generalized. Without doubt numerous changes would be made in them if there were many more stations in the area under consideration.

The positive contours are shown in black and the minus contours in red. The zero contour is shown by a heavy red line. A positive anomaly corresponds to an excess of observed gravity and a negative anomaly to a defect.

Illustration No. 16 shows the anomaly contours for the new method of reduction. In each of several places where two or more stations are very close together the mean anomaly was used in the interpolation of contour points. These pairs and groups were Nos. 10 and 11; Nos. 21, 22, and 84; Nos. 26 and 27; Nos. 29 and 30; Nos. 42 and 43; Nos. 50, 51, and 52; and Nos. 68 and 69. After being fixed by direct interpolation the contours were modified somewhat in southern Texas, and also in New York southeast of station No. 32, where the −0.020 contour was modified to avoid an absurdity.

Note that on this illustration, as well as on illustrations Nos. 17 and 18, the stations Nos. 53 and 56 at Seattle, Wash., have been used in constructing the contours, although in certain other parts of this investigation these two stations have been rejected.

There is no apparent relation between the contours on illustration No. 16 and the topography and there is no great preponderance of positive over negative areas or vice versa.

The Bouguer anomalies are shown in illustration No. 17. In each of several places where two or more stations are very close together the mean anomaly was used in the interpolation of contour points. These pairs and groups are Nos. 10 and 11; Nos. 21, 22, and 84; Nos. 26 and 27; Nos. 29 and 30; Nos. 42 and 43; Nos. 50, 51, and 52; and Nos. 68 and 69. The zero contour in the southeastern part of the United States was somewhat modified, from the form given by direct interpolation only along stated lines between stations, in order to avoid a very slender strip of positive area which would have appeared to extend from station No. 4 to station No. 18 past station No. 16, at which point it would have had zero width.

Illustration No. 17, showing the Bouguer anomalies, stands in decided contrast to illustration No. 16, showing new-method anomalies, in the following respects:

First, on illustration No. 17, the negative (red) areas cover nearly the whole map, the only positive (black) areas in the interior being a small one surrounding station No. 74 in Minnesota and one of moderate size surrounding stations No. 13 and No. 6 in Louisiana and Arkansas. All other positive areas are confined to the vicinity of the coasts, and in the aggregate they are small. There is no such great preponderance of negative areas on illustration No. 16, though the negative areas cover somewhat more than one half of the map.

Second, it is evident from illustration No. 17 that the negative Bouguer anomalies tend to be greater, the greater is the elevation of the earth's surface. Their average value along the coasts is nearly zero. In the interior in the comparatively low eastern one-half of the United States their average value is apparently between −0.020 and −0.030, but in the comparatively high western one-half of the country the average value is more than −0.100. Two large negative areas surrounded by contours marked −0.200 occur in the highest part of the Rocky Mountain region. No such relation of anomalies to topography shows on illustration No. 16.

Third, the anomalies shown on illustration No. 17 are much larger than those shown in illustration No. 16; about four times as large on an average.

These three contrasts are strong evidence that the assumptions involved in the new method of reduction are much nearer the truth than those involved in the Bouguer method.

The free-air anomalies are shown on illustration No. 18. The mean anomaly was used for each of the following pairs or groups of close stations in constructing the contours: Nos. 21, 22, and 84; Nos. 26 and 27; Nos. 29 and 30, and Nos. 50, 51, and 52. The contours were smoothed out slightly in southern Texas in the vicinity of stations Nos. 9, 10, 11, and 62.

The anomalies for stations Nos. 43, 55, and 69 were not used in constructing the contours on illustration No. 18. No. 43 is on the summit of Pikes Peak, much higher than the two adjacent stations, Nos. 42 at Colorado Springs and No. 44 at Denver, which were used in constructing the contours. No. 55 is on Mount Hamilton, much higher than No. 54 at San Francisco on which the contours in this vicinity are based. Station No. 69 is at the bottom of the Grand Canyon of the Colorado, far below the general level of this region. The contours near this locality are based on station No. 68 on the rim of the canyon. The difference between the anomalies of the high and low stations of each of these pairs is great and in each case the station which has been rejected in drawing the contours is far above or far below the general level of the region and has a very large anomaly. This is the characteristic of the free-air reduction and is a strong indication that this method is far from the truth in mountainous country.

This rejection of stations Nos. 43, 55, and 69 in constructing contour lines on illustration No. 18 has made these contours show much more favorably for the free-air method of reduction than they otherwise would do, for in each case the contours have been based upon the station of the pair which has the smaller anomaly. Even with this discrimination in favor of illustration No. 18 it still compares unfavorably with illustration No. 16, as indicated in the following paragraph:

A close comparison between illustration No. 18 and No. 16 shows that in general the same areas of excess and of defect show on both, but as a rule the maximum anomaly in each area is greater on illustration No. 18 than on illustration No. 16, as indicated in the two tables which follow:

Negative areas, gravity in defect.

States in which the maximum anomalies occur	Maximum New Method anomaly, Illustration 16		Maximum Free-air anomaly, Illustration 18	
	Station	Amount	Station	Amount
New York	32	−0.025	32	−0.027
South Carolina	17	− .023	17	* − .014
Georgia	15	− .025	15	* − .018
Ohio	34	− .021	34	− .026
Michigan	89	− .022	89	− .029
Oklahoma	12	− .029	12	− .035
Texas	9	− .022	9	− .026
Texas	61	− .031	61	* − .029
Colorado	44	− .018	44	− .040
Utah	47	− .023	47	− .073
Arizona	64	− .052	64	* − .021
California	66	− .052	66	− .059
California	54	− .025	54	* − .013
Washington	53	− .095	53	− .122
Mean		− .033		− .038

* These 5 are the only cases out of 14 in which the maximum in a given area is less on illustration No. 18 than on illustration No. 16.

Positive areas, gravity in excess.

States in which the maximum anomalies occur ·	Maximum New Method anomaly, Illustration 16		Maximum Free-air anomaly, Illustration 18	
	Station	Amount	Station	Amount
New York ·	87	+0.019	86	+0.029
New Jersey, New York	26	+ .022	27	+ .024
District of Columbia, Maryland	22	+ .037	20	+ .042
South Carolina	16	+ .013	16	+ .018
Florida	2	+ .016	2	+ .040
Arkansas, Tennessee	13	+ .028	14	* + .023
Minnesota	74	+ .057	74	* + .045
South Dakota	75	+ .050	75	+ .087
Texas	72	+ .030	72	+ .030
Texas	62	+ .029	62	+ .035
Texas	8	+ .025	8	+ .033
Mean		+ .030		.037

* These 2 are the only cases out of 11 in which the maximum in a given area is less on Illustration No. 18 than on Illustration No. 16.

In general the anomalies by the free-air method are distributed in much the same way as those by the new method, but they are clearly larger as a rule. The assumptions upon which the new-method computations are based are evidently somewhat nearer the truth than those on which the free-air method is based.

Illustrations Nos. 16, 17, and 18 thus confirm the conclusions reached on pages 76–80.

INTERPRETATION OF ANOMALIES IN TERMS OF MASSES.

In order to obtain a clear conception of the meaning of the new-method anomalies it is desirable to interpret them in terms of excesses and deficiencies of mass.

If, after computation by the new method, the anomaly at every station was found to be zero, one would be certain that everywhere the isostatic compensation is complete and uniformly distributed to the depth of 113.7 kilometers, that being the assumption on which the computation was made.

In the actual case the anomaly at each station by the new method is found to be small but not zero. This indicates that there exists a close approach to the condition indicated in the preceding paragraph. The departures from this condition may be expressed in terms of excesses and deficiencies of density, or in equivalent terms of excesses and deficiencies of mass, these being reckoned from the condition of complete compensation expressed in the preceding paragraph as a standard.

In general a positive anomaly—that is, an excess of gravity—must be produced by a net effective excess of mass below the horizon of the station. In some rare cases in which the station is below the general level of the region surrounding it a positive anomaly may be produced by a defect of mass in that portion of the topography lying above the station, the material above the station having a density less than that assumed in the computations, namely, 2.67. Similarly a negative anomaly—a defect of gravity—must in general be produced by a net effective deficiency of mass below the horizon of the station, but may possibly be produced by an excess of mass above the station.

The guarded expression "net effective excess of mass" is necessary for correctness. It has been shown that to compute gravity at a station with the required degree of accuracy it is necessary to take into account both the topography and its isostatic compensation to a long distance from the station (p. 71). So it is necessary in interpreting the anomaly in terms of excesses and deficiencies of mass to consider the excesses and deficiencies to a great distance from the station. Within the large area of influence considered for any one station there are in general both excesses and deficiencies. It is, therefore, the net excess or the balance of excesses over deficiencies below the horizon of a given station that produces an excess of gravity at that station. Moreover, a given mass has a maximum effect in increasing gravity if it is immediately below the station and in the same vertical as the station; it has a smaller effect if it is in that vertical but far below the station, 10 miles or perhaps 50 miles below; its effect is still smaller if it is displaced horizontally from either of these positions so that the line joining the station with it is not vertical; and the effect is zero if the line from the station to the mass is horizontal at the station. In other words, a given mass is more or less effective in producing a vertical attraction at a station according to its distance and direction with reference to the horizontal from the station. All of these considerations must be kept in mind in connection with the statement that an excess of gravity at a given station must in general be produced by a net effective excess of mass below the horizon of the station.

The effectiveness of masses in different locations with reference to the station is indicated in convenient form for the present purpose in the following table:

[Each tabular value is the vertical attraction in dynes produced at a station by a mass equivalent to a stratum 100 feet thick, of density 2.67, and of the horizontal extent indicated in the left-hand argument, if that mass is uniformly distributed from the level of the station down to the depth indicated in the top argument and from the station in all directions horizontally to the distance indicated in the left-hand argument.]

Radius of mass	Depth—				
	1000 feet	5000 feet	10 000 feet	15 000 feet	113.7 kilometers
1280 meters (the outer radius of zone E).	0.0029	0.0018	0.0011	0.0008	0.0000
166.7 kilometers (the outer radius of zone O).	.0037	.0034	.0034	.0034	.0024
1190 kilometers (or 10° 44′, the outer radius of zone 10).	.0040	.0037	.0037	.0037	.0035

The value 0.0029 dyne in the first line and the second column means that a mass equivalent to a circular disk 100 feet thick with a radius of 1280 meters uniformly distributed around the station to the outer limit of zone E (outer radius 1280 meters) and to a depth of 1000 feet would produce a vertical attraction at the station of 0.0029 dyne. If, however, the mass were equivalent to a circular disk * 100 feet thick with a radius of 1190 kilometers distributed around the station throughout zone 10 and smaller zones to a depth of 1000 feet, it would produce a vertical attraction at the station of 0.0040 dyne, as shown by the last value in the second column. The very large additional mass beyond zone E in this case as compared with the first case has increased the vertical attraction by only 0.0011 dyne (from 0.0029 to 0.0040). Corresponding interpretations apply to each of the values in the table.

In each of the cases represented in the second column the mass considered is equivalent to a stratum 100 feet thick but is assumed to be uniformly distributed through a depth of 1000 feet. It corresponds, therefore, to an excess of density of 1/10 of 2.67 or 0.27. Similarly the values in the fourth column for the equivalent of a stratum 100 feet thick distributed through a depth of 10 000 feet correspond to an excess of density of 1/100 of 2.67 or 0.03. The values in the last column correspond to very small excesses in density, 1 part in 3700, 100 feet being 1/3700 of 113.7 kilometers.

If in any one of these cases the excess of mass considered corresponds to a stratum 200 feet (or 300 feet) thick with all other conditions as above, the excess of density is twice (or, thrice) that indicated in the preceding paragraph, and the vertical attraction produced is twice (or thrice) that shown in the table.

The table also applies to deficiencies of mass, it being understood that a deficiency of mass corresponds to a reduction in the vertical attraction at the station.

The second line of the table shows that a mass equivalent to a circular disk 100 feet thick with a radius of 166.7 kilometers uniformly distributed around the station to the outer limit of zone O would produce a vertical attraction at the station of 0.0037 dyne if distributed uniformly from the station down to the depth of 1000 feet, 0.0034 if uniformly distributed down to a

---

* Strictly the disk in this case is supposed to be saucer-shaped to fit the sphere, as that is the basis on which all the computations have been made.

depth of between 5000 and 15 000 feet, and only 0.0024 if uniformly distributed to a depth of 113.7 kilometers.

Let this table be now applied to an approximate interpretation of observed new-method anomalies in terms of excesses and deficiencies of mass.

The mean new-method anomaly without regard to sign is 0.017 dyne. (See p. 76 and illustration No. 16.) It is certain that a positive anomaly of this magnitude, 0.017 dyne, is not entirely produced by excess of density confined to the first 1000 feet of depth. For, if so limited, the last value (0.0040 dyne) in the column of the preceding table headed 1000 feet shows that even if the excess extended continuously in all directions from the station to a distance of 1190 kilometers, it would necessarily be equivalent to a stratum more than 400 feet thick added to the normal stratum 1000 feet thick, or in other words, the density of the 1000 foot stratum nearest the surface of the earth must be 40 per cent greater than the normal (2.67), namely, 3.74. It is certain that so great a mean density as this for so large a mass does not exist near the surface of the earth. Therefore, any actual positive anomaly of this magnitude must be produced in part at least by excesses of mass more than 1000 feet below the surface.

The other two values in the column headed 1000 feet show that if the excess of mass is supposed to be limited to the shorter horizontal distance from the station, to 166.7 kilometers, or 1280 meters, the excess of density necessary to account for the anomaly would be still greater.

Similar reasoning may be applied to a negative anomaly of 0.017 dyne and it may be shown that such an anomaly can not be produced by deficiencies of density confined to the first 1000 feet below the earth's surface.

On the other hand, it is possible that a positive anomaly of 0.017 dyne may be produced by excesses of density confined to the first 15 000 feet below the surface of the earth. The second value (0.0034 dyne) in the column headed 15 000 feet in the preceding table shows that an excess of mass equivalent to a stratum of normal density 500 feet thick * extending for 166.7 kilometers in every direction from the station and uniformly distributed to the depth of 15 000 feet would produce a positive anomaly of 0.017 dyne. Such a 500-foot stratum added to the normal stratum 15 000 feet thick without increase of volume would increase its density by only 1 part in 30 or from 2.67 to 2.76. It is possible that such an excess of density for a mass of this magnitude does exist at some places in the earth. Similarly it is possible that a negative anomaly of 0.017 may be produced by deficiencies of density confined to the first 15 000 feet below the earth's surface.

The last value in the column, 15 000 feet, shows that if the excess of density extends even to so great a distance as 1190 kilometers from the station each equivalent of a 100-foot stratum produces a vertical attraction of 0.0037 dyne, and the equivalent of a 460-foot stratum is necessary to produce an anomaly of 0.017 dyne.

The preceding considerations show that the typical mean new-method anomaly of 0.017 dyne may be produced by excesses (or deficiencies) of density confined to depths less than 15 000 feet but more than 1000 feet. But the evidence of the observed deflections of the vertical † indicates that probably these typical anomalies are ordinarily produced in part, possibly largely, by excesses (or deficiencies) of density more than 15 000 feet below the earth's surface, probably as far as 113.7, or 122, kilometers below, for the deflections of the vertical have shown that the isostatic compensation if uniformly distributed with respect to depth extends to a depth of 122 kilometers (113.7 according to the earlier investigation). Down to this depth there is a relation of subsurface densities to surface elevations. Inasmuch as this relation is apparently maintained with considerable accuracy even when the surface elevations change greatly during the progress of geologic time ‡ there is an apparent changing from time to time of subsurface densities to a depth of 122 kilometers. It is probable, therefore, that the typical

---

* The vertical attraction at the station produced by a mass equivalent to a stratum 100 feet thick being 0.0034 dyne, that produced by a mass equivalent to a stratum 500 feet thick is five times as great, or 0.017 dyne.

† This evidence is discussed in The Figure of the Earth and Isostasy from Measurements in the United States and Supplementary Investigation in 1909 of The Figure of the Earth and Isostasy.

‡ The Figure of the Earth and Isostasy, etc., pp. 166-168.

anomalies of 0.017 dyne are produced in part at least by very small excesses (or deficiencies) of density which extend to as great a depth as the isostatic compensation itself, 122 kilometers, and that the anomalies are produced in part at least by the failure of the processes (whatever they are), which produced isostatic compensation, to maintain the densities at the precise values necessary for perfect isostatic compensation.

The last column of the preceding table shows that if a positive anomaly, of 0.017 dyne is produced by an excess of density extending 1190 kilometers in every direction from the station and uniformly distributed throughout a depth of 113.7 kilometers the excess of mass is equivalent to the stratum only 490 feet thick, and that if it extends only 166.7 kilometers from the station it is still equivalent to a stratum only 710 feet thick. In the first case as 490 feet is only 1/760 of 113.7 kilometers the excess of density is only one part in 760. In the second case the excess of density is only one part in 530.

There is some evidence given later in this publication (under the heading ''Relations between gravity anomalies and geological formations'') which indicates that there is a relation between the new-method anomalies and surface geology. This evidence tends to indicate that the anomalies are produced in part by excesses and deficiencies of density near the surface.

The greater the distance from the station to which the continuous excesses (or deficiencies) of density extend the larger one should expect to find the separate continuous areas of positive (or negative) anomaly on illustration No. 16. This illustration indicates, therefore, that probably the continuous excesses (or deficiencies) of density around a station, producing its anomaly, are limited ordinarily to a distance much less than 1190 kilometers, possibly to a distance of the same order of magnitude as 166.7 kilometers.

Taking everything known to the writers into account, including the considerations enumerated above, it appears that the best mean value to adopt from the preceding table is 0.0030 dyne. As a mean working hypothesis it will be assumed therefore, that ordinarily each 0.0030 dyne of anomaly is due to an excess (or deficiency) of mass equivalent to a stratum 100 feet thick. This working hypothesis is equivalent, as may be seen by inspection of the table on page 109, either to the assumption that the excess (or deficiency) of mass is uniformly distributed to a depth of 113.7 kilometers and extends to a distance of more than 166.7 kilometers and less than 1190 kilometers from the station, or that it extends to a distance of 166.7 kilometers from the station and is distributed to an effective mean depth of more than 15 000 feet and less than 113.7 kilometers, or the working hypothesis may be considered to be a combination of these two assumptions.

On this adopted working hypothesis that 0.0030 dyne of anomaly corresponds to 100 feet of stratum the typical mean anomaly of 0.017 dyne corresponds to a stratum only 570 feet thick. In this typical mean case then the isostatic compensation is so nearly complete that at the depth of compensation (122 kilometers) the pressure is in excess of (or less than) the normal for that depth by the pressure due to a weight of a stratum 570 feet thick of density 2.67. This pressure is only 660 pounds per square inch. A safe working load for good granite used in engineering structures is stated by good authority to be 1200 pounds per square inch, and its ultimate crushing strength 19 000 pounds per square inch.* On this same working hypothesis the maximum anomaly observed in the United States, −0.095 dyne at stations Nos. 53 and 56 at Seattle, Wash., corresponds to a defect of mass represented by a stratum 3200 feet thick, corresponding to a deficiency of pressure at the depth of compensation of 3700 pounds per square inch, less than one-fifth of the ultimate crushing strength of good granite.

The new-method anomalies indicate, therefore, that at the depth of compensation the excesses and deficiencies in pressure, referred to the mean value, are upon an average but little more than one-half the safe working load imposed on good granite in engineering structures, which are expected to last indefinitely without deterioration, and that the maximum excess or deficiency in pressure at that depth yet indicated by observations in the United

---

* American Civil Engineer's Pocket-Book, Mansfield Merriman, editor in chief, pp. 498 and 577.

States is only about three times the safe working load for good granite and less than one-fifth its ultimate crushing strength. These excesses and deficiencies of pressure are a measure of the stress differences at that depth available to produce rupture. These considerations indicate that the material down to the depth of compensation behaves as if it were considerably weaker than is granite under the conditions existing at the surface.

From the evidence given by deflections of the vertical the conclusion has been drawn that in the United States the average departure from complete compensation corresponds to excesses or deficiencies of mass represented by a stratum only 250 feet thick on an average.* The gravity determinations indicate this average to be 570 feet instead of 250 feet. In neither case is the average value determined or defined with a high grade of accuracy. The difference between the two determinations of the average value is, therefore, of little importance, The determination given by the gravity observations is probably the more reliable of the two. Each determination is significant mainly as showing that the isostatic compensation is nearly perfect.

POSSIBLE RELATION OF NEW METHOD ANOMALIES TO OTHER THINGS.

The new-method anomalies though smaller than the anomalies by other methods are not zero. They represent, aside from errors of observation and computation, the departures of the actual arrangement of density beneath the surface from that postulated by this method of computation, namely, that the isostatic compensation is complete and uniformly distributed to the limiting depth, 113.7 kilometers. Are there no discoverable relations between these anomalies and other things? If any such relation can be found it may make it possible to take one more forward step in this investigation.

The following paragraphs are a summary of some attempts to discover such a relation.

Relation of anomalies to topography.—On illustration No. 19, showing the gravity anomalies and the residuals of solution H, in the Supplementary Investigation in 1909 of the Figure of the Earth and Isostasy, certain selected contour lines are drawn in order that one may note any general relation of the gravity anomalies to the topography. The writers have been unable to find any relation between the character of the topography, as indicated by the contours, and the sign and size of the gravity anomalies. Illustration No. 16 should also be consulted in this connection.

Relation of anomalies to the deflections of the vertical.—This subject is rather fully covered by the topic, "Discussion of other regional peculiarities." (See pp. 117–121.) It is sufficient to say here that the gravity anomalies corroborate the evidence given by the deflections. In no important case are the anomalies and deflections contradictory.

Relation of anomalies to erosion.—The writers can see no relation between the size and sign of the anomalies and the areas of erosion. It is possible that there is such a relation, but the effect of erosion apparently is so small in comparison with other effects that the connection can not be discovered. One might be inclined to expect that in the areas in which there has been much erosion in recent times gravity would be found in defect.

Relation of anomalies to deposition.—Similarly, one might expect the anomalies to indicate an excess of gravity at stations located at the mouths of rivers where there has been much recent deposition of materials. Station No. 8, at the mouth of the Rio Grande, has an anomaly of +0.025 dyne; station No. 5, at New Orleans, near the mouth of the Mississippi River, has an anomaly of −0.015 dyne; station No. 65, at Yuma, at the edge of a large region of deposition near the mouth of the Colorado River, has an anomaly of· +0.007 dyne; and station No. 80, at the mouth of the Columbia River, has an anomaly of −0.015 dyne. One must conclude from these four cases and from a general examination of illustration No. 16 that there is no appreciable tendency for gravity to be in excess in regions in which there has been much recent deposition.

Relation of anomalies to the contours of the geoid.—A study was made to see if a possible relation could be discovered between the gravity anomalies (shown on illustration No. 16)

---

* The Figure of the Earth and Isostasy, etc., pp. 164–166, and Supplementary Investigation in 1909 of the Figure of the Earth and Isostasy, p. 59.

on the one hand, and the geoid contours (as shown on illustration No. 17 of The Figure of the Earth and Isostasy) on the other hand. Though the evidence is not clear that there is a relation, there are four points of resemblance which seem to indicate that regions of excess of gravity (even after the corrections for topography and compensation have been applied) tend to coincide with high areas on the geoid.

First, the center of the area of excessive gravity in northern New York on illustration No. 16 coincides with a summit on the geoid.

Second, according to illustration No. 16, as one proceeds from east to west along the thirty-ninth parallel in Colorado the anomaly in gravity changes from negative to positive and reaches a positive maximum between longitudes 108° and 109°. This area of excess has a long extension to the northwestward. Similarly on the geoid a maximum elevation in Colorado along the thirty-ninth parallel is found in longitude 107°, but little to the eastward of the maximum excess of gravity, and an extension of this summit to the northwestward is indicated by the geoid contours.

Third, on illustration No. 16 a negative anomaly in gravity is shown in Utah in latitude 39° and longitude 110°. Similarly on the geoid a point lower than its surroundings is shown not far from this location in latitude 39° and longitude 114°.

Fourth, on illustration No. 16 a well-marked defect of gravity is shown in the southern part of California near station No. 66, Compton. On the geoid the contours in this vicinity all have a sharp curvature around this location, indicating a valley on the geoid with steep slopes.

It is believed, however, that these coincidences are in part accidental. The contours of the geoid are drawn from deflections of the vertical, uncorrected for the effect of either topography or compensation, and are largely dependent upon the topography for their position and shape. The gravity contours show no appreciable relation to topography. (See p. 112.) Hence, though the geoid contours may corroborate to a certain extent the evidence given by the gravity contours, yet the geoid contours probably can not be used with much success for predicting the sign or amount of the gravity anomalies. The effects on the geoid contours of the excesses and defects of mass below sea level (which produce gravity anomalies) must ordinarily be masked by the greater effects of the topography and its compensation.

RELATION BETWEEN NEW-METHOD ANOMALIES AND GEOLOGIC FORMATIONS.

The 88 stations * used in this investigation are located geologically as follows: Seven stations (Nos. 15, 16, 43, 45, 57, 58, and 75) are in areas of the pre-Cambrian formation; 19 stations (Nos. 12, 14, 20, 28, 29, 30, 32, 33, 34, 35, 36, 37, 38, 39, 74, 78, 85, 88, and 89) are in the Paleozoic; 17 stations (Nos. 10, 11, 23, 24, 25, 40, 44, 46, 47, 55, 60, 61, 62, 70, 71, 76, and 77) are in the Mesozoic; 20 stations (Nos. 1, 2, 3, 4, 5, 6, 7, 8, 9, 17, 18, 48, 53, 59, 64. 65, 66, 79, 80, and 83) are in the Cenozoic; 19 stations (Nos. 13, 19, 21, 22, 26, 27, 41, 42, 49, 54, 63, 67, 68, 69, 72, 73, 82, 84, and 87) are unclassified, as it was found in each case that there are two or more formations near the station; and 6 stations (Nos. 31, 50, 51, 52, 81, and 86) are in intrusive and effusive formations.

The decision as to the surface geological formation on which the station is located was based entirely upon the geological map of North America bearing the following title: "Carte Géologique de L'Amérique du Nord, Dressée d'apres les sources officelles des Etats Unis, du Canada, de la République du Mexique, de la Commission du Chemin de Fer Intercontinental, etc., Henry Gannett, Géographe, et Bailey Willis, Géologue, Echelle, 1:5 000 000, 1906." In using this map all formations from pre-Cambrian to Neo-Algonkian were classed as pre-Cambrian; all from Paleozoic-Metamorphic to Permian, inclusive, were classed as Paleozoic; all from Triassic to Laramie as Mesozoic; and all from Eocene to Quaternary as Cenozoic.

Among the 19 stations which are placed in the unclassified group there may be mentioned as typical the 3 stations, Nos. 21, 22, and 84 at Washington, D. C., station No. 41 at Wallace,

---

* There are really 89 stations, but only one of the two stations at Seattle was considered, as they are very near together, and the same very large anomaly, —0.095 dyne, is found at each. The introduction of the other station in the table would have made the means for the fourth group slightly larger and so would have merely emphasized the conclusions drawn.

Kans., and station No. 73 at Dennison, Tex.   A boundary between formations of very different age runs through Washington.   Each of the Washington stations is either very near this boundary or else in such a position that it is known that both formations underlie the stations, one at the surface and the other at a small depth below the surface.   In these cases it is uncertain which of the formations should be expected to have the greater influence at the station.   Each of the other two stations cited, Nos. 41 and 73, stands on a long narrow strip of one formation bordered on each side by another formation of much greater horizontal extent on the surface. In these cases also it is uncertain which formation should be expected to have the greater influence upon gravity at the station.   It seems best to include in the unclassified list stations at which there are such uncertainties.

Stations No. 31 at Calais, Me., and No. 86 at Lake Placid, N. Y., have been classified as being on intrusive and effusive formations, as they are so shown on the map cited above.   Other authority indicates that these should be classed as being on pre-Cambrian formations.   There are other stations on which authorities differ as to the formation; also there are various stations for which it is difficult to decide whether the station should be put in the unclassified list.   The writers believe, however, that while the classification here given would probably be changed in a number of cases by substituting other geologic authorities for the map used, and by substituting judgment of other persons for that of the writers,* the net result of the revision would be simply to make minor changes in the figures in the following table without changing any of the conclusions drawn from the table.

The table shown below gives the means of the anomalies with and without regard to sign for the several groups mentioned above.

Geological formation	Stations	Mean with regard to sign	Mean without regard to sign
		Dynes	*Dynes*
Pre-Cambrian	7	+0. 019	0. 026
Paleozoic	19	− . 005	. 015
Mesozoic	17	− . 002	. 015
Cenozoic	20	− . 011	. 021
Unclassified	19	+ . 008	. 018
Intrusive and effusive	6	− . 001	. 009
	88		

The evidence given by the above table is clear that, on an average, at the stations located on the oldest geological formations, the pre-Cambrian, the topography is undercompensated and gravity is in excess, and that on the most recent formations, the Cenozoic, the topography is slightly overcompensated and gravity is in defect.   The means with regard to sign, +0.019 and −0.011 dyne, are so large as to make it reasonably certain that they are not due to accident. It is noticeable also that the means without regard to sign for these two groups, 0.026 and 0.021 dyne, are larger than those for any of the other groups.   Of the 6 stations among the 89 having positive anomalies greater than +0.030, two, Nos. 57 and 75, are on pre-Cambrian formation; one, No. 74, is on a Paleozoic formation; and three, Nos. 21, 22, and 84, are at the edge of a Paleozoic-Metamorphic area.   These exceptionally large positive anomalies confirm the general conclusion drawn from the table that stations on very old geological formations tend to have large positive anomalies.

The only one of the 7 gravity stations on pre-Cambrian formations which has a negative anomaly is No. 15, at Atlanta, Ga.   It is noticeable that this station is in the prolongation of a narrow area of Paleozoic formation nearly 200 miles long, which apparently ends within 10 miles of Atlanta, according to the map used.

Of the 5 stations among the 89 having negative anomalies greater than −0.030, four, Nos. 53, 56, 64, and 66, are on Cenozoic formations and the remaining one, No. 61, is on a Mesozoic

* The writers gratefully acknowledge here valuable assistance given them by Dr. U. S. Grant, of Northwestern University, in preparing this topic.

formation. These exceptionally large negative anomalies confirm the general conclusion drawn from the table that stations on recent geologic formations tend to have large negative anomalies.

Of the 20 gravity stations which stand on Cenozoic formations, 9, nearly one-half of them, have positive anomalies, but the remaining 11 negative anomalies are sufficiently large to make the mean of the 20 equal to -0.011, as shown in the table.

Among the 19 stations on Paleozoic formation, No. 74 at Minneapolis, Minn., has the largest anomaly, namely, $+0.057$ dyne. This station is near the edge of a great Paleozoic area in a point extending from the main body of that area into a pre-Cambrian area. The large positive anomaly found at this station is the prevailing characteristic of stations in pre-Cambrian areas.

The evidence of correlation between the prevailing signs of new method anomalies and the geologic formations on which the stations stand which has here been set forth is weak in certain respects. It deals with present surface geology only, as seen in large areas on a small scale geologic map. A thorough study of the evidence should deal with past as well as present surface geology, should deal with the subsurface geology taking into account as far as possible the thickness of the strata of various formations, and possibly also the details of the geology in the immediate vicinity of the station should be considered.

Nevertheless, it is believed that further evidence will support the generalization now made for the United States that at stations in pre-Cambrian areas gravity tends to be in excess and at stations in Cenozoic areas tends to be in defect. The first case corresponds to excess of mass or undercompensation of topography for all land stations, and the second case to defect of mass or overcompensation of topography for all land stations.

In general pre-Cambrian formations are of greater density than Cenozoic formations. Hence, the correlation noted is of the character to be expected if one considers that surface densities, that is the density of masses near the station, have more influence over gravity at the station than the density of masses lying deeper and, therefore, farther from the station. This slightly predominating effect of surface densities is very clearly shown in the first line of the table on page 109, the mass being considered limited to a horizontal distance of 1280 meters from the station. On the other hand, in the last line of the same table in which the masses considered are assumed to extend to a great distance (1190 kilometers) horizontally from the station, the predominance of surface effects is much less pronounced. In the latter case the attracting mass is, to the first approximation, a flat plate of indefinite extent. The attraction of such a plate upon a point outside it in the direction perpendicular to the plane of the plate is independent of the distance of the point from the plate. It matters comparatively little, therefore, in the case represented by the last line of the table whether the attracting mass is distributed through a large depth or is concentrated near the surface. Even in this case, however, variations of density near the surface have greater proportionate effects than variations of density which may occur deep beneath the surface.

Measured in terms of strata of normal density on the hypothesis used on page 111 the excess of mass in pre-Cambrian areas corresponds on an average to a stratum somewhat more than 600 feet thick and the defect of mass in the Cenozoic areas to a stratum somewhat less than 400 feet thick. The considerations stated on pages 109–111 indicate that this excess or defect of mass is probably distributed through a depth at least as great as 15 000 feet.

When one attempts to study the possible correlation of new method anomalies and geologic formations simply by comparing illustrations Nos. 16 and 19 (in the pocket at the end of the volume) with the geologic map of North America which was used, two apparently significant coincidences are noted.

First, three comparatively small detached areas of pre-Cambrian formation are shown in the United States on the geologic map, each far from any other outcrop of the same formation, one at the Black Hills near the boundary between South Dakota and Wyoming, one in Texas west of Austin, and one in Missouri about 50 miles to the southwestward of Chester, Ill.*

---

* On the map this area is so small that it is difficult to be certain about the geological symbol with which it is marked. The writers have, however, been assured by a geologist that this is a pre-Cambrian area and that the authors of this map must have intended to have it so marked.

Illustration No. 16 shows a region of positive anomaly surrounding station No. 75 near the Black Hills, and another surrounding station No. 62 in Texas and overlapping the pre-Cambrian area mentioned. No gravity station exists near the Missouri pre-Cambrian area, but on illustration No. 19 an area of supposed excess of mass is shown in this locality which was drawn originally * on the basis of evidence given by deflections of the vertical before the author knew of the existence of the Missouri pre-Cambrian area.

Second, a great Paleozoic area is shown on the geologic map extending continuously from New York State westward and southwestward and including parts of Pennsylvania and West Virginia, nearly all of Ohio, Kentucky, Indiana, southern Michigan, Illinois, Missouri, and parts of Tennessee, Arkansas, and Oklahoma. On illustration No. 16 there is a corresponding continuous area of small negative anomaly.

It is a very interesting fact that of the anomalies at the six stations in areas of intrusive or effusive rock formation, the mean with regard to sign is practically zero and the mean without regard to sign is only 0.009 dyne. This indicates, though not with much certainty, since the evidence from only six stations is slight, that areas of intrusive and effusive rock formation are very nearly in a state of complete isostatic compensation.

As the glacial ice which formerly covered the northern part of the United States was a large temporary load which has since been removed, and as the total amount of rock and earth moved to new locations by glaciers was large, it appeared desirable to look for a possible relation between the gravity anomalies and the ice sheet. The southern limit of the ice sheet was taken from the geologic map bearing the title, "Reconnoissance map of the United States showing the distribution of the geologic system so far as known, compiled from data in the possession of the United States Geological Survey by W J McGee, 1893." It was found that the following 28 † gravity stations are within the area which has been covered by the ice: Nos. 26–39, 53, 56, 57–60, 74, 76–78, 85–89. The mean anomaly with regard to sign for these 28 stations is −0.002 dyne and the mean without regard to sign, 0.017 dyne, agreeing very closely with the corresponding means for all stations, and thus indicating that no correlation exists between the ice sheet and the gravity anomalies.

On illustration No. 16 a very large area of negative anomaly is shown in the western part of the United States including all the region between the Pacific coast and a zero line which runs southward through eastern Washington and Oregon and southeastward through Utah and New Mexico, with the exception of a small area near Yuma, Ariz. The geologic map used shows that in this region intrusive and effusive formations predominate and next in order of extent are Cenozoic formations. Less than one-fifth of this region is covered by geologic formations which are not effusive or intrusive and are older than Cenozoic. According to the generalizations which precede, this region should, therefore, be expected to be one of small anomalies with negative values predominating slightly. In fact the anomalies are all negative save one, and several of them are unusually large negative values. The most decided geologic characteristic of this region in contrast to other parts of the United States is the activity of recent mountain formation accompanied by increased elevation as a rule and the fact that this region is now subject to relatively frequent and severe earthquakes. It is possible that there is a relation between these particular characteristics and the large prevailing negative anomalies.

In looking for a possible relation of the very large negative anomaly at station No. 66 at Compton, Cal., to the geologic history of this region it was noted that according to good geologic authority ‡ a portion of the State of California in the vicinity of Compton was continuously submerged during a long interval of geologic time from upper Georgic (Cambrian) to the lower Mississipic (Paleozoic). During much of this time, according to the evidence cited, the portion of the present California coast which was submerged was a short section from 100 or 200 miles

---

* See Illustration No. 3, Supplementary Investigation in 1909, of the Figure of the Earth and Isostasy.

† Stations Nos. 53 and 56 are counted as one, because they are close together and have the same anomaly.

‡ Paleogeography of North America, by Charles Schuchert, Bulletin of the Geological Society of America, vol. 20, pp. 427–606. See especially plates 51–78 and 80 at the end of this publication.

long having its center sometimes as far southeast as Compton and at other times as far northwest as Point Conception. The submerged region included Compton continuously, and much of the Santa Barbara Channel (which the deflections of the vertical also indicate as a probable region of defective density *) was included as a rule. During much of this long period the submerged area extended across the present coast line nearly at right angles and far northeast and northward across the present States of California, Nevada, and Utah. The contour lines on illustration No. 16 indicate that along a line extending from station No. 66 at Compton, Cal., to station No. 47 at Green River, Utah, and approximately following the line of this old submerged area, the negative gravity anomaly is greater than it is in the adjacent areas either to the northwest or the southeast of this line. This apparent relation between the present gravity anomaly and the geologic history may possibly be a mere accidental coincidence, but it seems improbable that it is so. The evidence of later observations of gravity and of deflections of the vertical in this region will be studied with interest.

DISCUSSION OF OTHER REGIONAL PECULIARITIES.

Illustration No. 16 shows by contours the regional characteristics as to sign and size of the gravity anomalies. Some comments on this illustration have already been made. (See pp. 106–108.)

From studies of deflections of the vertical corrected for topography and compensation the conclusion was reached, before this present investigation based on gravity observations was commenced, that there are 11 areas of excessive density and 5 areas of deficient density in specified locations in the United States. For 7 of these areas the indications are considered to be uncertain, but for the remaining areas the evidence was believed to be conclusive. The regions of excess or deficiency are stated on pages 73-76 of the Supplementary Investigation in 1909 of the Figure of the Earth and Isostasy, and the evidence is there commented upon. The areas are also shown on illustration No. 3 of that publication, which is reproduced here as illustration No. 19. On illustration No. 19 each gravity station and its anomaly are also shown in red. This illustration and illustration No. 16 may conveniently be used to ascertain whether the gravity observations confirm or contradict the observations of the deflections of the vertical. On illustration No. 19 an area of excessive density surrounded by a red line and marked by a plus sign is understood to be one beneath which, according to the evidence given by the deflections of the vertical, the mean density to the depth of compensation is greater than it would be if the compensation were complete (perfect). Similarly, under an area marked by a minus sign the density according to deflections of the vertical is less than it would be if the compensation were complete. If, then, the gravity anomalies by the new method are found to be positive in or near areas of excessive density and negative in or near areas of defective density, as marked on illustration No. 19, the gravity observations will thereby clearly confirm the deflection observations.

In the following paragraphs the 16 areas of excess or deficiency of density commented upon on pages 74–76 of the Supplementary Investigation, etc., are taken up in the same order as in that publication.

Southern Nevada.—The deflections of the vertical indicate that there is a defect of density within the area bounded by parallels 36° and 39° and meridians 112° and 118°, as shown on illustration No. 19. A gravity station, No. 67, was established within this area at Goldfield, Nev. Its anomaly is −0.015 dyne, which confirms the conclusion drawn from the evidence given by the deflections. Gravity stations Nos. 68 and 69, at the Grand Canyon of the Colorado, which are but slightly beyond the edge of this area of defective density as drawn on illustration No. 19, both have negative anomalies, thus furnishing additional confirmation. The contour lines on illustration No. 16 indicate that this area of deficient density is probably much larger than as drawn on illustration No. 19. It probably includes the gravity station, No. 66, at Compton, Cal., and possibly includes nearly all of Arizona, California, Nevada, Oregon, and Wash-

---

ington. On the mean hypothesis, explained on page 111, that each 0.003 dyne of anomaly corresponds to the equivalent of an added or subtracted stratum 100 feet thick, the anomaly −0.015 at Goldfield corresponds to a missing stratum 500 feet thick.

Southern Florida.—The deflections of the vertical at astronomic stations south of latitude 28° indicate a region of excessive density as outlined on illustration No. 19. This area includes Key West and extends along the coast from Cape Sable to Tampa and reaches eastward across Florida to the east coast in latitude 26½°. Gravity stations Nos. 1 and 3, with anomalies of +0.006 and +0.008, respectively, are within this area, and station No. 2, with an anomaly of +0.016, is just outside of it. These gravity anomalies confirm the evidence given by the deflections. Illustrations Nos. 19 and 16 agree as to the latitudes in southern Florida in which there is excessive density. Illustration No. 16 indicates that the center of the area of excess is probably somewhat farther east than it is located on illustration No. 19. The anomaly at West Palm Beach (No. 2), +0.016 dyne, corresponds to a stratum 530 feet thick in excess. The average anomaly indicated on illustration No. 16 for the part of Florida which lies south of latitude 28° is about +0.009, corresponding to a stratum 300 feet thick in excess. No elevation as great as 300 feet exists in this vicinity.

The mouth of the Rio Grande.—There is a region of excessive density, as indicated by the deflections, of uncertain extent along the Gulf shore in the vicinity of the mouth of the Rio Grande. Gravity station No. 8, just to the westward of this area, has an anomaly of +0.025 dyne. This is in agreement with the deflections of the vertical and indicates that this area of excess extends inland to the westward, as shown on illustration No. 16. The anomaly +0.025 dyne at station No. 8 corresponds to a stratum 830 feet thick in excess. No elevation as great as 830 feet exists within several hundred miles of this point.

Mobile, Ala.—No gravity station is located within or close to the oval outlining an area of defective density as indicated by the deflections in the vicinity of Mobile, Ala. Hence, no direct confirmation or contradiction is possible. It is interesting to note that the contour lines drawn on illustration No. 16 indicate that in this region gravity is probably in defect by about 0.017 dyne.

Relation of anomalies to the Gulf of Mexico.—From the deflections of the vertical the conclusion had been drawn that the isostatic compensation is nearly complete under the Gulf as a whole and that the two areas of excessive density near the shores of the Gulf are merely shore phenomena, not extending to deep water. This conclusion is confirmed by the gravity observations, since, as shown on illustrations Nos. 19 and 16, of the six gravity stations on the shores of the Gulf three (Nos. 8, 3, and 1) have positive anomalies, and the other three (Nos. 7, 5, and 4) have negative anomalies, thus giving an even balance of the evidence in so far as the Gulf as a whole is concerned.

McCormick, S. C.—The observed deflections of the vertical proved with considerable certainty that within a small area in the vicinity of McCormick, S. C., as shown on illustration No. 19, the density is excessive. A gravity station, No. 16, established on the edge of this area confirms the evidence given by deflections of the vertical, for it has an anomaly of +0.013 dyne, corresponding to a stratum 430 feet thick in excess. Compare illustration No. 16 with illustration No. 19 and note that the anomaly contours on No. 16, fixed by gravity observations, indicate that the area of excess is small, in agreement with the conclusion from the observed deflections of the vertical.

Savannah, Ga., and Fernandina, Fla.—The deflections of the vertical furnished somewhat uncertain indications that an area of deficient density exists near Savannah, lying mainly on the seaward side of the coast line, and that there is a small area of excessive density near Fernandina, as shown on illustration No. 19. The gravity station at Charleston, S. C. (No. 17), just outside the Savannah area of defective density, as drawn on illustration No. 19, has an anomaly of −0.023 dyne, thus confirming the evidence given by the deflections. As shown on illustration No. 16, the gravity observations indicate that this area of deficient density extends northward along the coast to include Beaufort, N. C. This is an extension into an area in which no deflections of the vertical are available. The gravity stations do not furnish a definite test of the possible extent of the small area of excessive density near Fernandina which is indicated by deflections of the vertical.

The Adirondacks.—The deflections of the vertical proved with considerable certainty that an area of excessive density coincides approximately with the mountains, and the limits of the area seemed to be fairly well defined.   The gravity stations Nos. 85, 86, and 87, in this immediate vicinity, together with stations Nos. 28, 32, and 88, at a moderate distance, serve to show the distribution of gravity in this region more definitely than for most parts of the United States. As indicated on illustration No. 16, the gravity observations agree with the deflection observations in showing that northern New York is a region of excessive density.   The gravity observations differ from the deflection observations simply in indicating that the region of excess does not extend so far to the southward and does extend farther to the westward and the northward than it had been drawn on illustration No. 19, based upon deflections alone.   This is not a direct conflict of evidence, for a reexamination of the residuals of deflection observations, as shown by the arrows on illustration No. 19, reveals that they are not inconsistent with the supposition that the area of excess has the shape and size indicated on illustration No. 16. Illustration No. 16 indicates that the positive anomaly in the Adirondacks is less than 0.010 dyne, corresponding to the stratum in excess only 330 feet thick.   The mean elevation in the Adirondacks is much more than 330 feet.   On the other hand, the anomaly +0.019 at Potsdam (No. 87) corresponds to a stratum in excess 630 feet thick, whereas the elevations in this region are much less than 630 feet.

Coast of Maine, New Hampshire, and Massachusetts.—There are no gravity stations within the area along the coast of New England shown on illustration No. 19 as an area of excessive density on the evidence of deflections of the vertical.   Stations Nos. 28–31, all near this area, have anomalies which do not contradict the evidence given by the deflections of the vertical.

Rock Springs, Tex.—From deflection observations the conclusion had been reached that an area of excessive density exists in Texas, having its center in latitude 30° and longitude 100°, as shown on illustration No. 19.   Gravity station No. 62, Kerrville, located within the indicated limits of this area has an anomaly of +0.029 dyne and thus decisively confirms the evidence given by the deflections.   In connection with the discussion of the deflections attention was called to the fact that the only area of pre-Cambrian rocks shown in Texas on a certain geologic map of North America lies about 100 kilometers to the northeastward of the center of this area of excessive density, as shown on illustration No. 19.   Gravity station No. 62 lies still nearer this lone area of pre-Cambrian rocks.   The region of excessive density around station No. 62 limited by the zero contour, as drawn on illustration No. 16 on the basis of the evidence from gravity observations alone, extends far enough north to overlap the pre-Cambrian area.   This suggests that possibly there is a real connection between the geological history of this region and the arrangement of densities put in evidence by the deflections and gravity observations. (See p. 115.)   On the basis of 0.003 dyne being equivalent to 100 feet of strata the anomaly +0.029 at station No. 62 is equivalent to a stratum in excess 970 feet thick.   On the other hand, if this anomaly be due to excesses of density confined to the first 15 000 feet of depth, as is suggested by the relation to surface geology commented upon, and if this area of excess extends for somewhat more than 166.7 kilometers around the station, then the table on page 109 indicates that each 100 feet of excess stratum would correspond to more than 0.0034 in the anomaly and that therefore the anomaly of +0.029 would correspond to a stratum of about 800 feet added to the first 15 000 feet.   This would produce an increase in density of about 8 parts in 150, or from 2.67 to 2.81.   This is within the range of possibility.

Sherman, Tex.—A possible area of excessive density in the vicinity of Sherman, Tex., with its center in latitude 33¾° and longitude 96¼°, of which the existence was considered to be doubtful when the evidence of deflections alone was available, has a gravity station, No. 73, near its center for which the anomaly is +0.003 dyne.   This anomaly is so small that it can hardly be considered sufficient proof of the existence of this area of excessive density; but the evidence, though slight, is in harmony with that furnished by deflections of the vertical.   The contours on illustration No. 16 show this region of excessive density as merely a connection between a much larger region of the same kind to the eastward including gravity stations Nos. 13, 14, and 6, and another to the westward including stations Nos. 72 and 40.

Chester, Ill.—There is a region in the vicinity of Chester, Ill., latitude 38°, longitude 90° (see illustration No. 19), where the deflections of the vertical indicate that possibly there was excessive density. No gravity station is located in or near enough to this area to furnish a decisive test.

Southern Michigan.—The deflections of the vertical furnished doubtful evidence that a region of excessive density exists in southern Michigan, as shown on illustration No. 19. The existing gravity stations do not furnish a decisive test as to the existence of this region of excessive density. It is interesting to note, though possibly it has little meaning, that the contour lines, as drawn on illustration No. 16, based on gravity observations alone, indicate gravity to be greater in this region than on either side, to the southward or to the northward.

Los Angeles, Cal.—The evidence given by deflections of the vertical made it reasonably certain that a very small area having a considerable deficiency of density existed near Los Angeles with its center about in latitude 33° 57′ and longitude 118° 14′ as indicated on illustration No. 19. To furnish a decisive test, gravity station No. 66 at Compton, Cal., was located as near as convenient to the supposed center, in fact only 4 miles south and 1 mile east of it. The anomaly there was found to be −0.052 dyne, one of the largest in the United States, a strong confirmation of the evidence given by the deflections. This anomaly corresponds to a missing stratum about 1700 feet thick.

Santa Barbara Channel, Cal.—There are no gravity stations within or close to the area of deficient density which the deflections of the vertical indicate as approximately coinciding with the Santa Barbara Channel. Hence the gravity observations furnish no test of the evidence given by deflections of the vertical.

Northern California, Oregon, and Washington.—The deflections of the vertical indicate that there is either a belt of excessive density to the westward of the primary triangulation paralleling the Pacific coast or a belt of deficient density to the eastward of this triangulation in northern California, Oregon, and Washington. There are four gravity stations, Nos. 53, 56, 80, and 81, within the affected region, but their anomalies throw very little light on the question because of the fact that they are within the belt covered by the triangulation. To test the question raised by the deflections of the vertical the most favorable locations for the gravity stations are on each side of the triangulation, to the westward close to the coast, or to the eastward well beyond the limit of the triangulation.

Washington, D. C.—The deflections of the vertical indicate a narrow area of excessive density in the vicinity of Washington and in Maryland and Virginia. Three gravity stations, Nos. 21, 22, and 84, in District of Columbia have anomalies of +0.035, +0.037, and +0.035 dyne, respectively, corresponding to an excess stratum about 1200 feet thick. Gravity stations Nos. 19 and 23 in Virginia and Maryland, respectively, are outside the indicated area and have minus anomalies. All of the evidence from the gravity anomalies confirms the conclusions reached from the evidence furnished by deflections regarding the existence and extent of this area. It is interesting to note that the area of excessive density near McCormick, S. C., as shown on illustration No. 19, which bears the same relation to certain Paleozoic-Metamorphic formations as does this Washington area, has also been proved to be such by the gravity observations.

Lake Superior.—The anomalies at gravity stations Nos. 57 and 58, the only ones yet available in the Lake Superior region, do not serve to locate definitely the areas of excessive or deficient densities which apparently must cause the very large deflection residuals in this region. The evidence given by these two gravity anomalies conforms in a general way to that given by the deflection residuals. There are no conflicts in the evidence.

In 10 of the areas of excessive or deficient density as indicated by the deflections of the vertical and shown by areas inclosed in red lines on illustration No. 19, there are gravity stations the anomalies of which confirm the evidence given by the deflections. In eight of these 10 areas the gravity anomaly was not known until after illustration No. 3 of the Supplementary

Investigation in 1909 of the Figure of the Earth and Isostasy had been drawn and the areas located thereon. In several other instances where the areas of excessive or deficient density were too uncertain to justify locating them on the map the evidence furnished by the gravity anomalies confirms the slight evidence given by deflections of the vertical.

A study of the gravity anomalies outside of the areas of excessive or deficient density drawn on illustration No. 19 shows that the evidence furnished by the gravity anomalies is consistent with that furnished by the deflection observations as a rule and serves to confirm and supplement it. Each of the two kinds of observations is evidently competent in many cases to locate regions in which there are small departures of the density from the mean values corresponding to complete isostatic compensation. Used together in the study of a given region the mutual support given by the two kinds of observations makes the conclusions drawn much more reliable than they otherwise would be.

Attention has been concentrated in the preceding paragraphs on the departures from perfect isostatic compensation, partly to ascertain how close an agreement there is between the evidence from the two kinds of observations, partly because these departures, slight as they are, may furnish a basis for future studies of the process of isostatic readjustment, and partly for the purpose of ascertaining whether they indicate any systematic errors in the processes of logic and computation used. This concentration of the attention on the departures must not be allowed to obscure the fact that the most significant thing about them is their smallness. Though the average elevation in the United States above sea level is 2500 feet, the departures from complete compensation as measured by the gravity anomalies are represented by strata of which the maximum thickness is 3200 feet corresponding to the defect of gravity at Seattle, and of which the average thickness is only 570 feet (p. 111). The pressure due to the weight of superincumbent masses is everywhere so nearly the uniform value at the depth of compensation (122 kilometers) which it would have if the isostatic compensation were perfect, that the departures are as a rule less than 1200 pounds per square inch. This is a safe working stress for good granite under compression in engineering structures which are expected to last indefinitely without deterioration due to pressure.

HYPOTHESIS OF HORIZONTAL DISPLACEMENT OF COMPENSATION.

In literature of isostasy the hypothesis has with various degrees of definiteness been put forward at various times and places that it may be that, although for each of the larger topographic features of a continent there is complete isostatic compensation, that compensation may not be directly below the features concerned. It is apparently believed that the compensation may be displaced horizontally many miles or even hundreds of miles from the topography to which it corresponds. It is apparently believed that the compensation for a mountain range may extend over a much larger area than the base of the mountain range, may even be to a considerable extent beneath an adjacent plain. This hypothesis has been made a basis of an expressed doubt as to the applicability to the gravity determinations which have been made in Switzerland of the method of computation set forth in this publication. Attention has been called to the fact that the computations of this publication are based on the supposition that the isostatic compensation of each topographic feature lies directly beneath that feature. It has been stated that modern geological theories indicate that there have been considerable horizontal displacements of the material now composing the Alps and that therefore the method of computation used in this publication is not applicable in Switzerland.*

It is desirable to test the truth of the hypothesis that the isostatic compensation for large topographic features or a considerable part of that compensation is in some cases displaced horizontally far beyond the horizontal limits of the topographic feature itself.

---

* Procès-Verbal de la 56ᵐᵉ Séance de la Commission Géodésique Suisse tenue au Palais Fédéral a Berne le 30 avril 1910, pp. 48–49. "Toute la méthode de M. Hayford repose sur l'hypothèse que les masses soulevées proviennent directement des régions sous-jacentes. Il n'est donc tenu compte que de déplacements dans le sens de la verticale. Cette hypothèse peut être considérée comme suffisamment exacte pour une étendue de terrain relativement plat et elle donne de bons résultats pour les États-Unis d'Amérique. Mais elle ne correspond pas généralement à ce qui se passe et s'est passé en pays montagneux. . . . Les théories géologiques modernes des déplacements considérable des plis dans le sens horizontal, pour les Alpes en particulier, ne permettent pas une application immédiate de la méthode de M. Hayford aux calculs relatifs aux stations suisses."

For the United States this publication furnishes a decisive test of this question. The values of gravity have been computed for 89 stations on the supposition that there is complete isostatic compensation directly beneath each separate feature of the topography large or small. These computed values have been compared with observed values of gravity, and the differences (observed minus computed) known as anomalies, are shown in tabular form on page 76 and graphically on illustration No. 16. If the hypothesis of horizontal displacement of compensation were true, evidence of that fact would be found in this table and this illustration. In regions adjacent to great mountain masses, for example, negative anomalies should be found corresponding to displaced isostatic compensation for the mountains in the form of deficiency of density underlying the outlying foothills and adjacent plains. An examination of the table and illustration fails to disclose to the writers any such arrangement of anomalies. Moreover, the anomalies found are so small, corresponding to a stratum only 570 feet thick on an average, that even if the negative anomalies were found to be adjacent to great mountain masses (which they are not) they would represent but a very small part of the compensation for the mountains, since the mountain masses in question in the United States rise much higher than 570 feet above the general level of the surrounding country.

In the great mass of evidence available from deflections of the vertical in the United States the writers also fail to find evidence of horizontal displacement of an appreciable part of the isostatic compensation for topographic features.

In Switzerland the method of computation advocated in this publication has been applied at 13 stations. This is too small a number to give strong evidence, but such evidence as these stations give seems to the writers to indicate that the method is as applicable in Switzerland as in the United States. The anomalies by the new method and by the Bouguer method of computation are shown in parallel columns for these 13 stations on page 47 of the Swiss Procès-Verbal, already referred to. Among the new-method anomalies for these 13 stations both algebraic signs are found and the mean without regard to sign is only 0.021 dyne, but little larger than the corresponding mean for the 89 stations in the United States (0.017 dyne). On the other hand, the Bouguer anomalies for these 13 stations are all negative—the smallest is −0.095 dyne and the mean without regard to sign is 0.118 dyne, more than five times as large as for the new-method anomalies. In Switzerland, as in the United States, the direct appeal to the facts seems to the writers to bring a positive response to the effect that the isostatic compensation is nearly perfect and that the isostatic compensation for each feature of the topography lies in general directly beneath that feature, not displaced horizontally. (See p. 102.)

COMMENT ON BOUGUER AND FREE-AIR ANOMALIES.

There is abundant evidence in this publication that the new method of computation of gravity is a closer approximation to the truth than either the Bouguer or the free-air method. The new-method anomalies are smaller than the anomalies by either of the other two methods. The anomalies by each of the other two methods show definite relations to the topography which are essentially indications of systematic error in the method of computation. The new-method anomalies show no relation to topography.

Are the observed relations between Bouguer anomalies and topography and between free-air anomalies and topography what one would predict upon the supposition that the new method of computation is a very close approximation to the truth? If so, these observed relations are in themselves evidence of the validity of the new method of computation.

The Bouguer method of reduction differs from the new method in that the Bouguer method (p. 75) takes no account of isostatic compensation and neglects all curvature of the sea-level surface in taking account of the effect of topography, the topography being treated as if it were standing upon a plane of indefinite extent. The new method of reduction takes full account of isostatic compensation, which is assumed to be complete and uniformly distributed to the depth of 113.7 kilometers, and in taking account of the topography assumes it to be on a sphere of radius 6370 kilometers, a close approximation to the actual spheroid.

On the basis therefore that the new method of computation represents a very close approximation to the truth, one should expect the Bouguer anomalies to contain the neglected effects of isostatic compensation (comparatively large quantities) and to contain the differences between the effect of distant topography computed as being on a sphere and computed as being on a plane of indefinite extent (comparatively small quantities).

Consider first the neglected effects of isostatic compensation, especially for areas within 2000 kilometers of the station. As shown on pages 19, 20, 23, and 24, and in the reduction tables on pages 30-47, the effect of isostatic compensation under a land area is to decrease gravity at the station of observation, and under an ocean area to increase it. There should, therefore, be negative Bouguer anomalies at inland stations around which land areas predominate; there should be positive Bouguer anomalies at stations at sea or on small oceanic islands around which ocean areas predominate, and the Bouguer anomalies at stations on the coasts of continents should be small as a rule, and should be positive if ocean areas predominate and negative if land areas predominate around the station. Moreover, since the amount of isostatic compensation is proportional to the elevation of the land surface, the neglected effects of isostatic compensation at land stations are in each zone around the station proportional to the elevation of the land in that zone. Hence one should expect the negative Bouguer anomalies at inland stations to be greater the higher the general level of the region surrounding the station and the higher the station itself. All these relations between Bouguer anomalies and topography exist. (Consult the tables on pp. 77 and 78 and the text on pp. 79-82.) For 16 coast stations the mean Bouguer anomaly without regard to sign is small, 0.019 dyne; for 18 stations near the coast it is larger, 0.031; and for the remaining inland stations much larger, 0.171 for one group (pp. 77 and 78). For the 16 coast stations the mean Bouguer anomaly with regard to sign is +0.005 dyne, corresponding to a slight predominance of oceanic effects. For 18 stations near the coast, the most distant being 325 kilometers from the coast, the mean Bouguer anomaly with regard to sign is −0.018 dyne, corresponding to a considerable predominance of land effects. Among the remaining 55 stations in the United States, all inland stations, there are 52 having negative Bouguer anomalies. The mean Bouguer anomaly with regard to sign for the 27 of these 55 stations which are not in mountainous regions is −0.043 dyne and for the two groups of stations in mountainous regions is −0.166 and −0.141, respectively. Moreover, even within some of these separate groups (see p. 80) there is an evident tendency for the negative Bouguer anomaly to be larger the greater is the elevation of the station. These relations are shown graphically on illustration No. 17 (in the pocket at the end of the volume). Note that on this illustration positive Bouguer anomalies are confined almost exclusively to the vicinity of the coast; that no negative Bouguer anomaly as great as −0.100 dyne exists east of the one hundredth meridian, in the lower half of the United States; that, on the other hand, in much of the region west of the one hundredth meridian, in the higher half of the United States, the Bouguer anomalies are negative and greater than −0.100; that in two areas of considerable size in the highest parts of the Rocky Mountain region all Bouguer anomalies are negative and greater than −0.200 dyne; and that the negative Bouguer anomalies decrease very rapidly from −0.100 dyne to about zero as the Pacific coast line is approached from the east. In the table on page 81 for 16 gravity stations not in the United States note that at 11 stations on oceans or on small oceanic islands the Bouguer anomalies are all positive and very large, that the minimum is +0.167 and that the maximum is +0.447 dyne.

Consider now the differences between the effects of distant topography computed as being on a sphere and computed as being on the plane of indefinite extent. For topography in zones 7 to 1, all at distances from the station greater than 2000 kilometers, the computed effect is practically zero if the topography is assumed, as in the Bouguer method of computation, to be on a plane tangent to the sea-level surface at the station, since that assumption places such topography very nearly in the horizon of the station. The Bouguer method, therefore, practically neglects the whole effect of such topography. As already noted, the Bouguer method also neglects the effect of the isostatic compensation of this topography, an effect of the opposite sign from that of the topography itself. The net result is therefore the neglect of the difference of the effects of the topography of distant zones and of its isostatic compensation. This difference is small, usually not greater than 0.005 dyne in the aggregate for zones 7 to 1, including all topography more than 20° 41' from the station. (See p. 71.) These small differences are too small to be easily discovered when merged with the much larger neglected effects commented upon in the preceding paragraph.

The free-air method of reduction differs from the new method in that the free-air method ignores both the topography and its isostatic compensation, and these are both taken into account fully in the new method. On the basis, therefore, that the new method of computation represents a very close approximation to the truth, one should expect to find in the free-air anomalies the neglected effects of topography and compensation which are shown in the seventh column of the table on page 74, headed "Correction for topography and compensation." These corrections follow rather complicated laws which are taken into account in the computation of the correction. The best available method of ascertaining whether the free-air anomalies include these corrections, and little else, is to compare three sets of values: First, the corrections for topography and compensation shown in the tables just referred to on page 74; second, the free-air anomalies shown in the last column of the table on page 76 and those on pages 77 and 78; and, third, the new-method anomalies, which are shown in the third column from the end in the tables on pages 76–78.*

Of the 89 corrections for topography and compensation only 22 are greater than 0.020 dyne. One must expect, therefore, that the effects of the omission of the remaining 67 corrections, none greater than 0.020 dyne and with an average value of probably less than 0.010 dyne, will be difficult to detect. At these 67 stations the free-air anomalies and the new-method anomalies differ but little.

In the group of 16 coast stations (p. 77) there are only 4 (Nos. 54, 18, 1, and 2) for which the correction for topography and compensation is greater than 0.020 dyne. For two of these (Nos. 54 and 18) the free-air anomaly is less than the new-method anomaly, and for the other two (Nos. 1 and 2) the application of the correction for topography and compensation made the new-method anomalies less than the free-air anomalies. In this group the balance of evidence is almost perfect.

In the two groups of stations, 18 near the coast and 27 in the interior (pp. 77 and 78), not a single correction for topography and compensation is greater than 0.020 dyne. Hence, little evidence on the point now in question is available in these groups.

Of the 16 stations in the mountainous regions and below the general level (p. 78) 7 out of 14 (after rejecting two Seattle stations) have corrections for topography and compensation greater than 0.020. Of these 7, 6 (Nos. 49, 79, 78, 69, 46, and 47) have new-method anomalies much smaller than the free-air anomalies, and only 1 (No. 67) larger. Moreover, in this group the means with and without regard to sign are −0.031 and 0.033, respectively, for the free-air anomalies, and the corresponding means for the new-method anomalies are much smaller, namely, −0.002 and 0.012 dyne. In this group the evidence is strong that the free-air anomalies are largely neglected corrections for topography and compensation.

The evidence is similarly strong in the group of 12 stations in mountainous regions and above the general level (p. 78). Eleven of these 12 stations have corrections for topography and compensation greater than 0.020 dyne. Of these 11, 10 (Nos. 52, 51, 48, 50, 20, 86, 75, 68, 55, and 43) have new-method anomalies much smaller than the free-air anomalies and only 1 (No. 64) larger. In this group the means with and without regard to sign are +0.049 and 0.055, respectively, for free-air anomalies and the corresponding means for the new method anomalies are much smaller, namely, +0.003 and 0.014 dyne, respectively.

Attention has already been called (p. 80) to the fact that within each of these groups the free-air anomaly tends to be larger the greater the difference between the elevation of the station and the general elevation of the region surrounding it. The anomaly is negative if the station

---

* The difference between any new-method anomaly and the corresponding free-air anomaly in these tables is nearly, but not exactly, the same as the correction for topography and compensation shown in the seventh column of the table on p. 74. There is a uniform discrepancy of 0.007 dyne (see p. 75) due to the fact that a constant correction of this amount was applied to the Helmert formula of 1901 in computing the new-method anomalies, whereas the Helmert formula was used uncorrected in computing the free-air anomalies in accordance with standard past practice.

is below and positive if the station is above the general level. This is also true of the corrections for topography and compensation. Among the 14 stations in mountainous regions below the general level, after excluding the 2 Seattle stations (p. 78), the mean correction for topography and compensation is +0.003 dyne for the first 7 stations, all less than 500 meters below the general level, and is −0.047 for the remaining 7, all more than 500 meters below the general level. Similarly in the group of 12 stations in mountainous regions and above the general level (p. 78) the mean correction for topography and compensation is +0.028 for the first 5 stations, all less than 250 meters above the general level and +0.071 for the remaining 7 stations, all more than 250 meters above. (Compare these means with the corresponding means of the free-air anomalies given on p. 80.)

The relations to which attention is called in the preceding paragraphs may be seen also in part by comparing illustrations Nos. 18 and 16 (in the pocket at the end of the volume). As the corrections for topography and compensation are small, less than 0.020 dyne, at three-fourths of all the stations these two illustrations have a general resemblance to each other. East of the one hundredth meridian the resemblance is rather close. West of the one hundredth meridian, where the country is mountainous and a large proportion of the stations lie far below or far above the general level of the surrounding country, there is much less resemblance. It is very significant that even the general resemblance west of the one hundredth meridian would largely disappear if illustration No. 18 were drawn using all stations in that area, for the lines of equal anomaly on that illustration would then become very irregular and close together. In drawing these lines of equal anomaly on illustration No. 18, stations Nos. 43, 55, and 69, each lying either far above or far below the general level of the country, were rejected.

The evidence seems to be strong that at any station where the correction for topography and compensation is large this neglected correction forms a large part of the free-air anomaly for that station.

On the whole, it appears that the observed relations between Bouguer anomalies and topography, and between free-air anomalies and topography, are what one would predict on the supposition that the new method of computation is a very close approximation to the truth. Therefore, these observed relations are in themselves evidence of the validity of the new method of computation. As these particular observed relations of Bouguer and free-air anomalies to topography are known to be world-wide, having long been known and frequently commented upon in connection with gravity observations in other countries than the United States, this line of evidence in favor of the new method of computation is world-wide and correspondingly strong.

COMMENT ON THE FAYE METHOD OF REDUCTION.

The new method of reduction has been compared with the Bouguer and free-air methods of reduction, since these are the two methods which have been used as a rule during the past few years in the reports of the International Geodetic Association and elsewhere. The Bouguer method postulates a total lack of compensation and a consequent high rigidity of the earth's crust. The free-air method assumes that each piece of topography is completely compensated for at zero depth. In his investigation, published in Appendix I, Coast and Geodetic Survey Report for 1894,* Assistant G. R. Putnam also used Faye's method of reduction, which is a modification of the free-air method in that a correction is applied for lack of compensation. This correction is equal to the vertical effect at the station of the positive or negative attraction of an indefinitely extended horizontal plane of a thickness equal to the difference in elevation between the station and the surrounding country and of a density equal to the mean surface density of the earth. By this reduction Mr. Putnam obtained anomalies which were in general much smaller than those obtained by him in using either the Bouguer or the free-air reduction. After calling attention to this fact, Mr. Putnam, in the publication referred to, states that "it is probable that no particular significance attaches to these residuals remaining after the

---

* See especially pp. 24–27 and 29.

application of Faye's reduction for several reasons; other values would certainly result if a different area were considered in estimating the average surrounding elevation, or if weight were given according to proximity to the station in making this estimation; and the average elevations here given are subject to some uncertainty, as they were obtained from a small-scale map." None of the reasons given by Mr. Putnam for declining to attach particular significance to the smallness of the Faye anomalies applies to the new method of reduction set forth in this publication. A comparison indicates that the new-method anomalies are of about the same average size as the Faye anomalies at the 14 stations in the United States for which Mr. Putnam computed them.

SUMMARY.

This summary is written to help one to secure a comprehensive view in good perspective of this whole investigation. The page references given serve to help one in consulting the detailed statements.

This investigation is based upon determinations of the intensity of gravity made at 89 stations in the United States and at 16 selected stations not in the United States, 105 stations in all.

In the principal computations of the investigation full account is taken of the effect upon the vertical component of the attraction of gravity at the station, of all the topography of the world, and of the isostatic compensation of that topography assumed to be complete and uniformly distributed to the limiting depth of compensation, 113.7 kilometers.

For definitions of isostasy, isostatic compensation, and allied terms, see pages 6–10.

The most important novel features of the principal computations of this investigation are, first, that all of the topography of the world is adequately taken into account, not simply that which lies in the vicinity of the station, and, second, that the isostatic compensation of the topography is adequately taken into account.

The differences between the observed values of gravity at each station and the computed values by the new method of computation, differences known in this publication as new-method anomalies, are tabulated and fully discussed, since they necessarily contain evidence as to the validity and accuracy of the new method of computation (pp. 74–79).

For comparison purposes the gravity anomalies for these same 105 stations are also given as computed by the two methods of computation most generally accepted in recent years— the Bouguer method of reduction and the free-air method of reduction. The Bouguer and free-air anomalies are fully discussed in comparison with the new-method anomalies, with a view to ascertaining which of the three methods of computation is the nearest approximation to the truth (pp. 75–80).

The principal formulæ used in the new method of computations are derived directly from the fundamental formula $F = k\dfrac{m_1 m_2}{D^2}$ expressing in absolute units of force, according to the Newtonian law of gravitation, the attraction of gravitation between two masses m_1 and m_2 of dimensions which are infinitesimal in comparison with the distance D between them. The quantity k is the gravitation constant (pp. 13–17).

At various stages in the course of the derivation of the formulæ, and of the computations, it was found necessary to make an integration by one or the other of two methods, namely, by the calculus method after introducing such approximations as are necessary to make the problem found in nature fall within the grasp of known integral forms, or otherwise by the numerical method; that is, by computing a sufficient number of numerical values of the function to insure that by taking their sum an integration within the required degree of accuracy is obtained. In every case in which there was the slightest doubt of the ultimate accuracy of integration by the first or calculus method the second or direct numerical method was employed. Such cases were numerous and of fundamental importance (pp. 23–27).

The topography and its isostatic compensation were dealt with in 317 units of area each consisting of one compartment of one zone. Each zone is limited by two circles each having the station at its center. Each zone is divided into compartments by division lines which are parts of radial lines from the station. The 317 compartments together cover the whole earth

INDEX.

Adirondacks, positive area ... 119
Anomalies, apparent nature of ... 94
Anomalies, graphical comparison of ... 106
Anomalies interpreted in terms of masses ... 108
Anomalies, new, and contours of the geoid ... 112
Anomalies, new, and deposition ... 112
Anomalies, new, and erosion ... 112
Anomalies, new, and geologic formations ... 113
Anomalies, new, relation to deflections of the vertical ... 112
Anomalies, new, relation to other things ... 112
Anomalies, relation to topography ... 77
Area of a zone ... 26
Assumptions as to isostasy ... 10
Assumptions not claimed to be exact ... 11

Bouguer anomalies ... 122
Bouguer anomalies compared with new anomalies ... 79

California, northern part, anomalies ... 120
Cenozoic geologic formations and negative anomalies ... 115
Change of sign due to distance ... 65
Chester, Ill., possible positive area ... 120
Comparison, Bouguer and new anomalies ... 79
Comparison, free air and new anomalies ... 80
Comparison, graphical, of anomalies ... 106
Comparison, old and new anomalies ... 75
Compartments and zones, boundaries of ... 18
Compensation, depth of, defined ... 7
Compensation, depth of, tested ... 103
Compensation, horizontal displacement of ... 121
Compensation, regional versus local ... 96
Compton, Cal., anomaly and geologic history of region ... 116
Compton, Cal., negative area ... 120
Computation, errors of ... 88
Computation of limit of a zone ... 27
Computation of reduction tables for distant zones ... 23
Computation of reduction tables for near zones ... 19
Computation, rapidity of ... 95
Correction for elevation ... 13
Corrections, separate zones ... 53
Correction to Helmert's formula of 1901 ... 75
Criteria of accepted interpolations at outer zones ... 63
Curvature must be considered ... 71

Definition of isostasy and related phrases ... 6
Density, increase of, with depth ... 7
Density, mean surface ... 10
Deposition, and new method anomalies ... 112
Depth of compensation defined ... 7
Depth of compensation measured from solid surface ... 10
Depth of compensation, test of ... 103
Discussion of errors ... 86
Displacement, horizontal, of compensation ... 121
Distance, change of sign due to ... 65
Distant topography necessarily considered ... 71

Elevation correction ... 13
Erosion, and new method anomalies ... 112
Errors, discussion of ... 86
Errors due to estimates of mean elevation ... 90
Errors due to glaciers ... 91
Errors due to inaccuracy of compartment boundaries ... 92
Errors due to interpolations for outer zones ... 92
Errors due to manner of fixing depth of compensation ... 93
Errors due to maps and charts ... 92
Errors due to reduction tables ... 92

Errors due to substitution of sphere for spheroid ... 90
Errors due to uncertainty of gravitation constant ... 89
Errors due to uncertainty of mean surface density ... 89
Errors due to variation of elevation within a compartment ... 91
Errors from Helmert's formula of 1901 ... 88
Errors in corrections for elevations ... 89
Errors, none due to increase of density with depth ... 94
Errors of computation ... 88
Errors of observation ... 87
Errors, summary of, due to both observation and computation ... 94
Errors, the method not subject to hidden ... 95
Examples of computations of corrections ... 48

Facts for United States stations ... 72
Faye method of reduction ... 125
Fernandina, Fla., possible positive area ... 118
Florida, positive area ... 118
Formulae expressing attractions, derivation of ... 14
Formula, Helmert's of 1901 ... 12
Free air anomalies ... 122
Free air anomalies compared with new method anomalies ... 80

General statement ... 5
Geoid contours and new method anomalies ... 112
Geologic formations and new anomalies ... 113
Glacial ice sheets and anomalies ... 116
Graphical comparison of anomalies ... 106
Gravitation constant, the ... 13
Gravity, in defect, areas ... 107
Gravity, in excess, areas ... 108
Gravity, variation with depth and latitude ... 9
Gulf of Mexico, compensated ... 118

Helmert's formula of 1901 ... 12
Helmert's formula of 1901, correction to ... 75
Horizontal displacement of compensation ... 121

Incompleteness of compensation, defined ... 9
Interpolation, criteria of, for outer zones ... 63
Interpolation for outer zones ... 58
Isostatic adjustment defined ... 7
Isostasy, assumptions as to ... 10
Isostasy defined ... 6
Isostasy, effect of recognition of ... 5
Isostatic compensation defined ... 7

Lake Superior anomalies ... 120
Local versus regional compensation ... 96
Los Angeles, Cal., negative areas ... 120

Maine coast, positive area ... 119
Massachusetts coast, positive area ... 119
Masses, anomalies interpreted in terms of ... 108
Mass in unit column ... 7
McCormick, S. C., positive area ... 118
Mean values of anomalies ... 76
Michigan, possible positive area ... 120
Mobile, Ala., possible negative area ... 118

Negative areas ... 107
Nevada, negative area ... 117
New England coast, positive area ... 119
New Hampshire coast, positive area ... 119
Newton's law of gravitation ... 13

Observation, errors of ... 87
Oregon anomalies ... 120

	Page.
Peculiarities, regional	117
Pendulums, changes in periods of	87
Periods of pendulums, changes in	87
Pikes Peak, computation of correction	52
Positive areas	108
Possible relations of new method anomalies to other things	112
Pre-Cambrian geologic formations and positive anomalies	114
Radii of zones	18
Rapidity of computation	95
Reduction tables, computation of, for distant zones	23
Reduction tables, computation of, for near zones	19
Reduction tables, explanation of	28
Reduction tables for lettered zones	30
Reduction tables for numbered zones	44
Reduction tables, special, for sea stations	46
Regional peculiarities	117
Regional versus local compensation	98
Rio Grande, positive area	118
Rock Springs, Tex., positive area	119
San Francisco, Cal., computation of correction	49
Santa Barbara Channel, Cal., possible negative area	120
Savannah, Ga., negative area	118
Saving by interpolation for outer zones	64
Separate zones, corrections for	53
Separate zones, corrections for, stations not in the United States	84
Sherman, Tex., positive area	119
Sign, change of, due to distance	65
Stations not in the United States	81
Summary	126
Surface density	10
Switzerland, new method of computation tested in	122
Table, anomalies for stations not in the United States	81
Table, corrections for separate zones	54
Table, corrections for separate zones, stations not in the United States	84
Table, E for various depths	24
Table, E_T, E_C, and E_B for various values of θ	25
Table, effect of 1 square meter of topography	68
Table, facts for United States stations	74
Table, new, Bouguer, and free air anomalies	76
Tables, anomalies, in various groups with relation to topography	77
Tables, reduction, for lettered zones	30
Tables, reduction, for numbered zones	44
Tables, special reduction, for sea stations	46
Table, various facts as to interpolations for outer zones	62
Templates, use of	47
Test, by stations not in the United States	81
Test of depth of compensation	103
Topography and compensation, effects of, why combined	97
Topography, distant, necessarily considered	71
Topography, relation of anomalies to	77
Unit column, mass in	7
United States stations, facts for	72
Washington anomalies	120
Washington, D. C., positive area	120
Zone, area of a	26
Zone, computation of the limit of a	27
Zones and compartments, boundaries of	18